1095/-

PENGUIN BOOKS

FROM JHELUM TO TANA

A fourth generation Kenyan of Indian origin, Neera Kapur-Dromson was born and educated in Nairobi. She studied classical dance in India and continues to perform Odissi, a style of dance from the eastern state of Orissa. She also regularly writes articles on socio-cultural subjects; *From Jhelum to Tana* is her first book. Neera shares her time among France, Kenya and India.

GW00645353

From Jhelum to Tana

NEERA KAPUR-DROMSON

PENGUIN BOOKS

PENGUIN BOOKS
Published by the Penguin Group
Penguin Books India Pvt. Ltd, 11 Community Centre, Panchsheel Park, New Delhi 110 017, India
Penguin Group (USA) Inc., 375 Hudson Street, New York, New York 10014, USA
Penguin Group (Canada), 90 Eglinton Avenue East, Suite 700, Toronto, Ontario, M4P 2Y3, Canada (a division of Pearson Penguin Canada Inc.)
Penguin Books Ltd, 80 Strand, London WC2R 0RL, England
Penguin Ireland, 25 St Stephen's Green, Dublin 2, Ireland (a division of Penguin Books Ltd)
Penguin Group (Australia), 250 Camberwell Road, Camberwell, Victoria 3124, Australia (a division of Pearson Australia Group Pty Ltd)
Penguin Group (NZ), 67 Apollo Drive, Rosedale, North Shore 0632, New Zealand (a division of Pearson New Zealand Ltd)
Penguin Group (South Africa) (Pty) Ltd, 24 Sturdee Avenue, Rosebank, Johannesburg 2196, South Africa

Penguin Books Ltd, Registered Offices: 80 Strand, London WC2R 0RL, England

First published by Penguin Books India 2007

ISBN-13: 978-0-14306-215-8   ISBN-10: 0-14306-215-8

Typeset by Eleven Arts, New Delhi

Printed at Sanat Printers, Kundli, Haryana

Dedicated to the memory of our ancestors who braved their way beyond the seas and jungles—through dangers and perils—to build new lives.

In remembrance of my father, who left in me the fragrance of poetry and of drama

For my mother, an ever-welcoming smile on her face, a fountain of positivism

For Alain—a source of inspiration and constructive criticism

For Renu, Vimal, Sunil, Ashwin and Sanjiv—a childhood full of strong visuals

For Raji, Ranjana, Rohini, Sheri, Alain, Asha—for extending the family

For Neil, Ravi, Shiv, Karan, Amar, Abhimanyu, Rohan, Karishma and Kamal—so that they may not lose their heritage

For Vimli aunty—'grande dame' of the family

For Brinder uncle and Saroj aunty for friendly exchanges over glasses of wine and hot cappuccinos

For Krishan, Baldev, Ved, Sudesh, Surinder, Kaka, Biha, Lalita, Bim, Pole, Kiran, Sindi, Prem, Kanta, Toshi, Swaran, Mama

For relatives and friends all over the world for making me feel a part of a universal network

For Moilo, whose smile remains etched in my memory

Contents

Preface

Rama, I have been weaving for you
Take care. This is no ordinary cloth
Each fibre in it is vibrating with my gratitude
My love, my compassion, my prayer…
— Kabir

When I was first introduced to Lala Kirparam Ramchand, I was forty-two years old. The portrait on the wall—an oil painting in colour by M. Stano, an Italian prisoner of World War II—showed a stern-looking, stocky man of average height. There was something striking about the face. A large square forehead. A strong jaw. Thick knotted eyebrows and bags under the eyes lent a severe, tired expression to his face. The gaze was faraway, impenetrable. He was only sixty or so, I was told, but he looked much older. A flat-topped skullcap perched on his scanty hair. Apparently, he never removed the famous 'Bangalore' cap.

I caught snatches of his adventures from various people. They sounded like dramatic 'once-upon-a-time' stories. I craved to know more. Where did he come from? How did I, an Indian, come to be here—among the vast lands of Africa? Why was my mother born here, as was my grandmother? Who was this man who started his life in Africa over a hundred years ago? I had entered my history midway, but I knew that there had to be a beginning somewhere.

We were based in India during this time, so I got to know Indian writers in their late seventies who had been brought up in the North

West Frontier Province and north-western Punjab. I learnt that there were different Punjabi dialects spoken in that region, notably Lehnda, which I had heard as a child. Lala Kirparam Ramchand, my mother's grandfather, was from the part of Punjab now in Pakistan, from a little town called Miani on the banks of the Jhelum. When I first heard his name he had already been dead fifty years, his ashes immersed in the Tana river in eastern Africa—to flow out into the Indian Ocean.

The discovery that my ancestors had arrived from Pakistan of today, India before partition—was so new to me then. It took more than a year of getting used to. As if fate had ordained it, Alain, my husband, asked for a posting in Delhi, and surprisingly, got it. I had many times visited India, but never for more than several weeks each time. And it had always been difficult. I had always longed to return 'home'. Home was Kenya. I knew no other. Home was the land of my birth. Home was where I grew up, where I went to school. Home was also the land that saw the beginnings of my creative birth and growth. Home was where my mother was.

Years later, I was to say: India is my grandmother, Kenya my mother. India inspired and awakened in me a cultural consciousness. India and Kenya together sustained my physical and spiritual being. I needed them both; I couldn't do without either. Kenya and India became states of my mind. I realized that the past was not to be forgotten, but to be built upon.

Each winter, when the weather became unbearable in Delhi, I longed for the sun and the vast open spaces of Africa, and took a flight 'home'. A major part of my stories come from long hours spent at the breakfast table with my mother in her lovely garden in Nairobi surrounded by jacaranda trees. Without my mother's immaculate memory and visual detail, much would have been missed. She was wonderfully patient while I probed intimate details of her life: it certainly brought us closer. On another trip to Nairobi, I enjoyed long conversations (not forgetting endless cups of tea) in the spacious lounge of Bashir Mauladdad and his charming and hospitable wife Nusrat. And Saturday lunches with my great-aunt and uncle, the Shankardasses, in their beautiful garden in Kitisuru.

A sense of mystery surrounded Kirparam Ramchand. His unsmiling wrinkled face looked hard and cold. I learnt that in real life the man was gentle and independent, yet reserved. What started as a search for my ancestral history ended up in an exciting discovery of Punjabi culture in Kenya of the early 1900s—how it grew, and how Indian immigrants adapted to their new environment, culture shock, the lessons learnt, possible transformations and historical contradictions—in short, a peek through the keyhole into how they saw themselves in their little world.

Many of today's third, fourth and even fifth generation Kenyan Indians have never been to India, but have kept in touch with the parent culture through practice of traditions and religion. Oral transmission from generation to generation, Bollywood, and the latest songs have to some extent ensured its survival. However, westernization—rather, the ubiquitous American pop culture is fast alienating young Punjabis from their roots.

Out of the fog of a nostalgic past emerge some happy, some volatile sounds and sights. Alliances of love and hate. Family get-togethers on Sundays, especially for festivals, not forgetting frequent visits and long stays with maternal grandparents. Cuddled up in grandmother Yashoda's bed late at night, listening to her softly reciting tales of jungles in the Africa of her time, followed by episodes from the Ramayana and the Mahabharata—stories that lifted us from the ordinary into worlds beyond. These tales taught us in allegories and symbols the stories of cultures and civilizations.

Amma Yashoda's hair was white like the snow we had often seen on Mt Kenya. She had a quiet, calming dignity that brought a kind of comfort to my youthful restlessness. The simplicity in her voice gave a feeling of repose, peace and security. Immaculate in a white sari, long silver hair knotted loosely at the nape, a simple welcoming smile upon her lips—no wonder she was known as 'mama mungu'—'woman of god' in Kiswahili. She just had that air of goodness.

So handsome, with a dozen gold *murkian* in each earlobe, great-grandmothers Bebe Gurdei's and Chachi Bhagwanti's loud, lively conversations still ring in my being. Climbing *jamun* and *luqat* trees with cousins in grandfather's vast garden in Pangani, eating raw mangoes and guavas, cut in quarters and sprinkled with red chilli powder. Long marriage feasts with guests coming from all over the country, or hiring several train cabins to travel to distant weddings.

Each of my ancestors has left a little something of themselves in me: Amma Yashoda's sense of solitude—her need for space and private time—and a philosophical attitude to life, not forgetting an avid love of nature. Bebe Gurdei's simplicity and an intense child-like love of life. Lala Kirparam's sense of adventure and fair play, bordering on rebelliousness. Bebe Hardei's strength and determination and bold independence. Hiralal Kapur's punctiliousness—not forgetting his passion for theatre. Grandmother Pushpawati's spirituality, reaching out for the mysterious, the 'other' world.

Their frustrations, less endearing traits as well, have not been left out either and lurk deep down somewhere—including colitis and sinusitis! Bebe Hardei's fiery temper and frugality, interspersed with Amma Yashoda's self-pity, Bebe Gurdei's stubbornness or Paya Kirparam's contempt for societal values.

This book is a re-creation of tradition. A new vision of old dreams. A renewal. The boundaries of tradition must grow, change, expand; pave the way for new vitality and immediacy, for innocence and wonder. Now, I would like to be able to say: the whole world is my home.

The beauty was all around me
But a small candle had been preventing it
Because of the light of the candle
The light of the moon could not enter

— Rabindranath Tagore

This book is a yearning, a remembrance of things past. Stories about Indians, about the Punjabi diaspora in the late nineteenth century. This is also the story of 'dukawallahs', shopkeepers, as they were then known—dukan in Hindustani became duka in Swahili. I have tried to imagine the times of my ancestors. The tension between love and friendship, family tradition, and personal fulfilment, ethnicity and gender. Adaptation to a new environment structures the juxtaposed stories.

Perhaps it is also a historical, introspective account of myself. Torn between three cultures, problems of identity have haunted me for a long time. Kenyan? Indian? Kenyan-Indian? South Asian-African? Perhaps, now I can say: beyond the limits of geography, where space and time know no barriers, there my identity has been cast—in my state of mind. With a respect for individual histories out of which a world has been imagined, this has been a labour of love. I can only hope that some of this pleasure will filter through the pages.

ACKNOWLEDGEMENTS

A special *asante* to:

Baldev Kapila for long hours of patient answering. He passed away in Canada recently

Satish Wason in Timau, Dharampal and Vimli Sharbandass in Nairobi

The family of Lalchand Sharma in Nairobi, for letting me use parts of his manuscript

Bashir and Nusrat Mauladdad in Nairobi, for the many stories of Nairobi in the 1940s and 1950s.

The Vidyarthi family in Nairobi for letting me share their father's life

Durga Sharma in Nairobi for sharing stories about her father, Pandit Laxminarayan Shastri

Surinder Mediratta, Nira Kapila, Umadevi in Nairobi

Allaudin Qureshi, writer and theatre director in Nairobi

Ashok Bhalla, Vice Chairman, Rallies Commission, Kenya

Cynthia Salvadori, whose books, *Through Open Doors* and *We Came in Dhows*, were a source of inspiration and information

Dana April Seidenberg's *Uhuru and the Kenyan Indians*, a source of information

Usha Shah, social activist and former chairperson of the Hindu Council, Nairobi

Francis Nnaggenda, for use of his poem 'The Dead'

Rasna Warah, Zahid Rajan, Zarina Patel, Harsha Shah, Ulveena and Farah Dar, Nairobi

Tony Singh and family for hospitality and invaluable support in many ways, Delhi

Lynette Nath for her help in Delhi

Pran Neville, Khushwant Singh, Krishna Sobti, writers, Delhi

Rani Oberoi, Delhi for giving me contacts in Lahore

Ranbir Kalka, Mrs Kapoor, Delhi

Rubina and Syed Chaudhry in Lahore for their warm welcome

Mr Mehra in Delhi for his anecdotes on life in Behra

The Piracha family for their kind hospitality in Behra, Pakistan

Commissioning editor V.K. Karthika of Penguin, Delhi, for all her feedback and support for the book (and author)

Senior editor Manjula Lal, who very efficiently took the book through its last stages

Krishna Kapur in Nairobi, for the many stories that form a part of this book

Frederique Dromson and Jacques Aloka in France

Alain Dromson for his support and encouragement and for making it all possible in so many ways

Innocent Mwangi at the British Institute for Eastern Africa, Nairobi

British Institute for Eastern Africa, Nairobi, for use of their reference library

National Archives of Kenya, Nairobi

Teen Murti Library, Delhi

India International Centre Library, Delhi

Institute Francais pour la Recherche en Afrique (IFRA), Nairobi

School of Oriental and African Studies (SOAS) Library, London

Solitary sojourn

Kucci tutt gai jina di yari, patannan the rohn khadiyan
(When fickle lovers leave the beloved and go away, the beloved can do
nothing but weep by the riverside)

— Punjabi proverb

They called her Hardei, beloved of Hari. Hari is one of the
names of Krishna. Krishna had many lovers. All the human
beings of the world were his lovers. Each vied for his attention.
When Hari looked at one, embraced another, danced with a third
or held the breasts of a fourth, surely this caused a pang of jealousy.
But each one had to meditate and await her turn.

Hardei had also been waiting. Many years. For the man to
whom she had been wed several years ago. Now she was waiting
at the railway station. Perhaps six hours, maybe more. Her six-
year-old son was becoming restless. He was hungry, so was she,
but they had very little money left. Moreover, they had never seen
so many strange faces before. They did see some black slaves being
brought in at the port when they had arrived in Karachi, but she
had not expected to see so many of them in this new country where
she had just arrived. '*Habshi*!' she exclaimed unthinkingly, and
clutched the white *dupatta* as if to protect herself from unseen forces.
It was a first culture shock.

Chunilal pulled the *dupatta* off his mother's head, revealing
her bodice and the slightly greying hair. 'O *habshiya!*' she smacked
her son lovingly and quickly covered her head again. Despite her

embarrassment she laughed loudly at the child's playfulness. Soon Chunilal fell quiet, and Hardei's old mood returned. She recalled stories from her childhood. 'A *habshan* will take you away if you don't drink your milk quickly', that is how mothers would scare their children back home in Punjab. To the likes of Hardei, all people with black skins and frizzy hair were *habshis*. How or why *habshis* had acquired this feral reputation, Hardei could not for the world have told you, but the name evoked terror, and this she passed on to her child.

Abash, havash, habshi, habeshi were common terms for Abyssinians. A Semitic tribe of mixed Arab descent, these strangers originated in the north of East Africa, in what is now Ethiopia. With a legendary history extending back over 2,000 years, an almost unbroken line of kings to Menelik I, the son of King Solomon and Queen Sheba, the Abyssinians of the highlands considered themselves superior and highly cultured, with numerous rigorous religious festivals and austere fasts. However, Indians only noticed the colour of their skin.

'So many sahibs and memsahibs—the *firangis!*' Here she came across all of them, it seemed. Her father had talked about the foreigners, Hardei tried to recall why. 'Perhaps it had to do with some business deals. But they were also the rulers of our land!' she mumbled tiredly to herself. She closed her eyes briefly. Her father stood in front of her still-closed eyes. 'Hardei, my child, still daydreaming?' he seemed to ask her, caressing her head gently. 'Father, who are the *firangis*? Where do they come from?'

'The *firangis*, ah, my child . . . This was a name given by Arabs to Christians during the Crusades. Later, it became a common term for all Europeans, and then all fair-skinned foreigners . . .'

She cursed herself. 'Why have I come? Why did I leave the familiar world behind? Do I even expect to find him here? What if he refuses to recognize me?' A torrent of questions arose in her mind and her heart sank a little. In her anxiety she bit her nails. 'What if there is already another woman in my place? Seven years is a very long separation.' Hardei felt in her heart that no man could do without a woman for that long. If only she could capture his memory, he might yearn for her!

It was unusual for her to feel so unsure of herself. A Punjabi woman was known for her confidence, for strength of character, and for her physique. Perhaps, even a touch of aggression. Had they not fought and survived centuries of invasions? Countless battles had left scars but, more importantly, had helped forge the will to face new conditions with courage, fortitude and a sense of adventure.

The sun had just risen. The clouds that had settled were streaked yellow and blue. Was it going to rain? She couldn't say for sure; even the vast sky and the cumulus clouds appeared different here. Hardei took a deep breath and looked at her son. He had fallen asleep on the waiting bench. She smiled and took him in her lap. She was used to sitting cross-legged—on the rough-hewn floor, or on the charpoy, the thin ropes of the cot cutting into her soft bottom.

After Kirparam's parents had passed away, Hardei and her husband had had to share the house with his father's younger brother and his wife, his chacha and chachi. Chachi, especially, had been rough with Hardei. Still very young and naïve, Hardei easily felt the pain and the exploitation. 'By now they must have surely heard that I have left for Africa,' Hardei thought to herself. 'How difficult they made my life, especially when there was no news about my husband.' Curses and abuses she could handle, these she could manage. It was when she became pregnant that she decided to run away, back to what was once her home. She sought refuge with her brother, but there she had a stepmother to contend with.

Her son shifted in his sleep, Hardei patted him and lulled him back to sleep. 'Soja mere rajkumar . . . sleep my little prince', her heavy drone had a drug-like effect on the child. Holding him with her right hand, she patted a gentle rhythm on his head with the other. With her whole body swaying to the lullaby, the child was asleep in no time. 'Will Chunilal's father recognize his own son?' she wondered. She studied his face closely, searching for any resemblance to his father. 'The same large forehead.' She shook her head and broke into a big smile.

Time dragged by, according to the big clock at the Mombasa railway station. It seemed like a different age when she had left Miani, the little town on the Jhelum, in the north-west of Punjab. There too she had waited with her son for the train. Her brother had not come to the station to see them off. He did not want to spend two whole rupees on the return journey home. She knew him well, but it had hurt.

While no one had escorted Hardei and her little boy to Miani railway station, it seemed as if all the other travellers were accompanied by a dazzling fanfare of colourful, noisy ceremonies. Relatives and friends had come to the station with garlands— invariably of marigold, the saffron-coloured flower which wafted a very distinct fragrance, reminding one of temples and puja rooms. Others carried boxes of sweets. They waved a rupee note or two around the departee's head as *shagun*, auspicious money for the journey, and then thrust it into their palms.

All kinds of last-minute exhortations and advice were being hurled until the train was almost out of view. The dos and the don'ts, 'Promise that you will write . . . that you will not eat beef . . . that you will not come back with a mem[sahib] from Vilayat (originally England, but often used for all foreign lands) . . .' A few wept, others waved their right hands.

A distant hoot announced the train's arrival. Its arrival had become a major event. Every time it steamed into the town of Mombasa, it brought with it a festive air. The platform came to life again. Soon the station turned into a marketplace. Cargo wagons were loaded or unloaded. Domestic livestock and exotic trophies, rhino horns and elephant feet, Maasai spears, *kikapus* (baskets) woven from palm leaves, leopard skins, mangoes, coconuts, flour sacks and tea chests. A magic spell seemed to have been cast.

Hardei shook off the somnambulist lethargy and quickly regained some of her composure. She realized that she had to rush into the train if she wanted to find a seat for her son and herself.

'*Chungwa! Ndizi! Chungwa!*' African men in red blankets and bareheaded, beaded women were thrusting bananas, oranges, and even live fowl from the gravel platform up at passengers staring at them from the open windows, their hands outstretched to lift up the goodies.

The station master gave a signal—nearly all station masters were Indian. Packed high with branches of the acacia for use as wood-fuel, the train started moving. Enormous Garrett engines, the biggest and most powerful, had to be wood-fired. As usual there was a commotion and some inconvenience as passengers were still loitering outside, talking until the last minute. Then suddenly as if shot by a gun, they started rushing about looking for their baggage, their children, their carriage. It did not help that the port and the mainland never seemed to agree on the time. Their clocks always read a difference—two minutes, five minutes. Not surprisingly, people often missed their trains. It had been suggested that a gun be fired from the centre of Mombasa followed by a signal from Mombasa fort, so that it could be heard in Kilindini, but this had yet to be implemented.

Mombasa came up on an island site good for defence: two deep-water creeks joined together to enter the Indian Ocean. Kilindini, the 'deep water' modern port, was in the western harbour. Dhows, coastal ships and local fishing boats used the eastern port near Fort Jesus. Three days a week the train left this island in the Indian Ocean for the shores of the largest lake in Africa, Lake Victoria—source of the Nile—unknown to the outside world until the mid-nineteenth century.

The train began to climb, slowly and laboriously, through the forest of palms into the hills overlooking Mombasa. Especially suited to growing coconuts, Changamwe, the first halt, abounded with fertility. Large orchards of orange, banana, pineapple and lime were a feast for the eyes. Soon they gave way to a semi-desert, with dense thorn trees right up to the beginning of Tsavo, where all of a sudden the sun bared its ultimate ferocity. It was like being in a pan of smouldering iron. The variations of temperature could be brusque and excessive—the cold of the morning and the heat of the day. To the English this flat, dry, open, bare and treeless wilderness intersected by two rivers—the Sabaki with its origins in Mt Kilimanjaro, and the bigger river Tana—was the Taru desert; the Swahili knew it as the Nyika. It divided the coast from the highlands.

Meriakani, Maji ya Chumvi, Samburu, Mackinnon Road. The train seemed to halt at every station for at least ten minutes. Each time, an Indian station master would walk along the platform with his kerosene lamp and then disappear quickly. 'One night the station master lingered on the platform after the train had left; he was taken away by a lion,' a co-passenger told Hardei. She stared at him in disbelief. 'Another time, some young *firangis* arriving with endless bottles of *sharab* (alcohol) from Vilayat went wild and high. Forcing the engine driver out of his chair, they drove the train at a reckless speed to the next station!' The man tried to make further polite conversation, but Hardei's nervous expression and lack of response to his monologue dissuaded him.

The middle-aged man, a huge white turban on his head, made himself more comfortable by sitting on the seat with his dirty shoes still on, firmly tucked under his once-white pajamas. The floor of the cabin became muddy as he constantly poured water for washing his hands and feet. He took out a small brass tiffin-box from a white cotton sack, and opened it. A strong spicy aroma floated in the air.

'My name is Kohli,' he said, putting some chutney and curry on a chapati and offering it to her. Hardei hesitated. It was polite to refuse a couple of times. 'You must have some,' he insisted in the culturally accepted norm.

The chapati was by now soaking wet in his hand, the curry dripping to the floor.

'I am from the Koilawadi zila, district Jhelum.'

'Then that makes you my brother,' said Hardei, accepting the soggy food offering with both hands as if it was *prasad* (sanctified food). 'We are from neighbouring districts. I am from Shahpur district,' she said.

Her own needs forced Hardei to abandon her reticence and talk to the man. In rustic Punjabi, she slowly revealed something of herself, explaining why she had come to Africa.

Their conversation was interspersed with the shaking and shuddering of the train down the tracks. It puffed and blowed. One hundred miles away from Mombasa, the train finally steamed into Voi, the first major halt for the night. The passengers would spend the night here to continue next morning with a new guard, always Indian—and a fresh shift of drivers. The dak bungalow at Voi was reserved for passengers. Here they ate and slept. Meals were prepared by Goan chefs and served by Goan stewards in white gloves as numerous winged insects, attracted to the lamps, buzzed over each table, eventually to be found in the soup. Small fires sprang up behind the goods shed. Natives made their meals of maize and bananas. The Indians relieved themselves in the bazaar just behind the station.

Delays were frequent on this route. The tracks were often damaged by charging rhinos, or washed away in heavy rains, or there would be engine failure. The steam had to be kept up at all times to drive the engine. Sometimes the drivers drew off a pot full of boiling water from the boiler. Other times, they would stop the train near a wood and request passengers, 'Would you please help cut up some *kuni* (firewood) for the engine?' They were quite happy to oblige. The wood was fed into the boiler and—along with a dose of paraffin—soon started burning merrily. In a short while, the needle in the steam dial would begin to rise. It gobbled up tons of fuel. The wood-fed engine hooted a lot, then stopped at yet another station, where no house, apart from the station building, was visible. The driver opened the regulator to let off the steam . . . oof oof ooof chook . . . and the music changed.

In the best of British traditions, trains were compartmentalized into three separate classes. At the far end of the train were carriages reserved for 'Europeans only'. Some European VIPs were authorized to ride in front of the engine to view the great herds of game and the enchanting scenery; less important dignitaries used the carriage roof, clambering up the narrow iron rungs intended for the lamp-lighter's use at dusk. 'Amma, amma, look, look!' Chunilal cried excitedly on seeing the big wild animals as the train raced past—his body half hanging out of the huge window. Hardei held on to his legs, as hard as she could. With his feet banging hard on her thighs, and the small body dancing up and down, she was afraid that he might fall out. But she could feel some of the same thrill coursing through her veins. Apart from squirrels there were innumerable monkeys, which she had seen enough of in Miani—making away with your things—anything they could steal, from bananas and mangoes to combs and bedsheets. Hardei was witnessing this grand spectacle for the first time in her life, something she was to see again and yet again, though with diminishing zest. She spied herds of zebra, giraffes, Thomson's gazelle, *kudu, dik-dik*—although she could not distinguish some of them yet. Hardei's initial fear turned to enthusiasm. She felt her spirits lift.

A magnificent coat with brown polygonal patches and those long very sympathetic-looking eyelashes made her momentarily forget everything else. He stood a little distance from the rest of his group. From time to time he rubbed his long neck against his body. Slightly out of time with the rest of his body, the tall giraffe walked at a leisurely pace. The regular up-down swing of his long neck gave him a strange style. Hardei had never seen a creature like this before; she continued to watch in fascination. What she would never know was that the giraffe has only seven vertebrae—as many as a man has in his cervical column! Slowly, the giraffe lowered his neck to drink from a pool. He spread out his forelegs, but kept raising his head to observe his surroundings for any hostile presence. He would obviously find himself in a very inconvenient position in case there was a need to escape. Perhaps, he would not be able to quench his thirst! Every now and then he lifted his head abruptly—knowing full well that the least sound could be a threat, and that meant flight. Too rapid a flight and the poor beast could die of fright—with a heart too fragile for its 600 kilos!

Mother and son instinctively recoiled as the train passed a lazing pride of lions. The male was sprawled in the tall golden grass, looking slightly bored. He might be the king of animals, but right then he was also the king of inertia—nothing short of 12–15-hour siestas during the day. 'No need to panic. Don't worry, the lion usually hunts at dawn, or late in the evening,' Kohli said comfortingly. 'However, the last time I travelled, the train had to stop here for several hours. A *firangi* official had spotted a lion out of his window. He insisted on disembarking to hunt it, and we arrived half a day late in Nairobi!' continued Kohli, showing off a little.

The sun had risen in the last quarter of the hour. Its first rays lit up the snowy upper reaches of Mt Kilimanjaro, bathing them in total splendour. Part of a volcanic massif, this was the highest peak in Africa at 19,340 feet, extending 80 km from east to west. The sight of the snow-capped mountain in the distance was the real gift of their journey. It stood pure and serene, as if a piece of heaven had fallen on earth.

In 1848, when Johann Rebmann, linguist and explorer, claimed to have seen a mountain covered in snow not far from the equator, and a year later when Krapf saw Mt Kenya, also snow-covered, their claims provoked derision from armchair experts. The Royal Geographical Society in London dismissed the claim of snow on the equator as an illusion attributable to soil composition! Sadly, in 15–20 years, this might become true, as global warming takes its toll.

With her eyes raised towards the summit, Hardei gazed in silent admiration for a long moment before she could find words to express her emotions. 'Proud and royal, how like the Himalayas, the abode of the gods. Perhaps Shiva meditated here too', she told her little one, and bowed in salutation, pressing her palms together. 'Here also must live some gods,' she told herself. A little corner of her heart was illumined. She felt like a child full of wonder and belief in front of this majestic image of the eternal. Who was not inspired by a view of a snow-capped mountain? Was it like Mt Meru, described in the Hindu *Puranas*? Surely it was a symbol of aspiration, of optimum strength, just like Mt Kailash! For Queen Victoria and her imperial cousin Kaiser William II, the mountain had only been a bargained piece of land. A detoured border—a mountain given as a birthday gift and later promoted to a symbol of national identity.

The heavy but mysterious mists rose slowly towards the summit, rivalling each other in whiteness. A few seconds later, the snows disappeared, swallowed by the mists, which seemed to triumph in the conquest. A celestial splendour enveloped in clouds, the mountain began to disappear from view as the train sped on.

The few moments of beauty had cheered Hardei up. But as the train approached Nairobi, she grew increasingly nervous. What awaited her at this end? Did she even remember what he looked like? He had never been photographed, not even at their wedding. Such pastimes were reserved for British rulers, Indian royalty and westernized Orientals.

'Come to think of it,' Hardei thought, 'I had my first glimpse of the man long after the marriage ceremony had taken place, when I dared take a quick peek through my long veil while his *sehra* was being removed. We were so young then. He did not even have a proper beard, and I was still flat-chested. Who told us what to do? It had been so awkward!' she closed her eyes, sighing deeply within her soul.

Very soon, even before the colour of henna had faded from her palms, Hardei had been put to work in her new house. She felt sorry for herself: 'At least they could have waited for the honeymoon period to be over before they asked me to work in the *halwai* shop.' It had been hard, very hard. Up very early, at dawn, she would light the charcoal fire and help make all kinds of sweets and savouries— *halwa, jalebi, puri, pakora*. From time to time, Chacha would send his nephew to Karachi to buy spices. 'Better and cheaper there', he said.

The last time he left for Karachi, Kirparam did not return.

Hardei could still recall his goodbye; he had not lingered over it. Typical. A Punjabi man never looked back to wave in sentimentality. A quick 'Achha!' and he was gone. She had wanted to shout after him, 'Mein kya, you have forgotten your umbrella,' but the words froze in her throat. It was a bad omen to call someone back. 'He will buy one in Karachi. A better one,' she had smiled to herself.

Karachi was a busy port loaded with beautiful things from faraway lands—silk, spices, sugar, rice and cereals, indigo, wool and European goods. . . in her daydreams, Hardei often imagined herself in the port town, running from one shop to the other, admiring the beads, or just feeling the softness of the silky dress material. 'Even if I did not buy anything, just looking would have been so much fun', she sighed. 'Hai rabba, hai rabba!' Not once but many times she had called out to her god. 'Perhaps he will take me with him the next time he goes to buy spices,' she had tried to console herself. Such was not her kismet, for eventually when she did pass through Karachi all by herself, it was in a hurried and panicky state.

Day after day she had gazed through the small iron-barred window for the sign of his familiar shadow, the sound of his quick footsteps. At times she caught herself speaking to him 'Mein kya, I say . . .' She did not use his name, of course. No, no, she could not have called him thus; it was just not done. To draw his attention, she would just say, 'Have you heard . . .' Kirparam did not often address her by name either. They sought each other's attention indirectly—by a discreet cough, a clearing of the throat—sometimes, only a sigh.

No wife addressed her husband by his first name—or any other name. It was a sort of social taboo. If asked his name (in rare circumstances), a wife would probably seek refuge in metaphor: Krishan would become 'the one who plays the flute'. And if he was called Gulabchand (rosemoon), she may have said, 'It is a rose,' (gulab) and then point to the moon (chand).

The family had searched all over the village, spoken to his friends—to no avail. She wandered about, abandoned and forlorn.

At such moments she achingly felt the lack of the mother she had never seen: she had died in childbirth. Her father had remarried, almost immediately.

She had never been held in the arms of her mother, nor fed the milk of her breast. Nor had anyone related any stories. She had no idea what her mother looked like. Even her name was not evoked! Would she have given her a pet name, called her 'my little *bitia*', for instance? Hardei might have been different had she been brought up by a loving mother. But she had to fend for herself, grow up almost alone—to find her own truth. Those moments when a mother called out to her daughter and shared her growing up years, when family secrets were revealed, all these little pleasures had been denied her. Little was known about Hardei's parents, or about Hardei's own troubled youth—a dilemma that could perhaps be traced back to the womb.

Hardei woke up with a start, nearly frozen. Thick clouds had covered the sky. Tall trees darkened the forest they were passing through. The train had climbed higher into a comparatively cold zone. Chunilal drew closer to his mother. It seemed to be his turn to feel the sense of dread. She clung to him, held him close to her bosom, hoping to draw some courage into herself from this human contact. From the humid coast of the Indian Ocean at Mombasa, the train had climbed to just over 5,000 feet. From here it would later continue to climb to over 8,000 feet at Mau summit in the virgin forests of the East African highlands, before dropping down 4,000 feet at Kisumu, the terminus on the shores of Lake Victoria. It would have passed through jungles, swamps, deserts, the plains and snow-peaked mountains.

The train advanced towards its destination with great resplendence—before chugging into the tin city of Nairobi.

The service had been running for a few years, but every time the train steamed into the vicinity of Nairobi, many people would rush out and head for the station to enjoy the hustle-bustle on the platform. Such arrivals were everybody's business. The station became an arena of jubilation. The arrival and departure of trains was an event. It was good to see newcomers, to welcome new contacts, especially new women.

Very smart in his sola topee—the hallmark of colonial power—the guard adjusted his pith helmet yet again and blew the whistle; the train jolted to a halt. Hardei's hand automatically reached up to adjust the *dupatta* on her head. Her heart missed a beat. She quickly bent forward and tried to peer outside. Perhaps by some miracle he has come to receive us, she spontaneously thought for a moment. Immediately she chided herself, 'How can he know of our arrival?' Kirparam had never written to her. She would never have known of his whereabouts had she not heard some stories in her hometown from people who had returned from 'Afreeka'. A land that was very far away, across the big seas. There was much jungle, and wild animals, but also opportunities to make some money. 'He was not even aware that I was with child when he left,' she told herself.

The Indians sat on long low benches. When the train arrived, they rose like crows in a field and stormed the coaches reserved for Asians. The native coaches with their wooden benches exploded with people. It was hard to believe that so many bodies were packed inside. Bundle-clutching, *dhoti*-clad Indians hastened to alight. Others carried black steel trunks on their heads, their once elegant kurta-pajamas now limp and crushed. Perspiring profusely, they heaved and pushed their way through the crowd.

So great was the congestion, it seemed that everyone in Nairobi had converged there. Wagons, rickshaws and bicycles had become a familiar sight on the streets. The rickshaw was a cheap and efficient way to get around and the jingle of the bell anklets worn by the 'pushing' and 'pulling' boys made a lovely sound as the rickshaw edged forward.

Tall, thin, mustachioed, turbaned, complete with riding breeches and boots, with an immense whip under the arm, Ali Khan cut an impressive figure amongst the crowd. The first glimpse of him was unforgettable. Town-dwellers soon knew him as a reliable source of information, as he was accepted even amongst the *wazungu*—perhaps one of the few coloured men allowed to set foot in the town's 'for whites only' Hotel Stanley. He had arrived from South Africa with horses for sale, picked up along the Benadir Coast. The Pathan horse-dealer monopolized the town's transport facilities, owning a large fleet of horse-drawn carriages. He was always there to meet every train with his coach drawn by six horses. 'Is he a dark-coloured *firangi*?' Hardei wondered.

Every alighting passenger had perhaps a dozen persons to receive him. Some drove up in rickshaws pulled by sweat-covered Kikuyus. In *gharries*, in bullock *tongas*, in two-wheeled carts drawn by mules, driven by turbaned Sikhs. Four-wheeled *hamali* carts threaded their way between the two-wheeled *tongas* hauled by a pair of trotting oxen, the Sikh driver sitting on the pole between them pulling on one rope, and talking to their animals in Punjabi, '*Chal, chal. . .* The noise was unbelievable. Everywhere people were shouting, the rickshaw men were grabbing your luggage and making off with it. Everybody seemed to be in a hurry except Hardei. She looked around her. Turbaned men—Sikhs, Pathans, Arabs—and African families carrying bulging bundles on their heads, babies strapped with a colourful piece of cloth to their backs.

New settlers had arrived in the country. Civil servants in starched khaki uniforms and white topees, others in felt hats. Women in long flowing gowns, large straw hats and white parasols covering their heads in the day, full white gloves enveloping their arms and hands—Hardei stared at them for a long while and wondered why. Much later she learnt that they regarded the sun as a dangerous animal that would strike you down like a cobra. Few European women would expose their complexions to the harsh tropical sun. 'Ah . . . these memsahibs have not yet experienced the furnace of our country! What would they do in our hometown, Miani, where summer temperatures could really scorch you!' she had commented. For the English, brought up in a climate of perpetual drizzle, the sun was debilitating; they had to adopt all kinds of protective layers to guard against its intrusion.

Young and old alike wore some sort of a sun helmet. But her little Chunilal wore neither topee nor helmet. 'Why my little one, you will wear a pugree when you grow up, won't you?' He looked up at his mother as she continued, 'The earth preserves the fire of summer in her belly; real heat emerges from the ground, my son.' The little boy smiled as if understanding it all.

Hardei's hand automatically reached for her little son as if trying to retrieve some comfort, to relocate a much-needed security. And then she burst out in laughter. Beside her, he stood—all red. She caressed his face and said, 'Gulal!' For did he not look like little Krishna during the festival of Holi, all covered with gulal? Was it not like the first day of spring when one had the joy of dousing each other with brightly coloured water? The sudden strong rays of sunlight accentuated the reflection. She was now laughing and crying at the same time.

But then all other fellow travellers too seemed to have developed a ruddy complexion. She wiped her own face with the hem of her white dupatta; and it came off red. She looked down at herself. The ochre-red dust had penetrated everything. Clogging the clothes, eyes, nostrils, hair and pores of the skin with fine dust. All the disembarking passengers were united in one common colour! This time it was not the sun, but the fine dust of the African plains. Red ochre was the colour of the Maasai, the colour used by the Samburu, the colour of Africa. The brick-red earth enveloped each one; it welcomed every new arrival into the heart of its land. It stamped and marked every disembarking passenger from the train. For a day or two afterward, traces of the Taru desert and the Kapiti plains appeared as red streaks on the towel.

She waited. People were leaving. Newly arrived coolies carrying beds made of lemon wood and crisscross hemp on their heads, huge bundles in their hands. Slowly the station was emptying. Everyone seemed to have somewhere to go, except Hardei. She clutched her son's hand tighter, and picking up the little black trunk in the other, started walking towards the exit. A three-yard-long, one-and-a-half yard wide white veil thrown over the head fell in graceful folds nearly to her feet, a loose bodice to conceal the bosom, a pair of slippers on the feet, cracks clearly visible at the soles. No make-up. She looked forlorn, solitary and tired. She hesitated before joining a group of Indians as they left the station and walked down the main road towards the Indian bazaar, a mile from the station.

2

Across the seas

Dur de dhol suhane
(Distant drums sound better)
— Punjabi proverb

The decision to construct the Uganda Railway was taken in 1895. It was made with Indian knowhow, using Indian materials and labour. Next year, just when the revived Olympic Games were being held in Athens after a gap of several centuries, the British Government of India issued a notification amending the Indian Emigration Act so that Indians could emigrate to East Africa legally. The first batch of 350 Indian coolies arrived at Mombasa in January 1896. Blacksmiths, carpenters, masons, surveyors, draughtsmen, accountants and clerks were also recruited. Tailors, shoemakers, *dhobis* and cooks—they all came on their own. And, contractors took up the job of recruiting indentured workers for the railway.

Head-hunters were sent to various districts. Lahore, and later Karachi, served as recruitment centres where *jamedars* did the needful. A number of Indians, especially from Punjab and the North West Frontier Province, came on their own during this time—mostly as traders. Deployment of British Indian troops in East Africa in that decade strengthened the growing Indian presence in the interior and contributed to future immigration from Punjab, where most of the soldiers originated.

For young Kirparam, migration had been a spontaneous act. Adventurous, ready to face physical dangers and hardships of life in the unknown, an entrepreneur was in the making. While he was in Karachi buying spices for the shop, he heard about a cold land, but one of golden opportunities, where many Punjabis were heading. It was Vancouver, Canada. There were also tales of adventure and opportunities in 'Afreeka'. He had not hesitated. The hundreds of sailing vessels of all sizes and descriptions at the port lured him. The desert winds of the Sind brought relief, and a sense of freedom burst forth from within.

The port of Karachi already seemed a city of magic and mystery, of an opening and contact with connections to far-off places. Date palm, banana and tamarind—as each tree swayed, Kirparam's heart sang out in tune to its rhythm, and his vibrant spirit was propelled by the energy of perpetual discovery. He could not be held in captivity any more. Once the decision was made, he did not think of anything else. Not about returning to pack his suitcases, nor of saying his goodbyes. To whom? To his Chacha, or Chachi? His town Miani? Or to his wife, Hardei? Where was the private time or space? What would he have said? That I want to get away? That I want to discover? That I want to breathe in my own space? No, not even Hardei would have understood. Kirparam focused his mind fully on the journey. He was ready for the adventure and the new beginning. His new-found maturity necessitated freedom from the shackles of family life; he felt liberated. He could breathe at last.

Kirparam never spoke much of his lost childhood. The little that he did revealed an acute sense of deprivation and inner turmoil. His father died when he was no more than four years. Fate gave him little opportunity to emerge out of the umbra which had begun to envelop his life. What was dinned into him by his widowed mother only deepened his melancholy. And when he lost even his mother, it was the final blow—and a significant turning point in his life.

The elder brother had drowned while taking a swim in the Jhelum. Unable to bear the shock, his mother had jumped from the third storey amid festivities for the son's forthcoming wedding. With a broken leg, and a heart that refused to heal, she knew she would not live long. His mother had insisted on seeing Kirparam 'settled' before she died. Orphaned, he had been forced to live and work with his father's younger brother and his wife—a stingy, highly strung couple. On top of it all, the responsibility of a wife. It was too much, too sudden. He could not cope. He decided to take destiny in his own hands.

Bag, baggage, burdens and family—he left all these behind. He came alone. Anew. A new place invited a fresh start. A dream. An escape. A quest. A search for himself. With very vague ideas about the future—if any. Actually, he did not even need a reason: it was a primeval urge. With just about enough money to pay for his passage, Kirparam boarded the dhow. A Kotia type, or the bigger Boom, with planks of teak and palm wood tied together with cords of coconut fibre, bound for the east coast of Africa.

East Africa lies across the equator. Its location along the Indian Ocean led to trade with countries like Arabia, Persia, and India. Traders settled along the coast. They brought new ideas, new cultures, new languages and even new religions, century after century. Dhows, later ships, set sail from Asia to Africa and back again.

Sometime in the month of April 1898, three dhows set sail together from Karachi to East Africa, one of them carrying Kirparam. Each member of the crew carried with him a talisman. Some had Koranic verses concealed in little silver boxes tied around their necks or on the upper arms with black thread. Others carried idols of Ganesha, Amba or other *gram devatas* of their choice. They offered prayers to the mighty ocean. To Varuna—the overlord of the primordial waters riding on his fabulous aquatic vehicle, Makara the crocodile. The sailors sang in praise of Samudrimata, goddess of the sea, Shikotarimata, a goddess inspired by the island of Sokotra at the mouth of the Red Sea, and Hinglajimata, lady of navigation. Sailors, sea pilots, adventurers and traders, Hindus and Muslims—they all sought the guidance of local *pirs* and saints.

A warm ocean, often blue and pleasant, the Indian Ocean can sometimes be stormy and frightening, with strong steady winds blowing—the winds that divide the year into two main seasons, as described by early seamen from Arabia. The crew had to appease the water demons to bring luck to their venture. They lit a fire and burnt incense sticks, cracked open a coconut on the side of the dhow, placed rock sugar and a few grains of rice with it. And then the *khalassis* burst into song. As they swayed to the rhythm of drums, they appeared to go into a trance. Their excitement was infectious and passed on to the passengers. The festivities continued for a long time. Nobody seemed in a hurry to depart.

Kirparam had not thought of carrying any food with him; he had not even realized that the voyage would be so long and rough. He had not thought of asking practical questions. Just the thought of adventure and of getting away had been incentive enough. Luckily, he got to share meals with the group he travelled with: they mostly ate *dal* (lentils) and rice, and sometimes when the dhow did not rock too much, they were lucky to get chapatis. Different religious groups cooked their own food. A big sack of charcoal and the *angeethi*, their small iron burner, were kept in a corner together with each family's luggage. For the first few days, Kirparam could not eat—he constantly threw up. Those used to the travel were well stocked with fresh fruit and vegetables.

The hold was like a dungeon. Male passengers slept on the deck. Privacy was non-existent. Fresh water was stored in drums and controlled by the *nakhoda*, the captain of the dhow. No one was allowed to use this water for a bath. Those who couldn't do without the daily ritual brought up buckets of seawater with ropes. As soon as the weather started getting rough, drinking water was rationed. A cup each—just enough for drinking and cooking— and immediately the tanks were locked again.

For the first two weeks the weather was fair, and the three dhows sailed together. By the time they reached the Red Sea, the sticky heat had become unbearable. All aboard were exhausted by the strenuous voyage. If they fell asleep, they were soon woken up by the rats that swarmed the deck. Then suddenly, the north-easterly winds turned vicious. Within minutes a huge storm developed. The dhow now rolled and pitched more than ever. The experienced *nakhoda* screamed his orders. A sailor climbed up the tall mast and lowered the large triangular sail.

The sea was strong and powerful. The choppy waves pounded mercilessly against the dhow's hull. Kirparam tried to be of some help, but stood inert, rooted, without the kinetics. Desperate to relieve himself. The restraint caused his face to distort with tension. His hand went over his crotch; a hot liquid trickled down between his legs. Fear drained the blood from his face. He looked at the long drop leading to a small square basket at the outer side of the dhow and felt dizzy. But he was beyond thinking now. He crouched over the edge of the moving and heaving ship and relieved himself at last, with the furious rain and wind hammering away at him. The waves poured in mercilessly. Kirparam did not dare look into the roaring ocean. If the rope slipped from his hands, he knew it could be the end. He would be immediately swallowed by the angry waves. By the time he climbed out of the little basket, up the rope and back to the deck, he was completely drenched, but safe.

The storm raged on, increasingly menacing. Colossal walls of water rose around him, waiting to bear him away. 'We are going down,' he screamed, 'our little boat is ready to sink.' He gasped for breath and looked at the might of the water. All the passengers lay flat on the deck, their eyes closed in fervent prayer. Some started to cry, others vomited until they fell flat in sheer exhaustion. When the sail ropes broke, and the crew nearly lost control, they thought that the end had come.

Finally the storm moved away. The sky was still overcast. The clouds were grey, but the fury of the storm seemed to have abated. The sea was calming down. Charts were of no use in such conditions. And, they found themselves alone. The other two dhows were wrecked and everyone was lost at sea near Sokotra; all aboard perished. The voyage had been dangerous. The storm had been so bad that it took something like six weeks to cover the distance of 2,400 miles, instead of the usual four weeks. With its huge sail billowing, the *jahazi* rode the monsoon wind towards 'Zingibar', the land of the black people.

Zanzibar the beautiful. Fishing boats with colourful sails glinted in the sun. Under the palms, boatmen could be heard singing melancholy sea chants while working on their nets. Their long-drawn plaintive notes lingered in the air. The month of March, when the north-east monsoon, the Kaskazi, blows, heralds the arrival of all kinds of dhows in Zanzibar. Hundreds. Of different types—the Kotia, the Dhangi, the Boom—the largest among the dhows from Asia. Some of these dhows carried up to 300 passengers, as well as goods such as dried fish, dates, salt, henna from Oman, carpets from Persia, dry fruit, pottery and glass goblets, phials of attar of roses, brass oil lamps, tall pottery jars of oil and wine, tiles from south India, ghee from Sokotra. In April, on their return journey to Asia with the Kuzi breezes, the south-west monsoon, they took back with them coconut, soap, sugar, and rope made from coconut husk.

No one knows when it all started, the sailing of Persian and Indian dhows to and from East Africa on the seasonal winds. For centuries, traders came to buy slaves and ivory in exchange for perfumes, jewelry and cloth. The sea trade brought techniques from India, from the Middle East, from Arabia. Arab dhows sailed in large numbers from Iran and Iraq to buy mangrove poles. The Shirazis from Persia brought their precious skills with them. Together with the Arab colonists, Zanzibar became their headquarters. Many Arabs settled in the coastal towns after marrying into local Somali and Bantu tribes. As a result of this intermarriage, the Swahili (from *sahil* for coast in Arabic) began to occupy the coast from south Somalia to Tanzania and the islands off the coast—Pate, Lamu and Zanzibar.

Indians had for long been a business community along the East African coast, but by the time Kirparam landed in 1898, Zanzibar had lost its old commercial predominance. East Africa had already been partitioned among the European powers. Exploratory desires

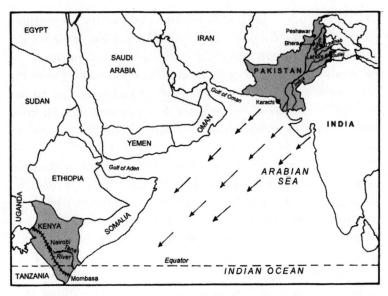

Lala Kirparam went from Karachi to Mombasa in a dhow blown across
the Indian Ocean by the north-east monsoon (indicated by arrows).
Pakistan and Kenya were part of larger British colonies at the time.

and the new missionary zeal to uplift 'backward peoples' plus
their need for vital raw materials brought about a 'scramble for
Africa': it was no misnomer. The continent was carved up so fast
that by the end of the nineteenth century the outlines of the various
empires were pretty much decided.

At least five European countries had jostled for control of East
Africa. Uganda, rather than Kenya, was the coveted prize. The
Anglo-German agreement of 1890 defined the boundaries of
German and British territories in East Africa. The colonial period
and its influences in so many ways gave the third world its present
shape. After slavery, colonization was the most crucial event in
African history. The old period of Arab ascendancy was at its end.
Zanzibar was still a maritime crossroad in the Indian Ocean. A
point of departure for explorations into the interior. Without docks,
however, ships had to stay out in the harbour; and little boats ferried
people and merchandise to and fro.

The lean ochre-coloured dhow in which Kirparam was travelling came sailing over the now calm waters. After weeks in the blazing sun and airless heat, and after surviving severe rainstorms, the odyssey of the dhow came to its terminus—the only dhow of the three to make it. Half-starved when they arrived, passengers joined the crew in a thanksgiving song for their safe arrival. Some cried from fear and exhaustion while unloading the meagre possessions that had survived the voyage.

Kirparam had had enough of travelling by dhow. He had lost count of the days that had passed since he had left the Indian shore, so he got off right there. Drunk in the soul and the eyes, he forgot all dangers, the uncertainty of arrival and the fatigue. Yet, ready to laugh at his folly in inviting misfortune. At that moment, he felt he could accept almost anything.

Coloured silhouettes outlined the waterfront. Woodworkers were carving beautiful chests and doors studded with brass. Tall stately palms, almost symbolic of the East African littoral yet not indigenous to Africa, swayed in the warm tropical breeze redolent with the aroma of clove and frangipani. Brought across the Indian Ocean from Malabar many centuries ago were papaya, banana, coconut palm, coffee and clove—the list was endless. Eighty-five kilometres of coral reef in the Indian Ocean, the place evoked romance and sorrow.

Wealthy merchants clad in elegant silks, their wives laden in gold but veiled, lived in luxury here. Large and populous, their many stone buildings with carved wooden doors were an obvious testament to their wealth. Strong emotions stirred in Kirparam's breast as he strolled in the lanes overlooked by balconies with intricately carved filigree balustrades that cast shadows across the narrow streets below. The heavy wooden doors intricately carved with symbolic patterns in abundance and studded with brass handles were very similar to those back home in Miani.

The day was punctuated with the muezzin calling the faithful to prayer. Women in black *bui-buis* held their veils with hennaed hands. Colourful *kangas* visible underneath, they walked along confidently. Small girls sold jasmine flowers in little baskets. Men in long white *kanzus*, embroidered *kofias* on their heads, strolled lazily. Islam on the coast was distinctly African. In the fruit and vegetable market, Africans, Arabs and Indians mingled together. The strong smell of clove and cardamom followed Kirparam everywhere. For a brief moment it brought back memories of his Chacha's little *halwai* shop. But the freedom, the adventure and endless new discoveries had completely engulfed him by now. The terrible sea voyage was very quickly forgotten. Just like a new mother with her baby—totally oblivious of the painful labour.

Dharamsalas, *musafirkhanas*, *sarais*, a few Indian hostels and the many Indian families on the island readily welcomed the new arrivals with free board and lodging. And endless stories about brave men who regularly travelled in dhows every season to and from Kutch on the western coast of India to Zanzibar. To them, Zanzibar was '*Cutcha-Sual*', the place of Hindus and *Suali*, men living in the *Sual*. The building of the railway was a popular topic that he heard discussed constantly, and at length. 'That is where job opportunities lie,' he was told. Without much money left, Kirparam made his way up to the mainland.

Mbuyuni. Under the baobab. *Miembeni*. At the mangoes. The native town of Mombasa, one of East Africa's oldest settlements—with a history of over 2,000 years—traces its name from these trees. Giant flamboyant trees—elaborate and extravagant—with rich, brilliant red flowers and row upon row of pink and white frangipani. The Nandi flame, with its resplendent flame-like ochre flowers. The jacaranda with its bell-shaped lavender flowers. Many-hued bougainvillea, in addition to huge coconut palms, gave the town that magical quality.

Mombasa was referred to by Ptolemy as 'Tonike' in the second century. By the seventh century, Arabs had begun to settle along the coast; Hindu traders followed soon after. Trade flourished and sailing vessels came from as far off as China. The rituals of buying and selling had their own currents of urgency. Frequent conquerors and the many explorers led to confrontation among cultures and religions. Mombasa then came to be known as Mvita, the isle of war. Centuries of trade with the outside world quickened its pace of life.

Sun, Islam, the Portuguese, the monsoons, dhows, traders—not necessarily in that order—but Mombasa soon grew into a strong urban centre. The hub of commerce was the old dhow port on the eastern side of the island. Here one would come across Somalis, Yemenis, Persians and Arabs in elegantly wound turbans and flowing robes rich in embroidery, daggers at the side, drinking *kahawa* bought from street vendors, going around with large brass pots, clapping two porcelain cups together to attract customers. One could see a Punjabi or a Chinese discussing the price of shark fin, spices and rice from India, and dates from Arabia. The old town became a cosmopolis. It certainly had the air of a city, yet its eclectic Swahili culture did not travel inland.

Rising from the heart of the town was Fort Jesus, silent witness to the town's occupation and turbulent history. The sixteenth-century Portuguese fort with its thick walls was to later serve as a military prison for Indian prisoners during the two world wars. Other than that, a main street named after the Portuguese explorer Vasco da Gama was the only reminder of Portuguese conquest. Much of the architecture—elegant fretwork balconies and shutters—was probably influenced by the Indian-style Zanzibari tastes of Omani occupiers in the nineteenth century.

African tribes, Swahilis, Goans and Europeans. These were the main communities in that melting pot towards the end of the nineteenth century, when Kirparam arrived. To him the habitation looked like an Indo-Arab town. The civilization was more or less Arab, but Indians—mainly from Kutch and Gujarat—in their colourful robes contrasted with the Arabs in snow-white *kanzus*. The Arab quarter was near the northern harbour. Shops, government offices and other European dwellings were situated on higher ground on the way to Kilindini. Facing the sea, ancient tombs lined the seafront. Africans and poorer Swahilis were located behind the old town in their rectangular huts roofed with *makuti* plaited palm leaf, so characteristic of the Swahili coast towns and much in contrast to the circular grass roofs found inland.

The Indian quarter, the more densely populated part of the town, lay further inland. Here was the Shiva temple, the Parsi temple and a beautiful Bohra mosque. Between Ndia Kuu and Fort Jesus lived Hindus and Muslims. *Mithaiwallahs* and *johris*—confectioners and jewellers. Bohras (from Vohoru in Gujarati, to trade), Khojas and Memons, Badalas and Kutchi Muslims.

A considerable number of Indian settlers were Muslims of the Ismaili Khoja sect, many of whom had arrived in dhows in the late nineteenth century, accompanied by their wives and children. Originally Hindus of the trading class, their weddings were sometimes conducted by Hindu priests. Khoja missionary Sadruddin, reputed to be the author of a version of the *Dasavatar*, the ten incarnations of Vishnu, explained that Imam Ali was the tenth incarnation of Vishnu. The tenth chapter became a sacred book in their scriptures. Read at religious services or recited at the bedside of the dying, it was a relic of their Hindu origins. They were to follow the Hindu law in regard to testate and intestate succession.

British East Africa was declared a protectorate in 1895. On 11 December, George Whitehouse landed at Mombasa charged with the task of building a railway from the Indian Ocean to Lake Victoria. He soon found out how difficult it was to get skilled workers here. Despite years of experience in similar work in countries like South Africa, Mexico and India, this was to become his major problem. The administrators were puzzled by what they saw as the Africans' indifference to the lure of money; they could not be induced to work for monetary gain on the construction of the railway. These people did not understand survival laws. So labour from India became the obvious choice. *Dhoti*-clad workers disembarked from ships carrying shovels and bedrolls.

In January the following year, masons, carpenters, clerks, surveyors of all categories arrived by steamer from India. Construction work on the railway line started a few months later.

By April 1898, the first train left Mombasa for its journey to Voi, one hundred miles inland. Thus began a new chapter in this part of the continent. 'The railway is the beginning of all history in Kenya.' These would be the famous words of Sir Edward Grigg, the new commissioner to British East Africa.

The railway was looked at as a way to ensure the influence of Great Britain. The 'dark continent' was undermined by the belief that before the advent of the white Christian people, it was inhabited by a barbaric people. Lacking a culture. Bringing civilization and Christianity were therefore 'noble' things to do. As early as 1901, Grigg began to encourage European settlement in the highlands. Indians were immediately confined to the lowlands.

On arrival in Mombasa, Kirparam had to undergo strict quarantine regulations. A camp had been pitched for medical examination of the new arrivals. Dirty clothes were disinfected as measures against the plague, the feet checked for hookworm. The first rail tracks had already been laid part of the way by the *dhoti*-clad workers with their shovels when he was recruited. His first job in Africa was to build banks of earth in the lower areas and cut a path into the hillside on reaching high ground. Once the ground was ready, they put the rails into place on top of metal bars. The task of plate-laying was arduous and dreary. A few hours under the sun, and their hands were scorched, their bare feet full of blisters, their legs showing under *dhotis* dyed in a reddish liquid. Patches of iodoform stood out here and there!

Drinking water was brought each day by train to this dry stretch of land. But it never seemed enough. When the supply ran out, they searched for water anywhere, even in dirty pools. This they strained through the ends of their muslin turbans and drank without a blink. The pugree—normal headgear for Indian males—certainly was more than a cultural tradition, a protection for the head from heat and cold. Kirparam also remembered making a rope out of their turbans to lasso zebras in the Athi plains, or when they were stranded for long periods in remote places without utensils. Their long—sometimes over six yards long—turbans were folded into the shape of a cup as workers cooked the rice therein—with the heat of the sand!

He would also recall the time Roshanlal was chased by a lion. Within seconds, he had climbed up a tree. He sat there for a long time while the lion hung around at the bottom—damn cunning animal. Then Roshanlal unwound his turban, lit it with his bidi and threw the burning piece of cloth towards the lion, scaring it away. Imagine if he had shaken with fear and fallen off the branch? Kirparam's laughter was still a little hesitant.

His reverie was rudely cut short by a harsh voice from behind. The huge man was shouting at Kirparam. 'I thought you come from a *halwai*'s family. Is this how they taught you to cook? The *dal* does not taste like *dal*.'

'Sorry, *praji* (elder brother),' replied Kirparam. 'But you can see that the firewood does not burn well. It causes a lot of smoke.' The lentil curry and *chapatis* were eaten yet again with an aroma of smoke.

They worked in shifts to prepare communal meals. From varying denominations, they cooked meals that conformed to the dietary restrictions of the Muslims, Hindus and Sikhs. Meat eaters refused to eat game meat—rhino, wildebeest etc.—that was easily available, while vegetarians often had to make do with an unbalanced diet. Some bought goats from natives for milk. They even tried to domesticate the buffalo for milk as was done in India, but the ferocious African buffalo refused to yield to such needs.

To break the routine of long hours of tiring and monotonous work, Kirparam had taken to helping in the canteen during the lunch break—a job he was most familiar with. Here he was happier. He came in contact with Punjabis, Baluchis, Sindhis and those from the North Western Frontier Province—people from his homeland. Bearded Pathans with flowing baggy trousers and clean-shaven Punjabis in straight pyjamas. Both wore turbans, but the Pathans wore a *kula* cap inside. You could tell a person's origins and trade from the way they wore their headgear—pugrees and topees. Up until the eve of the first world war, Muslims formed a large part of the Indian population in British East Africa. While the caste system as such did not exert its pressures, the social mobility of the individual and frequently his choice of employment continued to be influenced by considerations of caste and creed.

The Indian workers on the railway lived in crowded mud sheds or tents close to the rail tracks, without even canvas sheets to spread on the floor. Bonfires were lit to ward off the cold; the men were not supplied proper blankets. Kirparam too suffered. A strong draught made its way through the worn-out tent he occupied, peppered with holes—worn out by use and exposure to changing climatic conditions. It would be threadbare when Kirparam reached Nairobi.

At sunrise each day—Monday or Sunday—the labourers emerged sleepily from their tents to go to work. Lured by wily agents, some of these coolies had left their homes in India, little realizing that they were leaving not just their villages, but also the country! The agents never explained beforehand that they would have to work in the wilds of Africa amidst man-eating lions and hostile tribes. One poor fellow had understood that his job was to kill birds on a tree in a nearby village in India!

There was no fencing around the camps, and predators always lurked nearby. They could hear the roar of lions, laughter of hyenas, snorting of zebras, trumpeting of elephants. Attracted by food, safari ants often raided the tents and the food stores. Some nights, snakes slithered into the tents. There was no place to keep hard-earned money and other precious items. Once again, the versatile turbans came to the rescue.

The natives had lost most of their livestock in a severe three-year drought. A rinderpest epidemic decimated large domestic herds. Swarms of locusts and armyworm devastated grasslands and native plantations. Hunger could be seen on their faces, especially the Akamba and the Kikuyu. They started raiding tents, threatening violence with bows and arrows. The coolies had no weapons for self-defence; only officers and white subordinates were permitted to carry arms.

The rains failed again, resulting in widespread famine. Some places, there was only brackish water: it made them sick, especially at Maji ya Chumvi. They used salt water for all purposes—drinking, washing and cooking. Hot, dusty, exhausted, dehydrated men with no other recourse. Some strained this water through their turbans, but they still had stomach problems: diarrhoea with cholera, amoebic dysentery. Frantically untying their *dhotis* or pajamas as the cholera and dysentery opened their bowels, they squatted helplessly on the tracks. Even railway transport animals died drinking this foul water after grazing on the coarse dry vegetation of the Taru desert.

After the long drought came the deluge. Much of November, it poured. At first, the coolies were happy to take a bath after so long. They shouted with pleasure and jumped in the pools. However, ponds, rivers and streams were usually also frequented by wildlife. The rivers supported large populations of crocodiles and it was not unusual for men to disappear without a trace. Occasionally, a decomposed or partially eaten body was discovered—identification being possible only through the clothes. Sometimes, when men disappeared from camps without a trace, officers, even though aware of the harsh conditions in which the men were living and working, called it desertion!

The downpour continued and became torrential. Soon the air became humid and work on the line came to a halt. Very little work was done on the rails. And in the puddles, mosquitoes began to breed; an outbreak of malaria followed. Many lay immobilized again. The disease spread like fire through their rain-soaked tents. By December, the rain had not ceased. The drenched workers in their equally drenched tents waited for it to stop. As soon as it did, however, the fierceness of the sun took over. Once again, they lay immobilized by thirst; not a drop to drink. Stagnant water in the waterholes was again strained through turbans.

Moreover, ulcers caused by thorns in the dense scrub refused to heal in the coastal climate. Even minor scratches from the poisonous thorns of the euphorbia plant tended to go septic. Some thorns were soft and green; others hard and sharp, long as fingers. There were triangular ones, short and broad, but acute and bent at the point. These were the more dangerous ones because they cut through even the thickest cloth.

The workers had their *dhotis* torn to ribbons by the thorns, their shoes and slippers came off in halves while walking over sharp stones, and they were provided with neither protective footwear nor clothing. They had to make do with traditional homespun cotton cloth and slippers in the thorny jungle and stony terrain. They worked seven days a week for a sum of fifteen rupees a month.

The jigger was a pesky little insect accidentally imported from tropical America through cargo caravans to the East African coast. Very quickly, it became common in the red soil, and was found in abundance in freshly excavated rail tracks. The little insects would burrow under workers' toenails and lay eggs there, making the feet swell up. This spread rapidly in the coolie camps. Each night they would inspect their toes, and painfully extract the eggs with a needle or sharp penknife. It was important to make an incision in the flesh as soon as possible, before the eggs hatched and spread through the bloodstream. If that happened, the toe would have to be amputated.

They lay incapacitated by malaria, amoebic dysentery or pneumonia, gangrene from the mauling of a lion or leopard. At times like these, especially in the night sounds of the jungles of Africa, Kirparam would desperately wonder if he had done the right thing. The next morning, however, the sense of adventure and excitement, more often than not, overtook the melancholy.

Many chose to return to India, while several others died of dehydration and sunstroke. Out of a total of over 30,000 who had come to work on the railway, by the end only 6,700-odd remained. The railway budget did not make provision for illness, disability or death. It was a mean, stringent budget with provision for basic food and shelter. A meagre diet, often contaminated and unhealthy, meant that scurvy was common. Hospitals were poorly equipped, with too few medical staff and even fewer facilities and medication. But such issues were not immediately important; the colonials were in a hurry. There was quite a race to build the railway; the Germans were constructing a similar tract in German East Africa. Without these coolies, the railway may perhaps never have been built.

At a salary of twenty-five rupees a month, *jamedars* were delegated to collect men. Lahore and Karachi served as recruitment centres. Coolies were engaged on a three-year contract with return passage. At the railway site in British East Africa, *jamedars* were chosen for their disciplinary hand; they could be quite harsh. The coolies themselves could become a force to reckon with—when they had had enough, they took revenge, with all kinds of tricks and notorious devices.

The rails reached Mtito Andei, the vulture forest—where baobab trees abounded. According to African mythology, the first baobab planted by God was an ordinary-looking tree, but it refused to stay in one place, and wandered around the countryside. As punishment, God planted it back again upside-down and immobilized it. Baobabs may live well over 2,000 years

Beneath a baobab, Kirparam positioned himself in front of his provisions. By now, he had become a full-time employee of the travelling canteen. Wherever the train went, he and his employer, the *halwai*, went. With a small sack slung behind his right shoulder, he boarded the train with the other coolies. With the barest of equipment, he helped cook a surprisingly delicious Indian meal. Wooden packing cases were quickly turned into tables or shelves at every new stop. Feeding construction workers on the railway was more in his line of work. He felt freer. Work on the track had been harder. Fortunately, it had been a short phase.

He moved in with the *halwai*. The old man was called Gandhi, no relative of the future Mahatma, Mohandas Karamchand. *Halwai* Gandhi was a simple peasant from the plains of Jhelum district of north-west Punjab. Then, one night, thieves broke into their little camp. Kirparam was younger and stronger than his employer and was able to drive away the potential looters. The old *halwai* was grateful, but the incident had been too traumatic. He lost the will to fight it out under such harsh conditions. The same night, he confided to Kirparam that his only wish now was to return home, back to India.

'Would you be interested?' he asked Kirparam. For a minute Kirparam looked at him, baffled, but when he finally realized what the old man was proposing, he did not need to think. The decision was spontaneous. His luck seemed to be changing before he could even grasp the turn of events. He rifled through his pockets and found only five rupees. 'It's okay, my son.' Patting him on the back, the white-haired man continued, 'By the grace of God, you will pay me back in instalments through the mail.' The old man did not feel nostalgic, only thankful. He breathed a sigh of relief, and left the very next morning.

Kirparam did not sleep much that night: the excitement had been too much. Him, the owner of a canteen! It was better than his wildest dreams. Wasn't it only a short while ago that he had left India and embarked on a dhow in a state of loss? The recovery was remarkable. The glow on his face reflected a happiness he had not known before. Perhaps the impromptu decision he had taken in Karachi had been a good idea after all—to start afresh in a new country.

This was easier said than done, for life along the construction line was never easy. The tracks traversed a damp hot zone stretching about forty miles from the coast to the cold bracing air of the hills at Kikuyu 300 miles away. In between lay miles of dry country fed by a few small rivers and streams. Obtaining drinking water, meat or green vegetables was always difficult. Rice, *atta, dal, ghee*— all of these had to be imported from Punjab, as the staple food of the African was maize flour. Gujaratis and south Indians were quite happy with rice, but not these Punjabi men. They needed their daily stack of chapatis, though imported wheat cost three to four times as much.

Moreover, superior castes were hesitant to eat or drink from the hands of an inferior one. Kirparam was a Kshatriya, a caste below the Brahmins, and so he had to be careful with them; he only served them food purified by cooking on a fire. Water had to be served in a metal vessel scoured with earth.

The priestly class was looked at either as 'those who lived on charity', or those who had money and influence. From where he came, Hindus were generally less strict about purity rules, and Kirparam easily eliminated other limitations and restrictions he might have been burdened with. There could be no return for him to the 'purity' of these past traditions—if such a state ever existed.

Adaptable and culturally flexible, and therefore possibly better equipped to withstand the dramatic changes that he was experiencing, Kirparam's unusual range allowed him to easily shed the rigidity of caste and food taboos. He was equally comfortable with vegetables and 'forbidden' foods. Under the circumstances, he had no problem in throwing overboard most of the scruples of defilement. When necessary, he could go without food for days. An air of liberalism hung about him. He had a great capacity for excitement, curiosity and wonder—without this he could not so easily have crossed the wilds, jungles and deserts.

Sometimes, humble beginnings did not preclude sainthood. Baghali Shah had been a coolie on the first rail lines. He was killed at the site by a trolley that went out of control. They buried him at the spot at which he died, at Mackinnon Road in the Taru desert. In years to come, trains would slow down when passing by his simple grave—in respect, or in the superstitious hope of a safe journey. Baghali Shah had become a saint. Kirparam came to pay his respects and sat there all alone for a long while. He had never met Baghali Shah, but those who had, could only wonder and marvel.

Seyyid Baghali Shah had been a big strong man. He could lift more stones in his *karhai* than any of the other workers. Yet he was not the big bully that he could have been. His fellow labourers stood in awe of him. Even the white supervisors treated him with respect. Some kind of aura surrounded his being. One suddenly felt a little humbled in his presence. Those who worked closely with him swore that the *karai* of stones did not lie on top of his head—it floated above his head. It was also said that he spent much time in prayer, or alone in the forest surrounded by, and communicating with, wild animals. People insisted that he had some spiritual and magical powers.

A mausoleum was built at his grave. In death, Baghali Shah became a legend and a source of solace to the troubled. His departed soul emanated a certain kind of serenity; perhaps that was his power. Years later, people continued to visit his grave. Families ensured a quick halt en route to Mombasa, and again on their way back. They came with beautiful red or gold silk cloth to lay over his grave. They offered prayers and donated money. Many came especially all the way from Nairobi or Mombasa to ask for boons. Barren women asked for children. The sick appealed to be healed, the unhappy begged for peace. Worship transcended community and caste barriers; his apparent divine power attracted devotees regardless of their origin.

There was no one about, and Kirparam stayed on, thinking of nothing, emptying himself, becoming *shunya*, the void of the Buddha. The calm was broken by the fading light which descended precisely at 6.30 p.m.

The afternoon came to its end. The light dimmed; all at once night set in. The twilight was brief. At this latitude, the length of the day hardly varied: the sun rose at 6–6.30 a.m., and set around 6.30 p.m., with a very short dawn and dusk. The ordered regularity at the equator—twelve hours of day and twelve hours of night—seemed to have been ordained as the perfect rhythm. Kirparam knew he must return to camp.

Night was approaching. Once more, they were filled with dread. The terrified cry of 'Sher! Simba! Simba!' shattered the calm of many early mornings in the Nyika. The cry and the panic was infectious; it spread throughout the camp with alarming speed, continuing while coolies vanished. Some took to sleeping in trees, others dug holes and covered themselves with dry leaves and branches, some hid in huge pipes or built lion-proof shelters on top of elevated water tanks. Or they lit fires. Construction work on the site was delayed; many decided to leave the site in the hope of returning 'home'.

The Nyika was a flat, dry, treeless desolate region, the beginning of the Tsavo desert. According to the Wakamba, a certain evil spirit had a habit of enticing men away at night and after leading them down to the river, making away with them. They called this place Tsavo, which means 'slaughter' in Kikamba. Between Mtito Andei and Voi, near the Tsavo river, was where the famous man-eating lions roamed. Here, 136 miles from Mombasa, for three weeks, two cunning and voracious lions dragged Indian and African workers from their tents at night. They roamed in the darkness when all was quiet, when the men were asleep. The lions were confident of their timing. They struck at the darkest hour. The lions ate all—bones, flesh, skin, blood—leaving not a trace behind.

Suddenly, it became very cold. The silence of the tropical night was pierced by trumpeting. The roar of a lion was heard in the distance. Other reactions and replies followed: a frog or a toad vented his croaks, while crickets enveloped the area with their smooth-flowing chanting. It was a typically ferocious, bittersweet African night. Once more calm returned, but one could guess that not far off silent sufferings were imminent: the gashing of a throat . . . hacking of a vertebra . . . slashed limbs . . . a dreadful death.

The Maasai said they knew how to drive the lions away. They got together with all sorts of instruments to make a big din. They blew upon a spiralled *kudu* horn to call their people together. Vocalizing pathetic invocations to discourage the animal from attacking the area, they created an uproar. They knew that the lion did not like noise. That it operated in silence. But these two lions had gone beyond all reason. They had acquired a new taste—that of man. At first they were not successful in their efforts to carry off a victim, but as time went on, they seemed to stop at nothing, and indeed, braved any danger to obtain their favourite food.

After miles of thick thornbush, tsetse and mosquito, the rails slowly reached Simba. Clothed in sparse and stunted acacia, Simba lay not far from Makindu. The luminous plains were already yielding to highlands. It was seen as a fresh air camp. Even other animals knew it. There was a constant annual migration of large herds—duiker, antelope, *dik-dik*, giraffe, gazelle, zebra, onyx and *kudu*. They came here in search of water and greenery.

They would come in thousands, as they had been doing for generations, all headed in the same direction—south, towards what is now the Tanganyika border. In spite of its reputation as a 'man-eating station', Alladina Visram, an Indian pioneer entrepreneur who had dukas (small shops) all along the railway, had opened one at Simba station too. Kirparam was also following the railway line and pitched camp to set up his little *halwai* canteen, ready to serve *halwa* and *pakoras* to the railway coolies.

There were challenges upon challenges. The heavens had opened their gates: it rained without ceasing. There was water everywhere. It seemed as if the deluge was upon them. With the torrential rains came scorpions, snakes and disease. Just when it was thought that they had disappeared, the lions returned. One night, the coolies heard a familiar sound. It was the call of the lion.

Now the call came from across the river every night. It was obvious who reigned over the territory. They were cunning, these two. They could lie very quiet for much of the night, without the flicker of a blade of grass. At the peak of the night, when even the frogs had stopped croaking and the silence lay thick, when the bitter cold immobilized all living beings, they appeared. Mysteriously, as magical fabrications from thin air, as a play of light between late night and early dawn. Apparitions, creatures of imagination or hallucinations, mirage or reality—it was hard to tell. Hazy images, ambiguous states, elusive realities—were they or were they not there? Who could say? They were never seen, yet their baffling groans were real. And death was real.

Kirparam recounts a night he was almost killed by one of the lions: 'My heart missed a beat. I could hear them from somewhere. Then a shadow came upon me. I could feel it, but I could see nothing. I could sense hot air close to my face. My fists tightened. My limbs stiffened. I felt cold; then I became numb. Suddenly, there was a scream. At first, I thought it was me, but no: it came from my left side. What was real, what was illusion—I could not have said in those long seconds. Everything happened as if in a blur. I have been taken, I thought. How long do I have to live?

'Suddenly, my past came alive in front of me. I thought of my family. My mother is no more. I have a wife somewhere, far away. I can't reach her to even say goodbye—to tell her that I, Kirparam Ramchand, am being eaten, that I am dying. Her blurry image seemed to be receding far away, as if she was being swallowed into a dark tunnel. *Hardei, Hardei. . .* I screamed the name without opening my mouth. "Aahhh!" This time I knew the scream was not mine. There was movement right next to me. I couldn't budge. Paralysed with fear, I floated between light and dark.

'I had my eyes shut tight, but I was fully alert to the slightest reverberation. The silhouette moved; I felt it instinctively. I couldn't see the contours, nor did I have the courage to open my eyes. I felt that if I did, I might attract attention, and that could set my death-trap. When I finally opened my eyes, the place next to me lay empty. The mattress was still warm and full of his breath. But he was no more. *Pola, Pola,* I cried in my soul. But Pola was no more. He had been taken by the brute. I had heard Pola cry and scream, but I lay impotent, unable to move or ask for help. Pola's screams are still alive within my being.

'The night was an eternity, almost. I lay there immobile and held my breath as in *shavasana*, the corpse pose. Only, this did not have the quietness of a meditative posture. For a moment even my thoughts stopped, too stunned to surface. And when they did, dreadful images roamed the murky waters of my mind. My eyes did not shut the rest of the night. I tried to open myself to inner forces to receive renewed strength and inspiration. Rather, I tried to dispel the fear of what I might perceive.

'At last it was dawn. I was relieved. The beams of the rising sun covered the hill and the valley. They awakened a light in my heart. Ashamedly, I never felt so good to be alive. . . Many nights we heard the crunching of jaws. Surely, these were the dogs of Kali baying in the skins of the lions.'

'Kali' was a word constantly on the lips of these early Indian migrants. It got incorporated into the Swahili language with a similar meaning—fierce, terrifying.

The next day, bits of the man's body were found strewn here and there, at a distance from the camp. The coolies got together for the painful job of gathering the bones and performing the last rites. The body could not have been washed even if it were whole—there was no water to be spared. It was cremated in its bits, in its soiled and sweaty clothes, with thorny scrub insufficient to consume the fire. Without the sacred sandalwood, the marigold flowers garlanding his neck, or the ghee poured with each chanted mantra.

Unbathed mourners, clad in white garments, paid their last respects as they lit the pyre. There were Hindus, Muslims and Sikhs, and each recited prayers in his own way. Two days later, the ashes of the dead man were collected and put in an urn to be ultimately scattered in the waters of the Indian Ocean at Mombasa. When possible, ashes were sent to the family in India with a returning coolie. Sometimes deaths were not even recorded and it took a while before relatives came to know what had befallen their kin.

Kirparam never really got over the incident. Its memory would haunt him throughout his life. It was yet another episode that would change his outlook on life and death forever. For the first few days, he often thought: 'It could have been me that night. But it wasn't. I survived by inches. I know now that I have been given another chance. I must be prepared to appreciate this gift of life. And somehow, to give back a little of what I have received.'

He especially liked to narrate the tale to his grandchildren. He would laugh a little and say that the only reason the lion did not take him was because he had eaten a lot of garlic and chilli that night.

On cold August nights, around the warmth of his *angeethi*, where he could warm his hands and lower his eyes, he would look into the red embers, and invariably start with the story of Kali, the fierce one. Her body entirely black, a garland of white skulls around her neck, her protruding red tongue . . . and the children eagerly anticipated the gripping thriller.

3

Melting pot

Elala Onu Ai
(The eye of *Enkai* [God] is large)
　　　　—Maasai saying

D awn is the most beautiful phenomenon for the early gazer of the skies. In her he sees an image of the world anew. While everything else changes, she remains constant—never stooping, never withering. Emerging fresh and glorious every morning, ever ancient, ever young, dawn is the elder sister of the night. She awakes all creatures and puts everything into motion.

This day, the daybreak was disturbed by the piercing sound of a whistle shattering the silence. Such a sound had never been heard by the Maasai, not even since the white man came many moons ago. Young and old, it frightened them all. The animals that came to the pool for water were agitated and darted away without drinking. Loud and shrill, the sound challenged the entire history of their land.

This was the whistle of UR35, the first railway train heading towards Nairobi. Not that the sound was altogether unexpected. Work had been in progress for a while, and the railway line had slowly been advancing across the dry Nyika right up to the edge of the Kenyan highlands. The rails reached a screen of palms fringing a small tributary of the Athi river. Not far from here, the Ngong hills, rising 8,000 feet above sea level, stretched in a long ridge from north to south. One degree south of the equator, a small stream rose from the base of Mt Kilimanjaro. It was a meeting point of Maasai, Kikuyu and Akamba territories, and home to thousands of wild animals. At the foot of the Kikuyu hills, the gateway to healthy highlands, Nairobi stood at over 5,000 feet above sea level.

The route map prepared in 1883 by Joseph Thompson for the Royal Geographic Society of East Africa showed 'Maerobi' 120 miles south of Machakos. The chief engineer, George Whitehouse, chose Nairobi as his central site solely because of the change in gradient between Mombasa and the Nairobi river—a climb of 5,400 feet.

Shortly after the construction of the Uganda Railway had begun, Dr Boedeker, an Anglo-Indian doctor from England and one of the earlier pioneers of British East Africa, visited the area. Later, in the temporary role of medical officer, his opinion of the site of Nairobi was: '[it is] the worst possible choice for any sort of urban centre by virtue of its swamps alone. Even among the caravan leaders, the site had always been recognized as an unhealthy locality swarming with mosquitoes.' In October 1899, Ronald Preston, in charge of plate-laying, wrote of it as 'a bleak, swampy stretch of soppy landscape, devoid of human habitation of any sort'.

In the cool windy month of May 1899—during which time the young Mohandas Karamchand Gandhi was probably fighting the Boer War in South Africa—and the not-so-long-forgotten wife that Kirparam had left behind was giving birth to their first child in faraway Miani—Kirparam arrived with the rest of the railway party in Nairobi. Tents were pitched on the soft ground around the swamp. Mabati shanties, built from corrugated iron sheets, were constructed. Soon the place of cool waters for the Maasai, a swamp for others, took on the airs of a 'railway town'—the twenty-sixth station on the line, the last halt before the highlands.

It was a process of fertilization, germination and birth. From tents and aluminium sheets a new town was born. The swamp was to grow—not without its labour pains. Plague would break out before long; there would be death in its embryonic stages.

'The land belongs to *Enkai*, it is his property. It may be divided up for practical purposes, but no individual nor any family may own it,' the Maasai had always said. The land, to them, was sacred to the extent that they would not pierce it—not even to build a well, or to bury the dead. A Nilo-Hamite tribe—that had wandered from the regions of the upper Nile (and like to think of Egypt as the land of their origin) some time in the seventeenth century to a contrasting Bantu area in the east—came to be known as the Maasai. It was the allure of a bronze statue, a dark antique divinity, ready for warrior expeditions, for a hard life, for strict disciplinary rules, for complex initiation rites . . . will my son cry out while being circumcised? Will he bring shame upon himself and his family?

Their tall, slender bodies gleamed with cow fat and ochre. An exclusive diet of milk and blood combined with rigorous training in warlike exercises gave the Maasai those admirable proportions. They were always very scantily dressed and besmeared with red clay and oil. The long limbs accentuated with brightly coloured beads created a dramatic impact. By the eighteenth century, they had spread over much of the Rift valley. Because of the fertility of this land, people had been migrating here for centuries. Nilo-Hamitic tribes, mostly pastoralist groups—Kalenjin, Maasai, Turkana—came from the north and north-west of Africa. The Kikuyu and Akamba agricultural groups came from the west and south-east to central Kenya. The Maasai were fewer in number, but they held great power.

Maasai land begins in the south at Mt Kilimanjaro and Mt Meru, continuing up to Lake Baringo. It stretches from the Mau escarpment in the west to the Aberdare range and Laikipia plateau to the east, right up to Mt Kenya. Nearby, at mile 327, half-way between Mombasa and Lake Victoria, an engineer chose a place for the railway headquarters. It is known to the Maasai as Nakusontelon—the beginning of all beauty.

Nakusontelon was bisected by a small stream, which the Maasai called Uaso Nyarobae. Travelling caravans had often set up camp there. To the Maasai, it became Ngare N'erobi, a place of cold water. These nomads brought their herds here for water and green pasture. The river certainly had good drinking water. Ngare N'erobi became Nairobi, the place where Kirparam and Hardei would spend the better part of their lives, to have children, grandchildren and generations to come thereafter.

Much of the Maasai and other tribal lands were taken for European settlement. The lands the Europeans eventually occupied seemed to them unused, partly because they did not understand the indigenous system of land tenure. From an African point of view, all land was occupied, even when it was temporarily unused. However, the colonial government subsequently ignored the indigenous claims on land and decided to divide rights, privileges and living areas on a strictly racial basis.

In some cases, the British managed to make the Africans sign treaties, or they launched punitive expeditions. In other instances, resistance to British domination was fierce. In the case of the Maasai, the British took advantage of intra-tribal conflict, playing off one group against another. This enabled them to move the Maasai off their fertile land in the Rift valley to the Laikipia plateau up north and finally to a reserve in the south where the land was a lot poorer. The Maasai shifted their *kraals* (settlements) together with their precious herds of cows from the north of the river up to Ngong.

The Europeans were a new kind of foreigner, coming from a place nobody knew yet. The Africans thought that 'perhaps these people had no home of their own and were constantly wandering to look for a home'. So they came to be known as *wazungu*, the wanderers. A Swahili handbook of 1909 defines the word '*mzungu*' as a strange or startling thing. Whatever the true definition, the colour of the white skin was (to the African) unnatural and evoked some premature creature, whose lack of pigment proved that it was not yet ready for birth. The Indians knew them as *firangis* at first, then as *angrez*. Eventually, they came to refer to them as *wazungu*.

Before the British arrived in East Africa, the Maasai prophet Mbatian had predicted the arrival of an iron rhinoceros on the back of which a pink, strange people would be riding: 'The stranger will come and kick my people down and keep them under their feet, however brave and strong our people are.' 'An iron snake will one day cross our land . . .'—so ran the ancient Kikuyu tribal prophecy. The snake had arrived. The Kikuyu prepared to resist with a ferocity that could only be matched by the Maasai. But the iron snake survived and changed their lifestyle forever. The railway had opened the country up for colonization.

True, the Uganda Railway reduced the journey from the coast to Nairobi from six weeks or more to less than twenty-four hours. But the wildlife that had once roamed freely in herds of thousands— the graceful Grant's gazelle, Thomson's gazelle, reedbuck, duiker, hartebeeste, wildebeest, zebra, smaller antelope—were all frightened away by the clang of the rails and wouldn't come within a fifty-yard radius. The magic wrought by the Maasai foot-runner was also no more.

Life began to revolve round the railway. Administration headquarters shifted from Machakos, as it lacked water, to the mound above what some called a 'thoroughly English stream'. A flagpole and tin shack were quickly erected. At sundown the Union Jack was lowered. For a while the country was ruled from here. Nyarobe was reborn as 'Nairobi', an illegitimate child of the railway. Sickness dominated its conception. By the time the railhead reached the plain, many of the coolies were too ill to move.

Merchants and traders came to the new centre by bullock cart. Others travelled in *kaburu* carts—two-wheel wooden ox-carts— or four-wheel wagons brought in from South Africa by the Dutch. Generally travelling at night, they set up camp somewhere and lit a fire round the campsite to keep lions and other animals at bay. Walking around alone was not advisable, for the animals came out in large herds to drink. With an excellent climate and plenty of meat and green vegetables, the highlands became very attractive in no time. The Union Jack flew high each day. Government *bomas* (administrative centres), with their respective district commissioners and collectors, and police posts, with European officers and Goan clerks, were established. Asian traders soon followed, opening up little dukas—which were to flower as trade centres before long.

Opportunities were seen, and habitations sprouted like mushrooms overnight. Everywhere the train stopped, a new settlement arose. The nucleus of a community began to form before the end of the century. Nairobi remained a large encampment of tents until the beginning of 1902. Below the bridge, Alladina Visram formed the nucleus of a bazaar. Small in stature, but a powerful and well-established trader, he already had forty-three dukas between the coast and the Nile district. He was so rich that he was regarded as the uncrowned king of Uganda.

Machakos, Taita, Kibwezi and Voi already had flourishing Indian bazaars. Scenting trade, they came from Machakos to this new encampment. Little Indian dukas with rusty corrugated iron roofs multiplied rapidly. There was a narrow verandah for the customers, bags of grain and pulses and an array of goods. The small shops were crammed from floor to ceiling with every kind of ware, such as ghee in jars and jaggery in big brown sugary lumps. They started selling blankets, iron, brass, copper wire, beads, shirts, khaki trousers, lamps, cowries, cups, tobacco, matches, hoes, tea and sugar.

Bazaars and dukas in various parts of East Africa began to take shape. As their appetite for consumer goods developed, Africans from miles around started coming for the new products. And slowly, they started work for wages on roads and on European farms.

Many years later, when Kirparam had grown old and rheumatic, he would cry out in pain, lamenting that the right medicine was getting more and more difficult to find. 'What would one use in those days, Payaji?' the children would ask. 'Ah! Now that is the question. In those days, my child, I would have used the fat of lions,' he would say with a sly smile. He would sense their forthcoming reaction. 'The fat of lions!' they would scream in one voice. 'But that is not possible!' 'And why not?' he would ask.

'Mind you, lion fat was very much valued and sought after by many Indian traders. This they traded for other goods (and later for cowrie shells) from the Samburu or the Maasai who hunted these animals. In those days, lion fat was highly esteemed as medicine against rheumatism and impotence.'

'What is impotence?' they would want to know.

'General weakness of the body, or an inability to have a child. Since both the fat of the lion and the fat of the ostrich were regarded as "hot" substances, when rubbed on the legs or other parts of the body, they killed pain.'

'Did you ever try it, Bauji?' they would ask.

'No, I had no need!' Kirparam would roar. 'I was young then, like the lion himself. I didn't need the lion to heat me. My blood was already hot enough!' And they would all burst out laughing.

'Payaji,' Chunilal, the eldest, listening very attentively to his father, would ask, 'you said that you traded goods with the Samburu. Did money not exist in those days? What did one give them in exchange for the lion fat?'

'Money came in circulation a few years later, my son. At the time, trade was through barter. For example, the Samburu valued coloured beads.'

'Who are the Samburu?' another child would interrupt.

'Wait, wait. Patience. One question at a time. I can't answer all your questions simultaneously. Yes, where was I? The Samburu. This particular tribe is closely related to the Maasai. Now don't ask who are the Maasai, you have already seen them walking by our place up north in Nyeri. The name Samburu means butterfly, because they are always in the process of moving.'

'Then you were also a Samburu once, Payaji,' the youngest would say.

'Why?'

'Because you flew like a butterfly from so far away to come here!' And there would be another round of laughter.

'These butterfly men must be very strong if they can kill lions?' Chunilal would ask.

'Definitely, my son. It was nothing for a young *moran* (warrior) to walk one hundred kilometres without food or water, or track a lion only with a spear; their toughness is still legendary. And yet, they love to dress up, to do makeup, to wear a lot of coloured beads everywhere on the body. Beaded necklaces, beads on the hair and in the ears, bracelets, anklets . . . just like beautiful butterflies. Their almost effeminate looks belie their fearsome warrior spirit. I once asked a Samburu if he had ever been afraid. Do you know what he said?'

'No Payaji, but please tell us!'

'His reply was . . . "Of what?" They did not know fear . . . that is, not until the white man came with his gun. From the Samburu, we got grain. We gave them coloured beads in exchange.'

'Why did they want beads so much?' was another question.

'Why, to look beautiful. And to attract their women. These Samburu men spend a lot of time decorating their bodies, discussing their looks. An admirer gifts his girlfriend with strands of beads. The more she has, the more chances he has for an invitation to a proposal for marriage. One Samburu once told me that he had sacrificed his dinner to offer beads to his woman. Our banias knew this and sold them loose beads so they could thread them with palm fibre.

'The beads were given all care, for success depended on the aesthetic mixture of different colours that were harmonious and flattering to the eye. We must be careful to note that part of their dressing is highly symbolic. Ornaments made by women and medicine men often play an important part in rituals where they represent the female element. The small metal star on their foreheads is a reminder of their mythical origins in a world far removed from this one, the planet Venus. "May God put you where he has placed the stars"—this, I was told, is one of their prayers.'

His eyes would light up as the youngest child would say, 'I think it is a beautiful story.'

'The beads were all of the same kind?' Chunilal's perceptive question again.

Little was one to know then that this young man with his inquisitive mind would end up as a clever and well-travelled businessman, with trading interests far and wide. Kirparam would answer with pride, happy to arouse interest in his children about other peoples amongst whom they would live. This kind of conversation was not very common in most Indian homes.

'That is a good question. It is a good thing that I spent time up north, amongst these tribal peoples and can give some details. One could count at least 400 varieties of beads, with different names. The most common were in white porcelain. Most in demand were red enamel ones, called *samsam* or *kimara phamba*, which means "that which satisfies". Other than these they had bluish-black beads called *Asai*. These beads were the colours of the day and the night sky that God inhabits. Green beads symbolized peace, being the colour of vegetation after rainfall.'

'And where did the beads come from?' Chunilal would ask.

'Beads have been imported here for centuries. Glass beads came from Persia and China. Now of course we get them from Europe— Venice, Amsterdam and Czechoslovakia.'

Beads, belts, iron bells on the knee or the ankle, or cowrie shells reflected a man's wealth; clothes were never as central as jewellery. They sought copper and brass wire for ornaments, replacing the earlier iron jewellery. The importance of jewellery was so great that when tribes could not afford it, they began stealing telegraph wire. 'We performed the extremely useful task of initiating the exchange of commodities and gradual introduction of the use of money amongst the local people,' Kirparam would tell the children.

Payment was also made by cotton cloth cut into *dhotis*. *Bania* merchants imported three types of cotton cloth—the *merikani*, the *kaniki* blue indigo and others like *dabouani* from Muscat. *Merikani* (corrupted from American calico) was coarse unbleached cotton. 'Sheet' to the Americans, *lattha* to the Punjabis, the calico (the name is taken from the Indian town Calicut) was the most common.

'The Bhatia tycoon from Kutch—what was his name . . . let me think. I never met him, but a few years before I came, he was the talk of the town in Zanzibar. Ah yes, it was Jairam Sewjee. This young man was from a very poor family—yes, a rags-to-riches story. I believe it was his marketing strategy that was responsible for the popular name of *merikani*—much of which, by the way, is now manufactured in India. Richard Burton, John Speke, Henry Morton Stanley and David Livingstone—they all entered the mainland through Zanzibar. And while there, made most of their purchases—beads, brassware, cloth for the interior—from none other than the agents of Jairam Sewjee', Kirparam would conclude the lesson to the children.

Monetization crept in. The tribes even started beading the coins to wear as a neck ornament. They had no pockets in which to put the change in any case, for they did not wear trousers. And in the absence of pockets, their earlobes were stretched down to accommodate cigarette tins, hold monthly wages or little snuff gourds.

The traders introduced them to sugar, tea and blankets. Salt was one of the first goods introduced to the Africans. 'I was given a pinch of salt by a *Muhindi* (an Indian) and asked to taste it. I put it in my mouth . . . it was good, really good . . . I liked it,' said a Tetu (a branch of the Kikuyu tribe) elder. At the heart of the economic activity, the traders helped open up East Africa through trade, efficiently and cost-effectively.

Merchants, sailors, financiers, administrators and labourers helped bring the world there. From the vicinity of the railway and the administrative posts, Indian traders spread into the countryside to purchase a variety of local produce—ivory, rubber, grain, gum, copal, hides, horns, copra and ghee—in exchange for their trade goods. Darjani, 105 miles from Mombasa, was the fifteenth station on the line. It was renowned for its milk and ghee.

The old century passed without much fanfare. The empress

of the British empire, Queen Victoria, passed away. The town of Mombasa, then still the capital of British East Africa, plunged into mourning. All public places wore a deserted look.

The railway continued to progress. The Indian rupee quickly superseded the Viennese Maria Theresa dollar. It took the place of cowrie shells, of cloth, beads and wire. The National Bank of India became the authorized bank of the protectorate. The silver rupee with its sixteen *annas* and twelve *paise* became official currency. Indian holidays were made official.

For all practical purposes, the British protectorate was a province of British India, administered from Bombay. There were 2,000 Indians and only 500 Europeans; clearly Indians were the more conspicuous and numerous immigrants. However, the official sponsorship of Indian migration was very soon to be cut short. Confined to the building of the railway, the phase was over by 1901.

There was little difficulty in taking a census of Nairobi in those days. A transfer of the railway staff to Nairobi was the foundation of the resident population. At the turn of the century, the first town council meeting of Nairobi was held. The first police force was brought together—eight Indians and six Swahili were recruited. Their job was to keep the drains free of rubbish and to fill oil in the town's thirteen street lamps.

It was not rare to find someone in a ditch in the dark. Lanterns, still in use, were few and far between. The chorus of crickets and frogs drowned the hiss of lanterns throwing gentle, distorted shadows on the tin and canvas walls. Lions still roamed the streets. A walk at night could be quite frightening. Soldiers stood in sentry boxes at night—barefooted, blue-uniformed *askaris* in their famous felt hats, the red fez with black tassels. Not too long ago, they had carried bows, arrows, spears, javelins and lances to protect themselves and their communities. But now they just carried a whistle.

Nairobi grew in size and became safer—in a way. Until it had electricity, in 1908, there were still frequent fires and the wooden buildings went up like matchboxes. Gradually wood and stone structures came up and tin shanties disappeared. Barracks made of brick with corrugated iron roof sheeting for the railway maintenance staff lay along the tracks. These were known as *landhis*. Along the long rows of eucalyptus trees that lined the bare dusty streets was the post office, manned by an Indian. It displayed an array of flags indicating the movement of mail. A blue flag meant that the ship had left Aden for Mombasa with the post. A red flag symbolized the arrival of overseas mail, while a white one was for mail ready for distribution.

Fresh drinking water from wells was even now being brought in *debes* by train. The empty tin or *debe* (from the Indian word *dubba*) was vital. A four-gallon measure especially for transportation of water from the river, the *debe* became invaluable for gathering anything from ghee to oranges. Coffee pickers were paid by the *debe*, as were other harvesters. Charcoal prices were marked by the *debe*. The *debe* could be flattened and used for roofing or turned into a makeshift oven perched on three stones (stoves were imported only after 1906).

They rolled off their charpoys and resumed the daily grind. The turn of the century was a day like any other for small dukawallahs, for *babus* and for coolies. One phase of their history had ended; another was beginning. Kirparam had not even attempted to make an assessment of events. Even less, speculated upon what lay in store.

So much was happening in his life, and Miani seemed so far away both physically and mentally. The truth is that in the years he had been away, he rarely thought of Hardei, except in the few times of despair. The last time he had remembered her was when still in the town of Simba, that night when he could have become food for the lion.

It was the dawn of a new era for some, holding promise of hope and prosperity. For Beliram Parimal, the new century came with assurances and guarantees of affluence. Even before the new century had entered maturity, Beliram opened a provisions shop in Nairobi. It sold all kinds of groceries, wines and spirits, John

Hiralal Kapur in front of his *landhi*, a wooden house raised
on stilts, in 1927

Hague whiskey and gin. Soon the shop would expand and Beliram would become a man of some means.

Kirparam, who until now had been travelling with his *halwai* canteen, decided finally to stop in Nairobi. He joined up as Beliram's partner, and became a dukawallah. Stereotypical images of the Indian as the dukawallah were already beginning to take shape. Clad in a white *dhoti* and tight-fitting black coat, seated on a low divan surrounded by his ledger and account books, was the Hindu moneylender. The Bohra ironmonger wore a long white coat and loose trousers, while the bearded Sikh was the *fundi*—great with his hands and physical strength—a mender of all kinds of things. The slim Goan was the chef, or secretary. Insisting upon Portuguese cultural ties, he spoke Konkani at home, but denied any Indian background. In fact, the Goan was neither put at par with the Indian, nor was he under British rule. He was a Portuguese of Goan origin, and therefore, slightly higher in status and esteem than the Indian.

Drawn into the vortex of a new life, caring less and less for the life he had left behind, Kirparam began to enjoy his work. Challenging and adventurous, it had potential. There was room for growth, and the possibilities were infinite. However, a deep-seated isolation began to take root in him. An absence of a home and family life bothered him. For a long while, he lived anywhere, in makeshift places—in tents, on bare earth, in the bush. When things eased up financially, he found a little place of his own in a Grogan Road wooden *landhi*.

The working hours were long, the evenings lonely. Contrary to life at the coast, where social life was plentiful and colourful, the interior was dull. A sense of community life had not yet evolved. Few men, if any, had come with their wives. Life in the township offered few amenities and fewer excitements. There was little by way of recreation—except, perhaps, another woman.

The Kenya colony acquired the reputation of the 'Happy Valley' crowd—usually British aristocrats—who were good at handling guns, alcohol and women (not necessarily in that order).

A typical question was 'Are you married, or do you live in Kenya?' Even in London it was thought of as a place beyond the reach of social censure.

Some men were content with local women—Wakamba women, Wameru women. However, the Indian pleasure-seekers' paradise came from Hira Mandi in Lahore. All the way from that red-light district, a few women were invited across the ocean to East Africa for the pleasure of the railway *babus,* coolies and others. The old, the young, the rich, the married, the single—they all sought the company of singing and dancing girls. The men came from far and beyond to indulge their desires.

Some of the well-known *kanjariyan* (prostitutes)—including Amma Moti Jaan, Rehmat Bibi (also known as Mai Rehmo) and Gulzaar—were accepted by society at large. Later they married or adopted children, and were able to amass much land and property in the Pangani area. Kirparam found his solace with a Punjabi Sunni Muslim who continued to practise her faith. Kirparam's woman was not a great beauty, it was said, but he would be with her right to the end. It was in total defiance of all social norms and rules.

Nairobi as a location and a town began to gain strategic importance. In 1905, it took over from Mombasa as the capital of the British protectorate in East Africa. Government offices were moved to Nairobi. And a once-abandoned Hardei arrived to hunt for the husband she had not seen in the last six years or more.

The cool breeze cut through her body like a sharp razor, the thin shirt clinging to her now frail, but otherwise heavy frame. 'Before the railway was built, somehow Nairobi was even colder; the sun shone only in the afternoons', Mathuradass, at whose house Hardei had found refuge, told her. She did not reply, but stood silently, staring into space.

Her drooping shoulders reflected her unhappy state. She picked up a thick white *dupatta* and wrapped it tightly round her shoulders. Mathuradass's wife, though not a conservative Hindu— both she and her husband had 'converted' to the revolutionary Arya Samaj branch of Hinduism—looked at her white *dupatta* and winced. Since when did young married women cover themselves with a white *dupatta*? White was the colour of mourning. But she did not say anything.

Dark patches circled her eyes. It was apparent that Hardei had not been sleeping well. She looked tired and mentally exhausted. Terrifying thoughts continued to run through her mind. 'What will happen? Where is my husband? Is he still alive?' Sensing what was troubling her, Mathuradass' wife assured her, 'Nairobi is a small place, with a small Indian community; it will not be difficult to find *praji*, but for the moment, *penji* (sister), you must get some rest.'

Mathuradass, a cashier for the army recruited from Calcutta, knew the new area of Nairobi and its surroundings well. He had been here even before Kirparam had taken the dhow from Karachi, when the first batch was brought in. It was at a time when soldiers and sepoys were being recruited in India to police those states that came under British influence. Indian laws had been extended to Kenya to cover recruitment of labour from India. Peace and law and order had to be maintained. The penal code, criminal procedure code, the Evidence Act, the Police Act—the laws invoked were those of British India. Judicial appeals were heard in the high court of Bombay.

Many of his khaki-clad (in their well-pressed shorts, a khaki topee on the head) white superiors had spent time in British India, and spoke fluent Hindustani, if not passable Urdu. All their office work was conducted in Urdu. Police records in Mombasa, Nairobi and Kisumu were maintained in Urdu. Mathuradass had picked up enough Swahili when he had been based in Mombasa (Swahili being the lingua franca of the East African coast), like many of his contemporary Indian inspectors and deputy inspectors who had served in the police force right from the time of the building of the railway. However, almost none of them could speak more than a few words of English.

Mathuradass was more than a little nervous that day. He sat at the desk fidgeting with the accounts. For once, he wasn't making much headway. He knew that in a few days he must leave to go up north. As usual, he was not looking forward to it. The voyage was not without risks. Thinking of this made him even more edgy, although he was fully conversant with the routine. But, brooding over the trip did not make it easier. Like it or not, the job had to be done. Salaries had to be paid to the rest of the railway staff. He would do it, as he had been doing all these years. Towards the end of each month, he would begin the journey. Right up to the railhead and back. The construction staff had to be paid personally, and he was the head cashier. This morning, however, he was not so much worried about the trip-related problems, as he was about the meeting in progress at the Government House. It would make things more difficult—both for his work and for the lives of civilians in general.

The hall resounded with excited voices. The air was thick with expectation. The administrators, European farmers and other businessmen had got together in their black suits and cravats to discuss labour—mainly labour on their 'own' farms, lands that had once belonged to African clans and tribes. The immediate worry of European farmers was that the Africans were still not willing to work for money. It continued to cause them great alarm. The meeting was sure to end in pandemonium. They were all hoping for immediate solutions to their labour problems. 'The recently introduced hut and poll tax to force them into cash economy must be reinforced,' discussed the spokespersons for the government. 'They are resisting our work; we have to get them back on the farms. We will now not accept the exchange of goods in kind as payment of taxes. They will henceforth pay in cash.'

The introduction of the rupee had solved the problem of payment of wages to employees. The railway coolies, the police force, soldiers, and other related departments were being paid in Indian rupees. The rupee would now also be used for collection of taxes. Their stores of trade goods were to be closed down. Cows or agricultural produce, strings of beads, cloth and wire, mirrors, cowrie shells—and other such items that had been the medium of exchange so far—would be slowly disposed of.

Africans, who for years had lived without money, would now need money to pay this tax. There was only one thing for them to do—go and work on white farms.

The Africans saw it as a punishment. The exchange of money was a new evil arriving with the introduction of the hut tax. According to African customary law, taxes and other fines were paid by families or clans, not by individuals. While British law looked to the individual, the African tradition saw the group as a whole—that was the great difference. The new rule was to lay the foundation for nuclear families in African tribal communities.

They were told that they were paying for 'improvements'—roads, police, street lighting, etc.—which they had always done without. The two-rupee hut tax introduced in 1903 became an economic pressure, especially amongst the richer tribal people, for a man's wealth was partly weighed by the number of wives. Since each wife had her own hut, the husband was taxed accordingly! Counting hundreds of coins stuck together with hippo fat, writing receipts, checking registers, the 'friendly and child-like' African started learning the rudiments of tax evasion, borrowing receipts from those who had already paid. Indians were not new to tax collection and payment, nor were they novices at tax evasion. Their records were kept in a secret coded language which only they could understand.

'We worked very long hours. In the beginning when I worked as a *halwai*, running the canteen for the railway coolies, my turnover was so small that I counted the monthly profit in *paisa* rather than in rupees,' Kirparam would tell his expanding family, nearly twenty years after this development. 'It was difficult even for us to pay taxes then. Now that they are asking us to render accounts in English or in Swahili and written in Roman script, how do they expect us to meet such demands?' The new law of 1923 would arouse much objection from the semi-literate Indian petty dukawallahs. Their shops would remain closed for weeks, and they would refuse to pay taxes.

There were mass desertions. The Africans were badly treated and underpaid. Far from being anxious to work on European farms, once they earned enough to pay their hut tax, they were content to leave. A police force was employed specially to arrest deserters. Frustrated with the unreliable manpower, the Europeans became desperate. The Native Registration Ordinance made it compulsory for all adult male African workers to wear a chain with a metal container around their necks. It contained their identification papers. This was the infamous *kipande*, a means to control the movement of African labourers. The registration document was supposed to prevent desertion from European farms.

It endorsed his past and his present employment status. It had all the essential elements of the pass system. The *kipande* became a symbol of imperialism. Africans were forced to sell crops or go outside their reserves to work. The stock that an African could keep and the amount of land granted for cultivation was reduced, while the number of days they had to work for the white farmer was increased. From being independent producers, they were reduced to agricultural labourers.

Together with the hut and poll taxes that were introduced, the racist outlook would climax quickly and surely by 1922, and the three-tier structure—with the Africans at the bottom and Indians in the middle—would be reinforced. 'In 1914, Indian railway and public works department workers went on strike to oppose the poll tax', recounted Makhan Singh, founder of the trade union movement in Kenya, many years later. 'We must not forget that the colony was developed mainly by Indian and African labourers.' A self-declared communist, he would boast that he could not be deported out of Kenya. He was eventually, but not to India. He was sent to the northern frontier district of Kenya—a district hardly considered part of Kenya. Restricted to the area of Maralal, right up north near the Sudanese border, he would fast for three weeks to bring his case to the notice of the public.

* * *

One evening after work, two days after the labour meeting at Government House, a still-anxious Mathuradass took Hardei to the house she had waited for so long to enter. To be with her man—

in search of whom she had travelled across the seas. Hardei was already shaking, but neither of them was perhaps prepared for what she would later recall as the worst-case scenario.

A party was in full swing. Everybody seemed to have a bottle in hand. A big *sufuria* of chicken smouldered on the firewood *jiko* in the middle of the circle. Mathuradass became pale. Meat and alcohol, the two deadly sins, were right in front of his eyes, in plenty. He looked at the ground in shame. He wished he could leave, but he couldn't abandon Hardei *penji*. He felt trapped. Somebody cracked a joke in Punjabi, the whole party burst out in loud laughter. Many laughed till the tears ran.

Standing in her dark corner under a tree, Hardei appeared tired and fragile, older than her twenty-two years. Mathuradass stood right behind her, like a shadow. She looked around in disbelief, and then she saw him. Surely, it was Kirparam, the man to whom she had been wed seven years ago. He appeared somewhat changed. In fact she saw him anew, with the eyes of a stranger. A bit older perhaps, but healthier, and fairer in complexion. Neither too tall nor too short, he had a good build. Still clean-shaven (Hindus in those days did not often grow beards). The same restless eyes, but the man seemed more agitated. He was dressed differently. Trousers and jacket, shoes with laces, but no socks, a black Bangalore topee covered his head.

'He looks like a real *babu*,' she thought to herself. She wanted to rush to him with some tenderness, but at the same time, a desire to beat him was not far. She wanted to ask him 'Why? Why? Why?' a thousand times—why had he left her all alone? For the moment, she restrained herself. She noticed that he was now in very intimate conversation with the woman sitting next to him. He even touched her. Hardei's expression changed. A shadow of fear crossed her face. She held back her flood of tears with remarkable control.

The woman was about the same age as herself, dressed in *salwar kameez*, her head covered with a white *dupatta*—the typical attire of a Punjabi woman. At that time she could not have said whether the woman was a Hindu or a Muslim—not that it would have mattered. Hardei listened to them talk, but did not understand anything. She could not have known what they were talking about even though she was within easy reach, and their conversation loud enough. She was too engrossed in looking at this man, staring at him fixedly, studying his every aspect, thirstily drinking it all in, to be able to comprehend any words.

She stood there trembling, her eyes transfixed on them. Her breast heaved under suppressed sighs. Her heart was beating very fast as she took a few steps towards her husband. Her gait was heavy, as if she was very tired, but her step was sure. She placed her hand on his shoulder, and he turned his head sharply in her direction. Everybody noticed her now. Kirparam did not recognize his wife at first. It was three seconds before he did, but it seemed like eternity. He looked at her again in shock and recognition. Was he seeing a ghost? This was the last place he expected to see his wife.

Hardei could not hide her anger any more. The hurt that she had been nurturing for so long in her bosom erupted. Her fury knew no barriers. Raging and fuming, in one breath, she said it all—in front of the whole party. She was no longer willing to meekly accept her fate or to reconcile herself to its harshness. Her capacity for endurance had been tested beyond limit. She almost choked on her own words.

The group quickly sobered up, but the tension within Hardei did not abate—it only mounted further. Oblivious to her surroundings, the hand that had been digging deep into her own skin landed on his cheek with all its force. It happened so suddenly that for a long while nobody spoke. The silence hung heavy in the air. People looked at her as if she had gone mad. Perhaps she had. It was a paralysingly awkward moment. For her. For him. For Mathuradass. And for everybody else who was present.

Kirparam stared at her, aghast. His mouth and eyes remained wide open. The plainness of her features stood out; her determination and half-ironic tone made an impact. His hand slowly found its way to the cheek where she had slapped him. It hurt—the shame of it all. She had dared to insult him, humiliate him in public. Stimulated by the heady combination of shock and alcohol, his ego demanded vengeance. Disgraced, scandal-hit—he had to get even. Kirparam lifted his hand in retaliation but stopped, shocked at what he saw. The face in front of him was strained and fatigued—the prematurely grey hair, eyes that had lost their lustre— a testimony to her suffering and pain. It was not the face of an angry and vengeful woman. His hand froze in mid-air. He checked himself and swallowed the bitter insult, his heart filling with remorse. An acute sense of guilt overpowered him.

Hardei stood rooted, dumbfounded by her own actions. Husband and wife stared at each other for what seemed like eternity. Then she recoiled, mortified. She had hit him, but the pain was stronger within her; the anguish on her face gave it away. She knew that her behaviour was unpardonable. In her desperation, she had acted in panic. Another woman would not have dared. 'Perhaps he will repudiate me, punish me,' she thought. 'Worse still, send me back.' She oscillated between happiness at having finally found him and the fear of immediately losing him.

Kirparam slowly lowered his hand, and clasped the other hand in his lap. His face took on a grim look. His silent consent was enough.

She was home. The man so rigid on the surface agreed that his wife could stay with him.

4

Domestic disharmony

Une femme pardonne tout excepté
qu'on ne veuille pts d'elle

(A woman can forgive all, except being rejected)
—Alfred de Messet, nineteenth century French poet

After the fury died down, domestic harmony was elusive for a long while. But there was no running away from the situation. It was a period of many adjustments, both for Hardei and for Kirparam. Not forgetting their son Chunilal. The boy may not have understood everything, but the little that he did was perhaps enough to bring some discomfort to his formative years. With a father who was often absent from home and a frustrated mother, he perhaps did not have the best of environments for growing up. Even when father and son found themselves together, the bonding was uncertain.

Chunilal may even have felt that the father appeared from nowhere to disrupt the intimacy he enjoyed with his mother. But over the years, the relationship between father and son would mature. They would even set up business together. A certain formality between them, however, would never totally disappear. On the contrary, the rift would widen as Chunilal's literary education and socio-cultural milieu broadened. That would create a distance.

Like his father, who had braved his way to Africa and nearly lost his life in the adventure, Chunilal's journeys years later would take him to even further lands. He, however, would travel in style. Chunilal went all over the then apartheid Africa and continental Europe, hobnobbing with the white colonial regime. He settled business deals, stayed on the forefront of the political scene wherever possible, and became a Freemason under their influence. Eventually, Chunilal would serve on the pre-independent Nairobi city council as an alderman, get elected as president of the Federation of Indian Chambers and be awarded an OBE (Order of the British Empire).

Kirparam had always shied away from glory, titles and honours; they held little meaning for him. Faithful to his dharma, it was enough for him that he had been able to provide his son the best education and opportunities available to an Indian child of the time, and helped him to pioneer the opening of sawmills in Kenya and Tanzania.

As for Hardei, the euphoria of having traced her husband was momentary. Memories of the incident and the emotional imbroglio were raw and fresh in the subconscious. She was still very young when they started calling her Bebe. The title was usually reserved for an elderly woman, her hair whitened with the wisdom of experiences that life had laid before her. But ever since Hardei had displayed an air of authority, demanded her rights from her husband, she had gained a new respect in the family, in the *biradari* (extended family). Years of lone survival in India had taught her to be independent and forgo pleasure. She had cleaned pots and pans, tilled the land, grown fruit trees, but living with her stepmother in Miani had also meant constant nagging, and reminders that she was no more of 'this' house: 'A married girl is welcome only as a guest in the parental home,' she was relentlessly told.

Kirparam was uneasy, his discomfort great. They were like strangers. Attitudes towards each other were mercifully not hardened, and Hardei was not expecting any miracles, just hoping that the new beginning together would set them off on the right path. The dispute, although vicious, had not acquired any kind of savagery or violence. But the relationship lacked cordiality, so necessary for a meaningful and sustainable family life. On most days there was silence between them, but sometimes they brimmed with rancour, and harsh words were exchanged. 'Perhaps silence is more communicative than words,' Hardei began to think.

Many nights, she lay in wait for him. Eventually, in the wee hours of the morning, the smell of stale alcohol would penetrate the room. Feeling nauseated, her hand would automatically cover her nose. Unable to control herself, she would shout, 'So you have been drinking again!' Hands on hips, her sarcastic tongue would lash out all kinds of merciless accusations. She would rant, lecture and scold to the point of being incapable of genuine dialogue. The relationship seemed to be slowly coming apart at the seams.

Groping for ways to assert her rights and for a chance to make a lasting impact, she once screamed at him, 'At the wedding ceremony, you had taken vows to keep me happy, to look after my needs, but . . .' Even as she tried to air her grievances, she broke down. The already fading memory of the earlier good moments that they had shared rebelled against her expressions of gloom. Her nagging became in some part a kind of protest, and in another a spontaneous reaction gathered from childhood memories. Corrosive cynicism, the hallmark of women of her region, was a way to demonstrate disapproval. It rose to Hardei's surface now. Nursing resentment while trying to win him over was not the best way to make the new start she so longed for.

For the moment, the central element of the quarrel, as far as Hardei was concerned, stood defined. The *maas–sharab* (meat–alcohol) parties had to stop. This was something she could not, would not accept under any circumstances. How he had acquired these tastes baffled her. Hardei did not say it, but she was sure that with these two evil habits gone, it would also check the danger of that other woman. The atmosphere would no longer be awkward and unmanageable, triggering elemental impulses. It spawned fear, distrust, anger and hate—sometimes to the point of irrationality.

'That' woman remained a nameless enigma. 'Surely it must have been that woman who introduced the first two taboos to my man!

It must have been because of her that he started eating meat and drinking alcohol!' The fact that he ate with her, a Muslim, did not seem to bother Hardei—many of her own friends were Muslim. Caste defilement was never an issue with her, but meat and alcohol were of grave concern.

The seven-year gap had come with its vicissitudes. A different country with its new experiences had certainly led to unpredictable changes. Every little argument became all-consuming. Normal, often resolvable differences were blown into indefinable abstractions. Locked up in mutual distrust, the chain of action and reaction fuelling their passion brought their fears closer and closer to becoming self-fulfilling.

Sometimes Hardei felt as if she had reached a dead-end. Kirparam, on the other hand, was exasperated by her overstated cavilling, and took to leaving the house early in the morning, only to return late at night—very often, after an all-night party. These were usually all-male gatherings, and invariably tended to exclude the few wives who had arrived in town.

Less accepting than the other women, Hardei found it increasingly hard to reconcile to the situation. Why, when Kirparam had left home, she had been a young bride, her fiery passions not completely fulfilled. She still had young blood throbbing through her veins. Now she sought advice, but the other women only laughed at her.

'One evening, I added a lot of red chilli to his food; he screamed out in pain,' said one of the women.

Another told her, 'Sometimes, when I get angry, I serve burnt food, but then I have to put up with the consequences later.'

Others talked about throwing their slippers or utensils on the ground in defiance. Adding extra salt in the food, putting salt instead of sugar in tea, expending their anger on children, mumbling curses—these perhaps provided an outlet for repressed personal drives, a way to seek vengeance.

Rare was the woman who could have an open, mature and equal relationship of dialogue and discussion with her man. Most of them seemed to have accepted the inevitable, though perhaps only superficially. Resignation was perhaps easier to handle, and ignorance less painful. They were all equally vulnerable, their sexuality slotted and put in place, living similar lives. A spontaneous rapport came into play amongst them. Numberless features of a legacy of common backgrounds facilitated their bonding. The personal warmth amongst the women did not necessarily mean that they were always cordial, or that the relationship was always easy. On the one hand, they were well versed in the art of flattery when necessary. On the other, their little worlds circled around gossip, jealousies, rebellion, all of which they perhaps tried to counteract with endless rituals, loud vulgar jokes and incessant laughter. Eroticism found expression in many ways in their day-to-day conversation. Besides Lala Prasad's small temple, there was no community or social centre to go to. Life revolved around the common hearth and domestic chores. They turned their bickering into an art. Some took the help of *jadu tona* (magic) or other tantric rites.

One of these women was Leelawati. A pleasant, soft-spoken woman, Leelawati had been living a life of deep frustration because she did not have a son. The lack tormented her. She slept badly and had to force-feed herself. She lost weight and began to have deep bags under her otherwise beautiful big eyes. 'Go see a tantric priest,' an inner voice told her, and she did. 'Get some ash from the cremation ground. Press it at the back of the throat of a newborn male child until it dies,' he said. It seemed like she became demonized almost overnight. Each time she went to bless a newborn male child, the infant died soon after. How and when she did it was not known. One never saw her actually commit the act, but they said she had the evil eye. That just her look caused it. 'Surely she performs tantra-mantra,' they whispered. Connections between Leelawati and the death of infants began to circulate. Punjabi society in Nairobi was rife with all kinds of rumours, but none had the guts to confront her.

'As soon as we saw Leelawati in the distance, we hid our children and shut the doors,' said Darshana, one of the wives.

'And what happened? Was she sent to jail?' asked one new arrival, in shock.

'What can happen in our closed society! Nothing, of course. Who would take her to the courts of the white man? No one testified against her,' replied Darshana.

'And she had a son in the end! That's what really happened.'

* * *

Chunilal sat on the floor in his little shirt amidst his still warm pool of pee. For a moment he played about and then began to wail. Hardei ignored him before smacking him on the cheek. 'Such a big boy, but acting like a baby.' Her frustration was apparent. Bitterness and frayed nerves were hardly the ideal atmosphere in which to lavish attention upon the screaming child. She cleaned up the mess and sat on the charpoy in her usual cross-legged position.

An almost child-like smile crossed her lips: the smile of someone who knew that what was going on in her head risked being ridiculed, at best taken for a joke. No, she would never take help from tantra-mantra *shastras* to get her man back in line, she thought, but she would find another way. An unsuspected reserve of strength broke through the cocoon of a cultured naivety. At the back of her mind, though, a fear continued to nag her: how was she going to build the present when the past still haunted her and her future was a big question mark? Before long, however, she had thrown her head back in defiance, as if to display a determined durability to herself.

She stood up to him and made her position clear. She must set her house in order: Kirparam could not have it both ways—behaving strangely on the one hand, and being a family man on the other. Hardei did not mince words, even though she was afraid. In her heart she knew that the choices open to her were limited. There was no question of leaving—where would she go? But she was not willing to accept the status quo. Nor did she have the patience or the serenity of mind to wait. Kirparam's response, however, continued to be increasingly cool and detached. He became remote and impersonal, as if preoccupied by weighty responsibilities.

Faced with stark options, Hardei's morale fell lower than ever before. She would still not give up. Then she thought of Beliram. She was aware that Kirparam held Beliram, his business partner in the shop, in high esteem. This was a courageous woman who knew how to get around restrictions imposed by conventions. Arranging her starched *dupatta* over her head, she walked over to the shop at a time when she was sure that Kirparam was not in. Beliram was of course surprised to see her there, but he did not show it.

There were few customers about, as it was still early. 'Brother,' Hardei said hesitantly, 'Would you listen to a sister's woes?' Then she broke down. For a while there were more sobs than words. Beliram did not say anything; he waited for her to calm down. Slowly, she opened her heart to this stranger in total confidence. He was receptive and responsive. In him, she found maturity and understanding. He listened to her without interrupting, nodding his head from time to time. When she had finally said it all, he held his chin in his hand and was plunged deep in thought for a long while before he spoke. His response was full of empathy.

'It is not going to be easy,' he assured her, 'but I will talk to Kirparam. You can trust my word.' Hardei heaved a sigh of relief, fighting down the rising sense of euphoria.

* * *

A very pale blue light revealed the outlines of the new town. An aura was visible over the horizon. From time to time, the tin roofs sparkled and played with the light. Kirparam couldn't sleep and walked over to the river bank. It was 4 a.m. Dhobis were seen walking to Nairobi river. The birds had not yet started chirping and most people were still fast asleep. Here, along the river, the washermen set up a communal *ghat* to do the laundry for residents. Squatting close to the ground in long lines at the water's edge, they were barely visible against the faint light, as they began the daily ritual with the lighting of a fire. Dipped in soap-water solution, the laundry was boiled in huge brass basins before being beaten. 'Thud-thud thud-thud', the wet cloth was beaten against a rock.

He walked for a long time. Beliram's words continued to echo in his ears. The pre-dawn walk was a panacea for his troubled soul. As soon as the first light of day appeared in the sky, he started for home. The dhobis were already preparing to starch the clothes to lay them out to be sun-dried later. Back home, their womenfolk would be heating the imported brass irons from India with charcoal. Each one had two irons—as one cooled, the other was ready for use. How to use a charcoal iron without letting the cinders fly out and burn your clothes was an art in itself, and dhobans were mistresses of this art.

Kirparam stopped for an instant to watch the smoke from wood fires rising from most homes in the bazaar. By the time he reached the bazaar, the townsfolk were already cleaning their teeth with twigs of the neem tree while waiting for the bath water to heat up. It had been all quiet when he had started on his walk over an hour before, and this increase in activity in the bazaar gave him a new lease of life.

Beliram had not told Kirparam that Hardei had come to see him. 'You can no longer avoid facing up to the problem', he had said. However, he warned his junior partner to make a clear break from recently acquired offensive habits. As a mark of respect for a man so senior to him, Kirparam listened without interrupting or arguing. He remained quiet throughout. Beliram used the opportunity to puncture Kirparam's apathy and hammered in him a sense of urgency, telling him he could not afford to take the wrong turning. In an effective manner, he told him a few home truths, and brought him to his senses. Had Kirparam been sure of himself, he would not perhaps have put up with such tutoring. But the very fact that a definite change was clearly visible to all proved that Hardei's man had made an assessment of priorities. It was rumoured that Beliram had even removed his turban during the talk—as a mark of humility—quietly donning it after he had spoken, and that Kirparam had shrunk with shame.

The talk between the men made a difference. Kirparam started making efforts almost immediately. For the first time since Hardei's arrival, he faced his role more honestly. At least he started to assume the responsibilities of a husband, more importantly that of a father. He was quickly on the threshold to some kind of transition. And, transformation came swifter than Hardei could have dreamt. In no time Kirparam became a teetotaller. Once alcohol had been given up, becoming a vegetarian followed easily. Getting rid of gambling took time. 'Once he even staked all the jewellery that I had received as a bride. He was so ashamed of himself later that he vowed to quit the habit,' Hardei had confessed to her friends. 'And, he did. He almost became a *bhagat*—a man of god, a saint.'

Later, when their children had grown up, Hardei often told them that Beliram was her god. Typically, the quarrel was viewed as a drama with three actors—two contestants and a peacemaker. It was not the contestants but the peacemaker who was seen as a victor. Beliram had rekindled hope in her heart at a time when life was bleak. He had helped save her husband from a damned life, and her from one of condemnation.

Yet, even though the show of bad grace was almost over, Kirparam's one earthy impulse remained. When the other follies had been exposed, finished off and later cremated, this one weakness stayed. And it was to be a part of him for the rest of his life. This was the 'other' woman, the nameless enigma, the third taboo. She was always there—in the background, but very much present in Kirparam's life. Nobody talked about it, but everybody knew. It was hard for Hardei. The amorous liaison with a Muslim woman caused her pain and disturbed the harmony that was slowly building. However, their marriage withstood the strain. Hardei prepared herself to live in denial of the other's existence. Somehow, she learnt to accept her husband's aberrations, while Kirparam respected her independence. However, the results of such an arrangement were obvious. Frustration and belligerence in equal proportions were on their way to becoming part of Hardei's personality.

For years, after all, Kirparam had not spoken about the wife he had left behind. The truth is that in the years away from her, he had rarely thought about her. Too much was happening in his life at the time, and the routine of his hometown Miani had seemed so far away. The majority of men who came to work on the railway had come alone, without their wives or families. Many were from poor villages. The long hours and hard work put them in a very trying position.

As it was, the construction coolies were held in low regard by their bosses and the other *wazungu*, who were always ready to find fault with them: the camps are crowded with prostitutes, they raid and steal whenever there is an opportunity, they are unhygienic . . . the list went on. If these so-called 'railway lunatics' displayed signs of psychological stress, they were meted further harsh treatment. They were incarcerated in the Fort Jesus jail in Mombasa and given hard labour. A number of them died in captivity, others returned home demented.

In the proximity and intimacy of their dark tents, the coolies relieved their sexual urges. They took young African boys and African women. Others intermarried with them according to their ways and customs. In a community dominated by males, these men were not choosy about the colour of the skin of the women with whom they had sex. Nor did they ask after their caste. By 1904, prostitution was rampant. Sex workers and stolen goods were found behind Victoria Street and the more inferior cabins in the Indian Bazaar. Unofficially, the brothels' existence was sanctioned.

In the Meru area up to the north of Nairobi, an unspecified number of Sikh men took Kimeru wives, some with Sikh marriage rituals. Somehow Sikhs, with their reputation of being hunters and warriors, were more acceptable to Africans. One Sikh was even known to have paid the usual bride price of a certain number of cows for a Mkamba woman with whom he had claimed to be madly in love. However, when the Sikh community threatened to excommunicate him, he had meekly returned the wife to her father—much to the chagrin and disgust of the old Mkamba man.

The follies that these simple people could get away with, were not afforded to the more 'educated' ones who had recently come under the influence of the Arya Samaj.

Conscious of political rights as a result of the independence movement in India, the new wave of migrants came equipped with a stronger sense of cultural and national pride. On 5 July 1903, forty-five Hindu men got together at the house of Jaigopal on River Road to discuss matters of a serious nature—the 'failing moral standards of our Indian brethren'. They were dismayed as they watched their colleagues behave in a manner that deviated from the norm. 'Easily tempted, sometimes even bestial—the signs are not promising,' it was said. 'The impact of the new environment free from social constraints has led our young men astray. Nobody dictates standards to them. There is no community life to adhere to. They are without the stabilizing influence of a family. The consequences are dire.'

'*Om vaangma aasyay astu*,' chanted Mathuradass, reciting the mantras. His cupped left palm held some water. He wet the middle and ring fingers of his right hand and touched both ends of his mouth, touching the right side first. '*Om nasormay prano astu*,' he said as he repeated the exercise with his nose, eyes, ears, arms and knees. The purification exercise completed, he poured more ghee into the sacred fire, recited some more mantras and ended the ceremony with a '*swaha*'. Getting up with ease from his cross-legged position, he vowed to himself that he would direct the Hindu community towards social reform as declared by their guru, Swami Dayanand Saraswati. Mathuradass Arya, the one at whose house Hardei had first found refuge, may not have been a new-wave migrant, but he was among the most educated of the first batch of Indians to have reached the place where Nairobi now stands. Moreover, he was truly concerned about what seemed to him the sad state of his brethren.

Inder Singh, Kishen Chand, Lachman Dass, Bakshi Ram, Ganeshi Lal Arya, Bihari Lal and Wazir Chand were some of the support pillars of the new breed of Aryan intellectuals in the group meeting that night. However, Mahashaya Badrinath and Mathuradass Arya—both cashiers with the railways—were the moving spirits behind the movement in its formative years. They took it upon themselves to be the custodians of their tradition. With education up to matriculation level—a rare feat at the time— they had the desired respectability. In the dual roles of priest and singer, they guided the members in reciting mantras.

'It is not the failure of the individual, but the social and cultural bankruptcy of our community,' a member said, and the rest nodded in agreement. They made a pledge then 'to fulfil the deficiency in religious and cultural influences'. It was declared that 'our fellow men must be uplifted from shame'. These staunch disciples harnessed their energies. Nothing more radical than a quick round of swift and visible changes was called for.

Cut off from their cultural roots in India, facing rapidly growing Christian influences as also rivalry from orthodox Hindu sects, the Arya Samaj strived hard for the thriving of its faith. Militancy in approach became characteristic of the earlier activities of the Arya Samaj. A campaign on the evils of alcohol and 'flesh-eating' were made the starting points. Members were regularly checked and reported upon. Thirteen of them were immediately excommunicated. The Arya Samaj *priti-bhojan* of simple *dal* and vegetables with plain chapatis—neither too spicy, nor too rich— was encouraged.

The Arya Samaj, meaning a society of noble and faithful Aryans, was founded in Kenya. Its teachings included 'Be vegetarian'; 'Abstain from alcohol'; 'Perform the *havan* fire ritual'; 'Recite the Vedic mantras'; and 'So long as you can tie a white turban, you are a *khandani*, a worthwhile citizen'. It became a renaissance movement among the Hindus.

On the night of Shivratri, the followers of Shiva are required to stay awake and give food offerings to the deity. During one Shivratri, young Dayanand was struck not only by the behaviour of other believers overtaken by sleep in the depth of the night, but also by an incident where a mouse climbed the altar and munched the food offerings laid before the idol of Shiva. A doubt was immediately cast in his mind about the power of the idol: 'Thoughts upon thoughts crowded upon me. Question after question arose in my disturbed mind. Is it possible, I asked myself, that this semblance of man, the idol of a personal god that I see bestriding his bull before me, and who, according to religious accounts, walks about, eats, sleeps and drinks, who can hold a trident in his hand, beat upon his drum and pronounce curses upon men—is it possible that he can be *Mahadeva,* the Great Deity, the same that is invoked as the Lord of Kailash, the Supreme Being and Divine Hero of all the stories we read of in his *Puranas?'*

The temple episode generated a desire that impelled Dayanand to discredit idol worship. It marked the beginning of a crusade against idolatry that he was to undertake for the rest of his life. The incident laid the foundation of the Arya Samaj.

Nineteenth century India was dominated by the interaction of two civilizations—the Indo-Muslim and the western as introduced by British culture. A multiplicity of social, religious and intellectual movements arose from this interaction. The Arya Samaj was among the most significant of these. With uniform rituals and religious renaissance, the Arya Samaj caught the imagination of the Punjabis, becoming a dominant religious and social movement among educated Hindus of the Punjab and north-western India.

The movement did not take off in his state of Gujarat, but Dayanand Saraswati, who had established the Arya Samaj at Rajkot in 1875, tasted substantial success when he arrived in Lahore two years later. Beyond racial and caste barriers, his clarion call was 'Return to the Vedas'. This revival of the national heritage became part of the rising nationalist movement taking shape as a reaction to British rule. Many young men and women who later became prominent leaders of the freedom struggle came under its sway. 'Return to the Vedas' was really a call for regeneration in tune with the changed politico-economic and cultural climate of British

India. Besides trying to unite Hindus, the new ideology gave them nationalistic pride. It lessened the humiliation of colonialism by providing a new vision of a glorious past.

Until then it was known that 'a Hindu is born, not made'. Dayanand changed that in one stroke. He transformed it from a religion that did not allow new converts to one that was open to all, regardless of caste, colour, creed or community. 'The caste system must modernize; status should be acquired, not inherited,' he said . . . 'Untouchability is not a part of the Vedas and therefore obtrusive.' Members were encouraged to spread the faith with the zeal of a missionary. A few Africans in Nairobi did convert. They were accepted as members of the Arya Samaj and faithfully met with other members of the congregation to sing. Weekly meetings were generally held on Sundays out of convenience as it was the weekly holiday, even though any day could be and was regarded as holy according to the Arya Samaj. The African converts regularly participated in rituals with vigour under Dayanand's call of *Krinvunto Vishwamaaryam*' (make the whole world Aryan).

The short-lived conversion bore little fruit, however, partly due to the British administration discouraging the apparent closeness between the followers of the Arya Samaj and the few African potential converts. It seemed imperative to prevent any collaboration between Africans and Indians, especially because the Arya Samaj had political clout in India.

Master Jatiram and his wife had made a beautiful little temple in a small store. Here the family assembled each evening. As soon as Master Jatiram's little hand-bell was heard, the family knew that the sweet sound was a call to prayer. His loud and clear voice started the Gayatri Mantra, '*Om bhur bhuvah* . . .' and he led them through the daily *puja*. He regularly visited the Sanatan Dharam temple and prostrated in front of all the idols. He poured oil on the icons of Hanuman, the monkey god; he placed fresh flowers at the feet of Krishna . . . he was a true devotee. There came a day when he himself threw away all the adored objects of veneration. The once beloved idols, which he had lovingly polished every morning, were that day carelessly ejected from the house like pieces of rubbish. Members of the household had watched with shock and consternation.

This achieved without any semblance of remorse or emotion, Masterji sat cross-legged on a cushion in the middle of a small stark room to prepare the sacred fire in the altar. He poured ghee on the finely chopped pieces of wood, and, lighting a fire, started mumbling Vedic chants. The simple ritual established Masterji's entry to the Arya Samaj fold. It also displayed his renunciation of Sanatan Dharam's *murti puja*. 'Idol worship is wrong,' he had been told by the new Aryan missionaries. And he had slowly begun to see some sense in that. Master Jatiram converted to the Arya Samaj way of worship. The little family temple in the store was gone. The family no longer gathered together as it had done for years.

'Ram-Ram Masterji,' someone called out, and Master Jatiram's 'Namaste' in reply came a little hesitantly, as if the tongue had not yet caught on to the word. For a split-second he felt a little uneasy, but almost immediately lifted his shoulders and walked on. Someone else laughed behind his back and shouted, 'The Arya Samaj has taken you over, Masterji! How will you worship your gods now?' But Masterji did not stop to look back and walked on. He went about the *biradari* almost defiantly. And yet, the Arya Samaj was as Hindu in concept as any of the older precepts. Was it just a *nouvelle vague*? Or would it also be absorbed into the Sanatana Dharam Hindu fold? Time would tell.

Essentially Hindu, the reformist ideology of the Arya Samaj appeared to appeal to those groping for a new consciousness in the charged politico-cultural climate. It perhaps also relieved them from drowning in the ocean of vagueness and vastness of Hinduism. Progressive in some ways, yet perhaps more conservative and fundamentalist in others, the new convert seemed satisfied. The Arya Samaj movement in Nairobi took root, especially amongst the Hindu Punjabis. These were the Punjabis who were neither Sikhs nor Muslims but were either 'unreformed' Sanatanis or 'reformed' Arya Samajis.

In matters of uniform ritual, the simple Arya Samaj fire ceremony slowly caught on, even though many homes continued to have an icon in their homes. A dancing Shiva Nataraj, or a pot-bellied Ganesha with a *laddu* in his left hand, or a blue-bodied, saffron-robed effeminate Krishna, a flute in his hands—even coloured cut-outs and prints from calendars were pasted in cupboards, safely hidden from general view. Yet, their hands remained joined together in front of their chests. The new Arya Samaj greeting of 'Namaste' bowed to the eternal soul that abides in each one; it appeared more neutral than the otherwise popular salutation of 'Ram-Ram'.

'Idolatory and all its attendant ceremonies having no basis in the Vedas have no place in true religion', declared their religious leader. *Shraddh* rites on behalf of the dead were declared futile, as was the practice of bathing in sacred streams. Pilgrimages, use of beads, sandalwood marks, gifts to mendicants, and many other rites of popular Hinduism were also made redundant. The new Arya Samaj temple in Nairobi was to be austere—a plain hall with a *havan kund* (fire altar) in the middle.

No Shiva. No Lakshmi, Durga, or Ganesha. The new prayer hall would house no idols. No incarnations of Vishnu. Ram, the Indian ideal, Krishna, the Indian reality—objects of such popular adoration were treated as pious or powerful princes of an older time. Keeping the message of their spiritual leader very clear, the Aryans advocated, 'only rites authorized by the Vedas must be observed'. Bereft of most *Upanishads*, as well as other speculative tracts of the Vedic tradition and the *Puranas*. Negating Saivite, Vaishnavite, and Devi traditions.

'Vedic dharma *ki jai.*' 'Long live the Vedic religion', they chanted. 'Rishi Dayanand *ki jai.*' 'Arya Samaj *ki jai.*' The resolute Aryans persisted. Their determination bore fruit. As early as September 1903, the foundation of a building was laid—a date which was to mark regular anniversary celebrations of Arya Samaj *jalsas* in Nairobi. The ancient Hindu way of worship, the Sanatan Dharam—which does not owe its beginning to any prophet, but has god incarnating when necessary—still claimed the majority of the simple Hindu believers in Nairobi. They could only organize themselves by 1917.

Hardei did not convert to the Arya Samaj way of worship. Like the average villager from Punjab, at heart she was neither an absolute Hindu nor a Sikh nor a Muslim, but a combination of all these. She worshipped all things held to be holy—whether people, places, objects or nature—without thinking about it. Unfettered by a unified, organized form of ritual, she more or less concocted her own private ceremony based on what she had learnt as a child from the elders and from preachers.

Besides, she was a devotee of Krishna. At the end of the nineteenth century, a man called Lala Prasad had arrived from Vrindavan—the birthplace of Krishna—with two deities. The blue-bodied Krishna and his fair-complexioned Radha became a reference point for many believers. People came from far away to perform *puja* at Lalaji's shrine, especially on festive occasions. Lalaji had planted a peepul tree and carefully placed the deities underneath. The little statue of Krishna playing a flute, standing with his right leg crossed over the left, stood in all its composure under that peepul tree, in the bazaar area. The peepul was sacred. Devotees circumambulated it, finally joining their hands and lowering their heads in devotion and humility. Its wood was often used to light the sacred fire. Under the shade of its branches and leaves, the Buddha had been enlightened. In the *Atharva Veda*, the peepul was used to ensure a male child. The peepul grew and grew into other trees—uniting, penetrating and destroying. Its fierce powers were evoked in battle rites. The peepul was the cosmic tree of life.

It was here that Hardei started coming to worship. The peepul in the bazaar was still young, and allowed the first rays of the morning sun to bathe the dark face of Krishna. Krishna the black, taking on hues of gold—an antipodal pre-Aryan hero rising above the local nature gods. He is the god of transgression, with potent divinity because he rejected the rule of reason, and had a morality that was not fixed in formulas. The flute-playing trickster, his delirious dance with the *gopis* only added to his sacred charisma. Reputed to be a great lover, he led worshippers to catharsis and ecstasy. Krishna, the eighth avatar of Vishnu, was also the god of the Mahabharata, where, as Arjuna's charioteer, he advised and guided him to take the path of action versus that of inaction. Probably the most adored and most accessible of Hindu deities, in the person of Krishna, Hinduism underwent a transformation that brought about the appearance of the divine in human form.

Lala Prasad's small shrine even had its own full-time priest by now. Worshippers stood before him, their heads bowed and hands outstretched, right hand cupped on the left. With a murmured blessing *panditji* dipped his forefinger in the vessel of holy water and touched both eyes of each worshipper.

Hardei's eyes would be transfixed on the statue of Krishna. She would feel the marble stir to life. Krishna seemed to break into a smile. Focusing her entire being on the pulsating divine energies, the idol became a point of concentration. In no time, she would feel slightly intoxicated. Face to face with the deity, she could almost hear Krishna whisper within the battlefield of her soul: act according to your dharma. Far more inclusive than mere duty, dharma was a sacred responsibility. Hardei would feel strengthened and rejuvenated. A new energy would envelop her being. She would bow, eyes closed, and drink the holy water.

Her parents, the Diwans, had been a prosperous family of Haranpur, a town 8 km from Miani, on the other side of the Jhelum. To be from the Diwan *biradari* meant to be financially sound, of a privileged status, having power. Often it also meant being a moneylender and a landowner. In days gone by, Mughal kings gave this Persian title to their finance ministers. Even today, the name Diwan carries the socially identified aura of nobility around it.

Hardei was not literate; in fact, she had never gone to school. She could not even count properly. The first time she had to handle her own money and accounts, she had had to ask someone to count the money for her. The next time she did it herself. She learnt very fast. Money trade came easily to her—after all, she was born into a Diwan *biradari*. A family of means, with factories in Sarghoda manufacturing strings for tennis racquets, sitars and guitars. She quickly learnt the traditional family occupation—moneylending on commission. In fact, quite a few Hindu men and women established themselves as moneylenders in the Nairobi bazaar.

The prevailing rule of northern India, that a man must take a wife from a village other than his own, meant that Hardei's family looked for a suitable boy out of Haranpur. A name was suggested, the family was sought out, and with that her future was sealed. Still in her early teens, the young girl was quickly married into the Khatri caste of Wasans, to a man not much older than herself. A certain Kirparam, from a *biradari* of *halwais* of the town of Miani. Hardei was destined to become a *halwaien*, they said, the wife of a confectioner from a humble quarter . . . little did they know how things would turn out.

Miani was not even his ancestral town. Kirparam's father Ramchand had come down to Miani from a town further north-west, an even smaller town called Mardan. For a long time after his arrival, the father continued to talk about, remember, dream about and reminisce about this town Mardan. Vivid descriptions of the major military post—where British soldiers in their highly visible brilliant red and blue uniforms (making them easy targets of the Pathans) collected intelligence and tried to keep peace on the North-West Frontier—would converge upon his mind. Ramchand would talk about vast mountain ranges, arid regions, pasture lands, deep forests, valleys, lush orchards, and the many Buddhist monasteries that provided them a place of worship and of play.

Sometimes, Ramchand would spend hours in the courtyard lost in thought. It was many, many years since he had been separated from the rugged landscape, but as soon as he closed his eyes, Ramchand could easily slide backwards in time, up the mountains. When they saw his face glowing with pride, his eyes beaming with pleasure, the children knew that a story was not far away; they were in for a treat. They grew up on these stories, never tiring of listening to them umpteen times. The stories came easily, repeatedly, like the chants of a mantra. His old face shone, became almost childlike when he talked of his ancestors. A great change came over him when he spoke of Mardan. The mere thought of the town completely transformed him. As the story progressed, Ramchand's breathing would alter, his eyes once more fill up with wonder and awe with each dramatic incident that he narrated. In his excitement, he would become more imaginative and transform into a storyteller par excellence, a true *kathakar* mixing reality and fiction and the revealing aspects of *maya*.

There was no denying the fact that the area around what used to be called Gandhara, now the Peshawar valley, had a unique beauty. Peshawar had certainly been an important city in the history of Buddhism. Mardan too had been much influenced by Gandhara art, leaving behind strong legacies like the sculpture in stone of the fasting Buddha. Here, Buddhism had prospered, and Gandhara had come to be known as Buddhist holy land.

However, given their geographic location, climatically and strategically, this inevitably came with the unbearable harshness of marching armies and countless movements. At a certain point, migration became inevitable, and the young Ramchand had left. He never told his children why, and they had not asked. Stopping by in Peshawar near the mouth of the Khyber Pass for a while, Ramchand had continued down south towards the Punjab, finally terminating his journey in Miani. Perhaps Kirparam's urge for adventure and travel had been inherited from his father.

5

Early lessons

'Thinner than water
Sweeter than sugar
Whose coming and going none can see
What am I?'
'Sleep.'
— Punjabi riddle

The East African Turf Club, 3 km north of the township, with rules adapted from those of the Calcutta Turf Club, was founded in the same year as the Arya Samaj: 1903. White women in fashionable hats and parasols, upper-class Indian women in brilliant saris, men in flowing turbans—they all went to the races. The race week was a big celebration of fashion and elegance, of business and pleasure.

The 'railway capital' had gained a reputation as a sportsman's paradise. Maharajas from India, aristocrats from the United Kingdom and Presidents of the United States were among those who came to the country for big game hunting and shooting safaris, and this often led to further investment. Tourism came early to this part of the world. The role of the white hunter was created, romanticized and glamorized. Uniforms for porters came at incredible speed from the Indian tailors at Alibhai's or Ahmed Brothers—outfitting princes, nobles, the landed gentry and those commoners who could afford it. By 1905—just about the time that Hardei had stepped into the town—Nairobi was catering to approximately a thousand European visitors a year.

On the other hand, even before urban facilities had been set up, the first negative signs of urban decay had already established themselves. Besides the people who were suffering and who had already suffered, even the environment was being affected. The ravages were already visible. Countless herds of wild animals, which had been living in harmony with most of the tribal peoples, had already been eliminated to make room for western civilization. Hundreds of animals were shot, their heads proudly displayed and mounted on lounge walls. It became fashionable to keep leopard and cheetah skins in front of fireplaces. Thousands of elephants were killed regularly for their tusks. Exports were estimated at 120 tons per year. Ivory markets of Europe and the Far East flourished. Ivory was used for piano keys, billiard balls, carvings, handles, umbrellas, canes—the list was endless.

Situated 5,500 feet above sea level, Nairobi was laid out with large open spaces. The hotels were for Europeans only. European businessmen dressed as if they were on Oxford Street; farmers from coffee plantations and up-country ranches wore khaki. Here was to be found the hub of the settler population—the main street with its little shop of smart hats and gowns, a chemist shop, a tool shop and the National Bank of India, a short square tin-roof structure on stilts (to prevent water seeping into the building when it rained). The foundations of a modernized economy were beginning to be laid, with Bombay Mint supplying the copper coinage.

A wooden bridge was constructed to connect the road from the railway station to the area behind. It was named Parklands, and was intended for European residential settlement. The early layout of Nairobi was based upon segregation of colour and class. Olive Grey, an ex-Salvation Army major wrote of how 'the sticky morass of the Railway Headquarters contrasts with the palatial residences in the hearts of men that no plausible speech can eradicate'. A township with a semicircle of bungalows, a huge railway station, houses for workmen, a few European shops, and the bazaar—all laid out with rectangular symmetry, it resembled a mining settlement. With the exception of a purple and yellow market, a monument to the public generosity of A.M. Jeevanjee, nearly all the houses were constructed of white corrugated iron sheets left over from construction of the Mombasa railway.

A.M. Jeevanjee's wealth earned him the title of 'Seth'. A very rich Bohra who headed a firm of contractors and general merchants, he set up his Jeevanjee Market in the style of a Victorian church—including a tower and clock—with stalls and even stables for horses. Why he chose to paint his market yellow and purple, only he could have told you—perhaps to attract attention, or to give the town the colour that it so lacked. In the centre of the courtyard lay a magnificent fountain to further brighten up the atmosphere. A very useful outlet for African produce, Jeevanjee Market was certainly popular—even with thieves! Right opposite the market was Jeevanjee Gardens, complete with an imposing statue of Queen Victoria.

'The garden is a gift to the residents,' said the Bohra trader from Karachi who had prospered in Nairobi and made it his home. People taking a leisurely walk in the garden would stretch their necks to look up at the yet-incomplete larger-than-life statue cut in grey stone. She stood high on a pedestal, looking straight ahead, just as she had done in the more than half a century of rule over the British empire. A hard and cold gaze made the doppelganger profile impressive and dominating, both in its rigidity and the hubris it portrayed. A pompous Victoria was to grace the lawns.

Arches decorated the streets of Nairobi. With long earlobes hanging loose to the neck, Maasai and Kikuyu warriors were made to line the street as the Duke of Connaught arrived to unveil the statue of Queen Victoria in March 1906. Elaborate precautions were taken to ensure that all went well. But when they learnt that the duke's daughter Princess Patricia and her lady-in-waiting Evelyn Pelly were also travelling with him, the organizers panicked. How could the young ladies be expected to come face to face with so many underdressed Africans? Clad solely in their one-piece red *shuka* tied over the left shoulder, the Maasai would definitely be an embarrassment.

Every red blanket available in the market was bought for the Maasai to dress in. The rest of their tribe teasingly called them *amanyahanga*, people of clothes. Just as the guests were leaving for Government House, it began to rain. All the Maasai automatically twisted the blankets over their heads for shelter. They were wearing nothing underneath.

The 'cream' of Nairobi society was present. The duke and the duchess sat with the governor on the specially constructed high dais bedecked in blue, red and white bunting. Africans who were to appear before them had been clad 'decently'. But to the horror of the entourage, a naked Maasai appeared at the garden party and walked across the lawn in front of the royal couple.

'Indecent exposure' of course did not exist in the minds of the Africans, but the Nairobi Municipal Council decided it was time that Africans covered their nakedness in the name of decency. Khaki shorts and shirts were introduced. *Askaris* (guards) were posted at gates to ensure that unless men coming into Nairobi were 'properly' clad, they would not be allowed to enter. Some Africans started entering the gates fully dressed, to undress completely on entry— to the utter shock of the settlers and their wives and daughters.

One of the most swashbuckling and controversial figures of African colonial history, Colonel Ewart Grogan warned the government: rape or murder, you will never keep these savages under control with your handful of *askaris*. Build a proper European police force and introduce punishments. The concept of 'disciplining' the African varied. Some Europeans freely admitted using the *kiboko* (whip) to 'teach them a lesson'. To keep them in check for small pilferage or slackening in work, others used guns. Once, chasing after a worker in his car, one white man even drove over the poor fellow, while Colonel Ewart Grogan, his eyes glaring red with anger, publicly whipped a servant before a crowd of excited whites.

* * *

They had been up much of the night packing, but the work was yet not finished. Hardei bent to pick up a load from the floor and screamed in pain. She knew that the heavy work was not good for her back, nor for the child she was expecting. She looked at her husband. He merely shook his head, pulled the charpoy down and made her sit. Handing her a glass of water, he continued to fill up the cart with their household goods. Soon they were on their way to the new bazaar. Until then known as *njogu*, the peanut bazaar, it had been shifted once again in 1906; this became the famous 'Indian bazaar'.

Artisans, confectioners, tailors, shoemakers, barbers, carpenters, blacksmiths—they all returned to live and to work in the new shanties as before. Carts drawn by mules, or *hamali* carts pulled by men continued to ply up and down the street. Because it was difficult to rent shops in the bazaar, tenants resorted to illegally subletting their premises. This led to the bazaar exploding in chaos. Without clean water, sanitation or electricity, this was another clear invitation to the plague. In Lala Prasad's little shrine, another god—rather, goddess—was added. She had neither arms nor legs. Not even an image in human form. Just a slab of stone with two beady eyes. Goddess Sitala became the goddess of the plague. Hardei went to offer prayers in the hope that the child in her womb would not be infected with the dreaded disease.

A strong stench filled the air. She covered her nose with her *dupatta*, but it was already too late. The reek had filled up her nostrils. Immediately, she threw up. She felt faint and quickly held on to a broken wall to regain control of herself. But the stench would not go away. The open trenches were filled with sewage. There were no proper drains nor were there adequate toilets. The bazaar was damp, dark, unventilated and overcrowded. Squalor and filth covered the area. In the badly lit streets, people often fell into the grime at night.

Yes, Nairobi grew, but its growth aggravated its problems of health and sanitation. Low on water after prolonged drought, the town was wholly supplied from Nairobi river. Contamination led to many diseases. The shops and stores that served as living quarters became an ideal breeding ground for rats. The plague had come.

Once known as the place of fresh water, Ngare N'erobi had been contaminated. Water was still carried up from the river, usually in *debes*. They washed themselves in the water and yet never felt very clean. Clothes were washed here. Houses, latrines, even vegetable *shambas* (fields) sprang up here. The bulk of drinking water was also drawn from Nairobi river; it didn't taste 'clean' even after boiling. Not surprisingly there were constant outbreaks of dysentery; bilharzia became an added danger.

It started pouring, but the children refused to stay indoors. Chunilal ran barefoot in the quagmire with the others, kicking packing cases, which were soon to become soggy and harder to chase after. 'Come back!' Hardei shouted after him, but he had run far and she couldn't catch up with him. Hardei cursed under her breath. Her belly was getting heavier now. She moved about the mess with difficulty. The corrugated iron roof of their house had rusted and fallen in. The bazaar had turned into a soggy morass. She was sure that the paleness of her son's complexion was somehow connected to the lack of a proper sewage system. 'All this filth is the root of our constant illness!' she muttered in irritation.

Practically every afternoon it poured. East of the Rift valley, the rain falls in two distinct seasons of the year—the intervening seasons remain drier, but are often cloudy or misty. During the months of long rains (March to May) and short rains (November to December), the road that led to the railway offices near the station—a track of black cotton soil—turned to deep mud. The swamp spread its softness under their small huts. Bullock carts used for goods and passengers further muddied the road. The poor dukawallahs sank packing cases into the mud for stepping-stones. Eventually, as the rains continued, even these stepping-stones were lost in the glutinous liquid. Shacks and shanties were moved to drier ground. Hardei's tasks seemed endless, and the plague was advancing once again. Hardei was worried that the unborn babe in her womb might already be infected.

The first sign was a dead rat or two. Very soon many more were found. The 'black death' started spreading with alarming speed. Workers, relatives and friends succumbed to the disease, one by one. As dangers from the lions decreased, hazards from plague increased. Shops were closed down. Business came to a standstill. The first outbreak of the disease was in 1902. Fresh epidemics continued until at least 1913. On the basis of his experience in India, Dr Ribeiro diagnosed it as bubonic plague. The medical officer gave the order to burn down the rat-infested shanties that served as shops and homes.

Dr Rozendo Ayres Ribeiro, Nairobi's first medical practitioner, arrived from Goa towards the end of the nineteenth century. Nairobi as a town was just taking root; people still lived in tents and camps, and work on the railway line was far from complete. Here, he set up his first medical practice. He took to visiting his largely Indian clientele—along with a few Africans and some settlers—on the back of a zebra. The chubby Goan on his tame zebra became a familiar sight in the bazaar. In fact, the photograph of him on his zebra became an icon of early Kenya.

At first his tent, which he shared with C. Pinto, his assistant, was pitched on Whitehouse Road. Ribeiro and Pinto were often found sitting late into the night, writing prescriptions by the light of a candle or a kerosene lamp. Dr Ribeiro had a neatly trimmed black beard, and his waistcoat buttons were done up tight enough to fly off any moment. He made his rounds cutting across community barriers. His malaria cure was especially renowned—he eventually patented it and sold it to an international pharmaceutical company. In a country infested by mosquitoes, the secret formula was much sought after.

Hardei prayed constantly. When she was working, her lips mumbled all sorts of entreaties. When she retired for the night, Krishna's name was still on her mind. On 6 June 1906, a girl was born to Hardei and Kirparam in their tin shack in the bazaar— their first child since their reconciliation. Others would be born in quick succession in British East Africa, which by now had become seriously infected by yet another disease—the virus of racial prejudice. Hardei, herself the beloved of Hari, chose to name the girl Yashoda—the foster mother of Krishna. In Sanskrit it meant 'glorious'. Perhaps this was Hardei's symbolic gesture to the god who had traced the new path in her life; Krishna had once more descended to save her. But she could not help wondering what lay in store for the child. What sort of country would she inherit?

Kenya lies astride the equator on the east coast of Africa. The most striking physiographic distinction is between the high altitude tracts, encompassing roughly the south-west half of the country, and the remaining area, consisting of low plateaus and plains. Lying east and west of the Rift valley, the highlands are the only sizeable area—other than the coastal belt—that can count on generally reliable rainfall; they also have most of the good soil.

A striking feature on the eastern side is Mt Kenya, the country's highest point at 5,200 metres above sea level. The area east of the Aberdares range, populated by the Kikuyu, the largest ethnic group, offers a cool bracing climate with mean temperatures of 22–26 and 10–14 degrees centigrade, humidity approximately 90 per cent in the early mornings, dropping to about 40 per cent mid-afternoon. The combination of moderate temperatures, adequate rainfall and good soil brought thousands of settlers to these parts—which were to become famous as the 'white highlands'.

One of the healthiest districts in British East Africa, the highlands could be made to look like the landscapes that the whites had left behind. Many of the settlers had been army officers in British India. In 1904, hundreds of white South Africans, also known as the Kaburus, had been invited to settle. Some stayed in Nairobi, others moved on to the Uasin Gishu plateau, where they grew wheat and raised sheep. No sooner had they come, than they encouraged the regime to look less to Bombay and more to South Africa for markets, legislation and planning. They called for more European supervision, namely, an introduction to labour laws and a system of identification for the 'natives'. A year later, the colonial office took over responsibility for the protectorate from the foreign office. A new Constitution was introduced and a governor appointed.

Hardei had not yet arrived when there was also talk of Zionists being offered the Uasin Gishu plateau as an 'ante-chamber' to the Holy Land. This part of Kenya could easily have become the 'land of the Jews'. In 1902, the secretary of state for the colonies, thoroughly impressed by the land and the climate, offered a free grant of 5,000 square miles to Zionists looking for a home. Jewish commissioners came to inspect the 'promised land' two years later. (Neither the settlers of the colony, nor were most Zionists in favour of the idea.) The commissioners camped at the edge of the forest. They heard the trumpeting of the elephants and encountered the Maasai Morans in full war regalia, bare limbs glistening with castor oil and ochre and faces done up in war paint, wearing long ostrich feathers and anklets of black and white colobus monkey fur, brandishing their long spears and shields. The 'new Zion' was very quickly reported as 'unsuitable' for fugitive Jews from Russia.

Many British soldiers who had served in the Boer war in South Africa also ended up in Nairobi. The magic of open spaces and the freedom was like a balm to their soul. England was too tame for them, its conventionality an anathema. In 1908, 250 other Boers arrived in Mombasa, to head upcountry the same day on special trains. They came fully equipped, with horses, wagons (from the backs of which swung carcasses of meat strung on iron hoops) and stock. A small township was created in Eldoret. Indian traders soon followed the Boers to set up dukas.

Kaburus—from the word 'Boer'—spoke Dutch, Afrikaans, broken English and a smattering of Kikuyu or Kiswahili. Mostly from the Natal province, to them all Indians were coolies because of the Indian porters on the railways in South Africa—'low-class coolies with their corrugated iron-shanties by the roadside'. Most Indians were not in commerce, nor were they all small dukawallahs. Most were employed as clerks—both for European concerns and Indian—or they were civil servants. They were also in a wide range of skilled professions—tailors, smiths, carpenters, auto mechanics, construction workers, etc.

Not all of them were racist, but generally Kaburus stayed aloof out of fear of their own society, which did not value such an interaction. Clearly, they were uneasy, apprehensive about being labelled 'friends of coolies'. Boers frequented Indian dukas for their own needs, but if the Indians went to their farms, they did not want to know them. They never let them into their homes.

Kirparam had his own encounter with them. One afternoon, when the heat was quite oppressive, he had stepped out for some fresh air. On his return, he had taken not more than three steps towards the door when someone called out, 'Hey, babu.' Kirparam turned and saw the Boer. A gauge of the hubris, the man stood proud and arrogant. The short babu walked towards the man without showing any signs of intimidation. '*Saab log* (sahibs), big people; they rule over us,' he thought to himself and went on to serve the man. Kirparam was not particularly ashamed of being called babu, even though he knew that it was meant to offend him. He belched. The acrid smell of ghee hung on his breath. The Boer's red nose flinched in disgust.

The black Bangalore topee clung to Kirparam's head as if it formed part of the skull. He hardly ever removed it. Most people had never seen him without it. When he did take it off at night just before sleeping, he quickly covered his head with a towel. Why Kirparam took to wearing this topee in the first place, rather than the traditional voluminous pugree, was beyond them. It gave him the look of a babu.

'Babu' was British colonialism's insulting term for Uttar Pradesh and Bengali clerks in India who knew English. The mocking title was in turn passed on to simple government clerks of Indian origin in the protectorate who handled all aspects of British administration. They came to be known as railway babus. The *wazungu* enforced their authority but rarely deigned to mix with such ordinary people. They looked at babus as passive, underdeveloped, uncultured, but cunning. No matter which caste he belonged to—Brahmin or untouchable—the Indian was a coolie or dukawallah, or at best a babu.

Lala Kirparam with his wife Hardei in a photo taken in the 1930s

In the Hindu *biradari*, they called them babuji or Bauji. All elderly men were Baujis. And it was said the way it was meant to be—with utmost respect. An expression for a father, an elderly person, a person of rank, a distinguished one at that. Babuji, or Bauji was a polite, deferential form of address. The railway *bau* was an educated person. Baujis were brought hot lunch—a spicy meal of lentils, vegetables and chapatis in a three-tiered brass tiffin (called *dissidabba*)—at their railway public works department workshop each noon by *totos,* young African houseboys. Children would hush when Bauji came home; daughters-in-law would cover their heads with their saris. '*Pairi pona Bauji*', they would say, touching Bauji's feet. In some houses, this touching of feet would be a daily morning ritual.

The feet of elders were venerated, while those of the divine were worshipped. Touching the feet symbolized a range of emotions—from love to devotion, to humility and humiliation, to begging for forgiveness, and to being pardoned. The settlers would only have laughed had they seen the contours of a thin darkie in his *dhoti* or in his white pyjamas, a pugree or black topee on the head, blessing figures touching his feet. Such humility and meekness was not the stuff that rulers were made of. Rulers and pioneers 'created' a new country; they were 'endowed with the necessary statures and powers'. They calculated manœuvres, devised strategies, made tactical decisions. Their actions required dexterity and skill.

The settlers increased their power in the council, and managed to influence policy to suit their own needs. A white man's country was being founded in the South African image with 'no nonsense about equal rights for black and white'. Their farming methods, control of labour, political techniques and objectives were founded on white South African precedents. Before World War I, they were the most dominant group—both in political expression and in numbers.

Through a deliberate policy of divide and rule, they secured colonial rule. They tried to poison race relations amongst the

800 Europeans, 76 Eurasians, 590 Goans, 3,171 Indians, and 9,524 Africans. Goans and Parsis enjoyed a reputation for efficiency and loyalty to the British. Mostly of Christian faith, the Goans quickly picked up English, although they continued to speak Konkani, a language close to Marathi, at home. And, except for an intellectual few like Eddie Pereira, most were not happy to be called Indian. Goans were especially famed as caterers, stewards, wine merchants and dealers in European groceries.

'One would scarcely believe that a centre so new should be able to develop so many divergent and conflicting interests . . . the white man versus the black, the Indian versus both, the official class against the unofficial, the coastal against the highlander . . . all these different points of view, naturally arising, honestly adopted, tenaciously held and not yet reconciled into any harmonious general conception, confront the visitor in perplexing disarray,' wrote Winston Churchill in *My African Journey*. Then under-secretary of state for the colonies, Churchill paid a visit to Kenya in 1907, mainly to smooth out difficulties concerning land laws. He was not certain, he said, that the exclusion of British Indian subjects from the highlands could be regarded as a valid policy.

Hardei was well into yet another pregnancy. Some women, not much older, had already given birth to seven or eight children. By the time they were forty or so, they had had as many as twelve or even fourteen children, many of whom died before they were four. More than the physical pain of continual pregnancy, though, Hardei's biggest discomfort was the number of times her bladder had to be emptied. Her nightmare was going to the toilet late at night, or in the early hours of the morning, especially when the drivers of the night-soil carts came to collect excrement from each house.

The toilet was a small shed with a pit latrine—actually a hole in a raised platform. Under this, a bucket was placed. The rear end of the shed opened to a sanitary lane. Buckets were emptied each night into a tank mounted on a municipal cart pulled by oxen.

Barrel-shaped containers on metal-rimmed cartwheels were driven to the river for disposal.

One morning around 4 a.m. she felt the need for the bathroom. She heaved and turned in her charpoy, but sleep did not come. 'May as well go to the toilet and relieve myself', she thought. Just as she was making the decision to get up, she heard loud voices in the distance. The *churas* were announcing their arrival. The drivers of the night soil carts were already on their way.

Many of them were outcastes. Others had converted to Sikhism to escape the stigma. She could hear the *churas* clearly now. They were very close, they could be heard urging their oxen to move on. She waited until they had left, their voices fading into the distance. A kerosene lamp in one hand (she kept it lit throughout the night as her pregnancy progressed), and a small tin of water in the other, she made her way through the cold Nairobi night to the toilet which lay at the far end of the house. It had rained at night, and once again the soil was mucky.

The place was without air or electric light. Going to the pit latrine was a hazardous business, especially in the dark, or when it rained heavily. A wrong turn and one could land a leg in the hole, if not the entire body. Pouring water into the hole after use, she was just about to leave when light from her small lamp illuminated a dead rat in the corner. She felt sick and quickly left the toilet, only to throw up just outside. She turned down the wick of the hurricane lamp next to her cot and lay down. They have come again, she thought, and took several deep breaths to try to calm down. She was right. She found another rat in the gunny sack containing grain in her store the next morning.

'*Haiza. Haiza. Haiza.* It is back with us. We are ruined,' the screams were heard throughout the bazaar. Once again pandemonium broke out. All hell broke loose. Almost every household was in mourning. Death was thick in the air. The plague had returned. It was to return again, and yet again, over the next three years. Many Indian traders were put under quarantine. It claimed many lives and rendered others homeless as the bazaar was repeatedly burnt down. Their shanties that served both as shops and homes were razed to the ground; stocks were destroyed. Quarantine quarters were set up in tents. There was fear that if you went into quarantine, you would not come out alive. But people were forced to remain in quarantine for up to six weeks.

Their third child had high fever. At first they thought it was just due to the cold. When she started trembling and the pain spread all over the body, they were afraid. The fourth child, the youngest of all, followed suit. That night she too had fever. The whole family panicked, and lay awake through the night. Before the night was over, Kirparam knew that if he was to save the rest of the family, he must make quick decisions. He had to send them away somewhere, somehow. Before dawn, Hardei, Chunilal and Yashoda were packed off to Ruaraka.

The authorities came knocking on the door very early next morning, checking on all households. 'Quarantine it has to be,' Kirparam was told when they saw the fever-ridden children. 'They are just babies. I can't let them go to that place of death all by themselves,' he cried in pain, and insisted, 'Let me nurse them at home.' 'What home?' the authorities shouted back. 'Every house in the bazaar is going to be razed to the ground, do you hear? Is that clear? We have enough work to do here without your adding to the problems.' Kirparam then asked if he could accompany the girls into quarantine. 'You will be risking your own life,' they said, but eventually they let him. He sat by the girls all day, doing what little he could to make them somewhat comfortable. He lay down on the ground next to their little cots by night, but stories of the Punjab plague, when several million had become victims, recurred again and again; his mind was totally tormented. He closed his eyes, but the images were still there. He cried himself to sleep—only to be woken up a few minutes later.

The older girl was mumbling something in her delirious state. The wick of her bedside lamp began to flicker. Kirparam was not unduly superstitious, but at this moment it seemed an inauspicious sign and he felt uneasy. 'Lila,' he called out to her softly, 'Do you know that you are very precious to me? When you get well, I will take you up to the mountain, the mountain covered with snow, the mountain that you like so much.' Kirparam continued to talk to her, thinking that this might keep her conscious and improve her state. 'Do you know why I chose to call you Lila? It is because when you were born, you looked so playful. You were so full of life, of amusement. You made us laugh. We loved to play with you.' His voice broke even as he spoke; he could see that her condition was worsening. Her lymphatic ganglions had swollen up. The strain was too much for her frail body. Kirparam knew that the worst was not far away.

The younger girl's condition was no better. Both had become victims of the dreaded disease. All it took was the bite of a small flea normally found on the back of the rodent. The fragile ones—very often children—were easily infected. Kirparam and Hardei lost both girls that night. Kirparam's heart broke. Sounds of pain and suffering from other patients surrounded him. He could offer them neither hope nor comfort. In the badly lit quarters, smelling of all kinds of disinfectants, he felt as if he would suffocate, unable even to give vent to his pain. At this moment he needed to be alone. He went out of the tents and immediately burst into a flood of tears.

They called them backward. They called them unhygienic. They called them lazy. Now, after the plague, the Indians were insulted further. 'They are foul liars, drunkards and thieves,' said a certain Lord Cranworth. 'They live in conditions under which no English farmer would dream of keeping his pigs.' 'To be in measurable distance of an Indian coolie is very disagreeable,' said Lady Delamere. 'Most Indians belong to the lowest class and are prone to unsanitary habits.' Plague, venereal diseases and other contagious ailments were attributed to them.

The new outbreak in the bazaar precipitated yet another attack on Indians by the settlers, initiating a move to reinforce residential and commercial segregation. Using the excuse of sanitation rules, they proposed zonation along racial lines: 'Racial segregation in towns is necessary to maintain proper sanitary standards.' The intentions of their slogans were clearly racist. The aggressors forgot that overcrowding was mainly due to unavailability of space for expansion and that there were no proper drainage or sewage systems. 'The bazaar must be demolished,' they said. And it was.

'Owing to the unsanitary habits of Asiatics and of Africans, they are not fit persons to take up land as neighbours of Europeans,' said Colonel Ewart Grogan of *Cape to Cairo* fame. Having trekked the entire distance from Cape Town in South Africa to Cairo up north to obtain the hand in marriage of Gertrude Watt, he wrote an account of his trek; it became a best-seller. Not satisfied with that, Colonel Grogan continued to speak out against Asians and Africans. He asked for their exclusion in the same way as in South Africa. Grogan, the lumber king of Kenya, with his 1,00,000 acres of land, declared in 1915, 'Land outside the municipal limits, roughly lying between Kiu and Fort Ternan, can only be given to white settlers'.

Ewart Grogan and Lord Delamere, another major controversial figure, vied with one another as to who could do most to further colonization. It took only twenty-two of them to band together an organization against Indian immigration; this was way back in January 1902. Segregation was not institutionalized, but from then onwards it continued to smoulder steadily. The Indian problem became immediate: Indians had to be stopped at all costs from acquiring any land suitable for white settlers. It was referred to as the 'Indian Question'—although there was no 'question' about the efforts to keep the highlands white. The corresponding rise in European demands for reservation of land gave birth to the 'white highlands'. Thus, on the slopes of the Rift valley, a white country was born.

The Rift valley emerged as a result of a monstrous geological accident. It is an immense scar, a gorge in the earth's crust

40–120 km in width. From Lake Baikal, through Lebanon and the Red Sea, to Mozambique, the valley stretched for over 5,500 km. Considered to be the cradle of mankind, it was seen at its most dramatic where it cut through the highlands of the British protectorate before descending into the Maasai plains.

The highlands lowered themselves in front of the second highest peak in Africa, Mt Kenya, an extinct volcano in the heart of British-occupied territory. A forceful chain of the Aberdares dominated the eastern highlands and gave birth to the river Tana. The highlands were clearly linked with the Rift valley, the slopes of Mt Kenya and the Aberdares range to the south. They formed the largest area of continuous mountainous country in East Africa. From Lake Victoria in the west to Mt Kenya in the east, the highlands covered nearly one-fifth of British-occupied territory. Again, the Maasai with their cattle were moved from Naivasha and the surrounding areas of the six million-year-old Rift valley with its string of glittering lakes and rugged extinct volcanoes. The treaty with the displaced Maasai to move out of the Rift valley was not honoured, causing them much angst.

At an altitude of over 5,000 feet, and with the equator running across the highlands, the days were generally warm to hot, the evenings cool; nights could be bitterly cold. The air was alive over the land. One could breathe easily. Around broad acacia trees, the settlers built beautiful houses on the pattern of those developed by the British in India. Yet, 'home' to these English pioneers continued to mean Great Britain; it became part of the colonial jargon. They clung to the word no matter how much land and property they had on African soil. Children were sent 'home' to boarding school. 'Home' would be a refuge when things went wrong in British East Africa. Home was not yet in Kenya.

'The highlands comprise only a small area in the protectorate which is suitable for European residence and effort,' they said. 'The highlands are unsuitable to Indian agriculture'. Once secure in the highlands, the settlers objected to Indian landholding in any part of the country. By 1912, almost a fifth of the alienated land was owned by five *wazungu*. Plots of land up to 5,000 acres were given to settlers. A relatively small number of Europeans dominated economic life; it was a period of intense colonial experience. A colonists' association in Nairobi formed by European settlers presented a petition to the government attacking the Indian role in the country and the prevalence of British Indian methods of government.

'The East African Protectorate is governed as if it were a province of India. The sooner the sorry farce of Indian laws, Indian currency and Indian methods of government is abolished and the white community given their share in the government of the country, the better,' it said. Many of the leaders of the Colonists' Association were either South African by birth, or those who had resided for a considerable time in South Africa.

Meanwhile, the plague continued to ravage the bazaar. It would be burnt and rebuilt, only to return to the filth. Once again, the fragile ones were the first to go. Two more of their children died later. Kirparam never fully recovered from the traumatic experience of losing four children to the plague. Hardei's eyes remained dry. Was it because she was stone-hearted, or did she have so much pain that she preferred to shower her energy on the children still alive? Her state of mind will, perhaps, remain an enigma.

They continued to die in the bazaar. The Indians' issue was one of survival. As for the European leaders, they continued with meetings to sustain their demands of 'highlands for whites only' and 'restriction of Indian immigration'. They met to consider the 'untenable position of their women and children' if the principle of segregation was not recognized.

Petition after petition was drafted and redrafted. A cable was sent to King George's wife, Queen Mary, in England. 'We, the women of Kenya humbly implore your assistance to protect us and our children from the terrible Asiatic menace that threatens to overwhelm us . . .' Another went to the king informing him that the flower of Christian faith so recently planted in East Africa may be choked by the quick growth of eastern religions. Settler missionaries joined in. 'Indians exercise a baneful influence on the character of natives. The mind of an Indian is fatal to good health'. In their minds, Kenya was a land in which British ideals, British civilization and traditions and the British way of life must prevail. An 'anti-Indian' European delegation was sent to South Africa and Rhodesia–Nyasaland to obtain support for the formation of a 'United White Africa'. The white South Africans strongly influenced Kenya's development.

The seat of government moved from Mombasa to Nairobi— which remained village-like in character for years to come. The new hill capital was divided along racial lines into seven distinct areas. There was a European business and administration centre, and European residential suburbs with enclaves in Ngara, Parklands and Muthaiga. Colour, religion and social standing were always under scrutiny; the differences could never be ignored. Even amongst their own, rank stood ground. First-class European officials who lived on the Hill would not dream of having tea with the lesser, scattered European Parklands residents.

Indians were confined to the bazaar area near the railway terminal and River Road, where lay the dhobi quarter and little vegetable *shambas* along the river valley. On the borders of the swamp, houses were occupied by labourers on the *shambas,* and some native prostitutes who paid rent to the Indian owners. As late as 1928, Indians as a general rule were not allowed to move beyond the Nairobi river. They could live in 'European' areas as servants, but not as subjects. African families were similarly restricted to the reserves or worked on European farms, forced into employment far removed from their homes. A Swahili town on the road to Muthaiga Club and a Somali township were founded. A few young Somali women lived in the Indian bazaar.

A place of gentle valleys channeled by the Mathari, the Nairobi, the Masongawai and the Ngong streams, Nairobi was still a new town, with bush on all sides. Government Road and Victoria Street were north of the station. There were no 'real' roads, only rough tracks. One led from the railway station to the crest of the hill; another started at the same point, and after traversing the Indian bazaar also led by a circuitous route to the hill. Important railway officials lived on the ridge in the hill area in their bungalows. The bungalow—originally a humble Bengali peasant hut, the *bangla*—became British architecture. Raised on a small plinth to guard against flooding, it was a form adapted to reflect the strengths of imperialism.

* * *

Mathuradass Arya walked from Government Road towards his home. Shop windows displayed luxury items imported from Europe, but he didn't even give them a glance. He seemed preoccupied, and continued to walk at a fast pace, indicating an agitated mind. Throughout the night, he had lain awake in a troubled state. His constant tossing and turning had awoken his wife, but he had not shared his concerns with her. She had known better than to persist when he had woken up earlier than usual to get dressed and do a *havan* that was longer than usual. He prayed to the Almighty to give him strength and wisdom to accomplish the task that lay before him. Then he drank a glass of warm milk, and without putting a morsel of food in his mouth, headed off to work. His wife silently handed him his tiffin.

The evening light was fading. The day at the office had been longer than usual, but Mathuradass did not seem to mind. In fact, he did not feel tired at all. Right now, his thoughts were projectiles that thrust him forward to an energized state. He turned round the corner, and wound his way to the bazaar. Excitement and nervousness crept into his being almost at the same time. He knew what he was going to do, but he was sceptical about reactions. We shall see what happens, he said to himself. He had already discussed the subject with other Arya Samaj members, some of whom had reservations. Others were cynical. Only a few were in total agreement.

'The time is not yet right, we must wait,' some had said.

'But it will never be right,' he had argued. 'Educate a girl and you educate the family, an entire community, in fact. Even Swami Dayanand Saraswati had to fight many such battles. Encouraging women's education, widow remarriage, raising the age of marriage both for men and women—Swamiji also had to face perpetual opposition!'

In his heart, though, Mathuradass knew that the small beginning he was hoping for was not going to be easy.

Born in 1867 in Ludhiana in the Punjab—a stronghold of the Arya Samaj—Mathuradass had directly or indirectly come under Swami Dayanand's influence. In the Arya Samaj of Nairobi, which he had helped establish, Mathuradass had already become a respected pioneer. He was a charmer with boundless energy, a dynamic personality with a contagious spirit of service. He hardly ever failed to instil his ideals amongst those he came in contact with. Uppermost among these was education. As if he needed to justify his opinion, he never tired of citing from Swami Dayanand Saraswati's reforms, wherein education of women formed an important part of the agenda. The Arya Samajis had not yet gained ground in Nairobi; the Sanatam Dharam was not as yet fully organized. Mathuradass knew that he was surrounded by a mixed lot. In this period of uncertain transition, the issue of educating girls would be looked at suspiciously.

At a time when schools for girls were a novelty even in India, Mathuradass campaigned to start a class for girls in his own small house. He knew that sceptics would try to deter his efforts, but he set about it with the determination and reformatory zeal that the venture demanded. Clean-shaven and small, Mathuradass' humility made him look even shorter. But his hard work and self-made stature elevated him, especially when he consistently refused positions of authority in the Arya Samaj organization. 'Too risky,' he would laugh. 'A position can easily give birth to an inflated ego. I still have much work to do.'

A mass of dirty shanties were huddled together in a haphazard way. The accumulation of rubbish and open cesspools loomed in every corner, and little children romped about barefoot. 'Look at them,' he thought, 'Here they are playing in dirty puddles, when they should be in school. How will they become responsible human beings?' At the doors of their duka-houses sat women and children in vivid-hued clothing. 'Namaste Chachi; namaste *beta*,' he wished a mother and her children.

Labo was sitting on the wooden steps leading to the entrance. A brown velvet *salwar* and a loose green *kameez* enveloped her big frame; a colourful thick *dupatta* covered her head. A young toddler clothed only in a white shirt sat in the mother's lap fondling his little penis. Two eight- or nine-year-old girls, their feet joined at the centre and hands clasped tight were moving joyously in a circle. '*Kikli kaleer di pag mere veer di . . .*' they sang along, their long skirts circumambulating to the rhythm.

'Ram-Ram, Mathuraji', they broke out aloud in unison.

'Is Bauji at home?' he asked Labo.

'The shop is still open in front, he must be there. Go *beta,* go and call Bauji', she said looking at the girls.

'No, please. Don't disturb yourselves. I will go to the duka myself.' And he walked to the front of the house. The shop was attracting a few customers.

Ramdass was also seated on the *thurra* at the front of the shop. His voluminous white *salwar* and *kurta* hid the shape of his body, and he had a white pugree on his head. His ten-year-old son in khaki shorts and striped shirt, already conversant with the trade, was collecting the money from a customer.

'Ram-Ram Mathuraji, what is this I hear, the latest rumour in town . . . is it true? You are not thinking of opening a school for girls in Nairobi?' asked Ramdass.

'Namaste, Bauji,' Mathuradass replied, his hands folded in

front. He smiled and sat on the raised platform next to Ramdass, and continued, 'May your words come true, Bauji. It is why I am here to seek your blessings. And I was also going to ask for permission for your daughter to attend. Your son is already attending the government boys' school, perhaps it would be good for little Kunti also to get an education . . .'

Ramdass did not let him finish; he had heard enough. 'Our daughter Kunti, thanks be to god, is a clever and obedient child. She is getting the necessary domestic training from her mother. She can even manage to look after the youngest child. In a few years we will look for an appropriate "match" for her. What need is there for her to read and write, we are not going to put her to work in an office!'

Mathuradass tried to hone his argument, to make Ramdass see his point, but the latter was adamant—in fact, he was almost shouting in anger.

Mathuradass folded his hands and walked out of the duka. It was definitely a difficult beginning. He even put up with some insults and a few humiliations to carry on with a mission he had full faith in. The predictability of it all depressed him. He started walking faster, as if speed would help lift his mood. He was paving the way to a social transition. Could he stay balanced with one foot in tradition and the other in a semblance of modernity?

The evening was drawing to a close. He had not eaten and the aroma of freshly prepared vegetables and chapatis emanating from houses in the bazaar assailed his nostrils. In another home, the aroma of lentils and rice freshly fried in clarified butter revived the cramps in his belly. His little home was not far and his wife was sure to be waiting, but how could he eat just yet, when he had not been able to convince even one family? 'I must try a little harder,' he murmured as he walked on. His shoulders had slumped a little more. He looked even smaller, the pugree hanging loose on his head. Like many of the older generation of Indians, he still kept to the voluminous pugree, while the younger men were trying to look smart in European garb.

On the surface, the bazaar was dirty and crowded, but beneath its appearance of squalor beat a heart livelier than many areas. It epitomized urban life. Here a little India had been created. One was transported as if by magic to the sub-continent, with rows of open-fronted shops. Gunny sacks full of grain and spices, sugar, salt and chilli. Bicycle shops, gramophone shops, sewing machine shops; stalls selling soda water, tea and sticky sweets. Cartridges, knives, guns, kerosene lamps, even prostitutes—almost anything was available here. The *mochis* (cobblers) were adept; they could offer you the style of your dreams. From leather chosen on the spot, these shoemakers sat on the floor working away at your orders, while Kutchi and Punjabi *mistris*, sometimes called *fundis*, hammered away in their carpentry workshops next door. The neighbouring *darzis* (tailors) could make you a suit in a day. Without furniture or even a counter, buying and selling in these shops was done on the floor. Even the *munshi* was seen squatting on the floor before a miniature desk to do all his accounting. And among all this, of course, Indian babus dressed like Europeans.

That evening a wedding was being held right in the middle of the bazaar. *Mandaps* had been erected, and the whole street decorated with jasmine and saffron-coloured marigold. During Diwali, shops were decorated with banana and mango leaves. Garlands of marigold were hung up everywhere. Little *diyas* lit up small dukas and duka-houses, while firecrackers illuminated the skies. For many years, this was home to most Indians. This was where they had their little duka, and the house just behind. There were Indians from different corners of India with their various languages and dialects, although the majority were from Gujarat, Kutch and Punjab.

The bazaar became the centre of the town's nocturnal life. There were cloth peddlers and street hawkers, Arabs in long *kanzus,* Sikhs in their voluminous turbans. Generally, only men were seen around shopping centres. Although there was the occasional Chinese or Japanese, one seldom saw an African. There were mainly Indians in the bazaar area, from the Parsi bank accountant to the *bania* dukawallah. A comfortably loose kurta-pajama on his body, his balancing scale by his side, the *bania* sat cross-legged on the floor—the client had no option but to do the same. The *banias* had infinite patience, and were content with very small profit. They did not mind any trade, even the retail of common articles of everyday use, so long as it was not regarded as conventionally polluting. In the Persian Gulf, apparently the word 'banyan' was given to a tree under which some *banias* had built their pagoda!

Mathuradass did not approach the Gujarati *bania*. Nor did he talk to the Kutchi, the *mochi* or the *darzi*. Used to living in more or less exclusive communities, their dealings with each other were pretty much restricted to business. Although Hindu, none of them were of the Arya Samaj persuasion. More importantly, they did not speak Punjabi, and very little Hindi. The intra-communal divide was far more language-based. With language came culture and mannerisms. Hindu Punjabis were more comfortable communicating with Muslim Punjabis than they were with Hindu Gujaratis. However, intimate social contact was generally limited to one's own community.

Due to its linguistic and religious groups, the Asian community failed to establish a firm, cohesive front. And because they were not one, the divisions—linguistic and cultural—were a persistent feature. Sub-communities insisted on establishing their own services (schools, hospitals, burial grounds), their meagre resources thinly spread. They had minimal contact amongst themselves. There was rivalry. Sub-groups did not often support other sub-groups. There were conflicts of interest.

It was no wonder then that the British played on these divisions to their own advantage. During the early years of British rule, the government paid very little attention to the educational needs of the growing Indian population. With commendable initiative and sacrifice, the more enlightened members of various Hindu and Muslim communities made their own plans to educate their children, usually financed by donations and the modest fee paid by parents. Owing to deep-seated differences of various groups, the schools sprang up on sectarian lines.

Perhaps even more than caste, ancestral villages and common language bound the people. Mathuradass only tried to call on those houses where he knew the families. Punjabi families, and more specifically, Hindu Punjabi families. He talked to his friends, persuading them to send their daughters on the grounds that the tutoring would come for free. Reluctant parents were assured that they would have no burden to bear, for this was not a business undertaking, and no fee would be charged to start with. In addition, he would take the necessary time off to teach the girls himself. When necessary, he assured them, he would not hesitate to pay the salary of a hired teacher.

He was sure that in spite of these guarantees, the first day would see few girls, if any. And he was right. Families procrastinated in a bid to see who dared to send in their daughter first. Mathuradass waited patiently. 'Even if one or two come, I will consider it a successful beginning,' he thought to himself. And when they started coming slowly, Mathuradass's heart danced with joy. He chanted the 'Om' mantra, giving thanks for this beginning.

The seriousness was evident on Yashoda's face, as if somehow she understood the importance of learning. A skinny figure in a long skirt and long top, with a coloured *dupatta* over her head, she seemed to be suddenly taller as she walked to Mathuradass' 'school'. Payaji had already bought her a slate and chalk—these she carried proudly under her arm. Mathuradass opened the door to let the four new students into his small two-room house. They sat on the floor, and he led them to the new start in their lives by chanting a prayer—loud enough for others to hear, and perhaps also loud enough to attract the attention of prospective new adherents. Rudiments of the Hindi alphabet and basic counting, besides the Arya Samaj principles, formed a part of their earlier curriculum.

Hardei had not been too keen on the idea, but Kirparam had not needed any encouragement to send his daughter to the new school—even though he was quite aware that it was based on the relatively new Arya Samaj principles. He was not exceptionally religious, and so it was he who motivated the young girl. He knew it would do her good. She was too quiet for her age, and hardly had any friends. So Yashoda was in the first batch of students at Mathuradass' school—not unlike elder brother Chunilal, who was among the first lot of students who joined the Government Indian Boys' School.

Kirparam and his children had been up for a while although it was only 4 a.m. Many other families were fast asleep. It was Sunday morning, and every Sunday Kirparam and his children went out for an all-day picnic. The children looked forward to it, as did Kirparam. Hardei did not join them; she always seemed to have other things to do. Cuddled under blankets in the ox-cart, sucking lemons to stave off nausea, the family was heading straight for the river falls in Thika.

The sun was high in the sky by the time they arrived. Kirparam watched the children swim. Yashoda only pretended to do so, barely soaking her tiny feet in the shallow pools. She loved being near the water. It was as if it allowed her to evoke the mirror of her hidden self; perchance, to daydream in this congenial setting. An incurable romantic, she gave the illusion of being happy.

Kirparam had dozed off for a few minutes on the grass. He woke up suddenly, totally rejuvenated. It was as if some genies had worked on his whole being during his short siesta, renewing his spirit. The rest of the children were still playing in the waters, but Yashoda maintained her posture of tranquil reverie. He looked at her anxiously, thankful that he had taken the step of putting his older daughter in school. How unlike her mother she is, he thought. Or me, for that matter! I hope this will help her gain some more confidence in herself. He began to peel potatoes to prepare *pakoras* while sipping on a cup of tea. Ever since he had stopped drinking alcohol, Kirparam had taken to drinking tea—all the time, litres of it. From his brass glass and saucer, he slurped his tea—'breathed' it in literally with a hissing sound: sweet, hot, sugary, milky tea that scalded the throat if you were not used to it: that is how he liked it.

He was taking the last sips of his tea when the children rushed out of the water and crowded around the fire. The aroma of hot, crisp deep-fried vegetables had brought about an insatiable hunger. Kirparam began to tell the children, 'Can you hear the rustling of the wind through the leaves of that tree? That echo, my little ones, is God. The sound of the water you are splashing, that is God. As also is the lashing of the sea, the symphony of the waterfalls, the soft murmuring of a brook. The trumpeting of an elephant or the roar of a lion. The first cry of a newborn babe, the last sigh of a dying man. The cooing of the cuckoo or the cackling of geese. What be the form of God, I know not. But nature I see all around. This to me is the true form of God,' he rambled on, thinking aloud.

Kirparam's own tutoring had excluded any mention of God as such, although he neither discouraged nor encouraged his children to adopt any particular way of worship or belief. He did, however, continue to whisper his avant-garde philosophy through anecdotes, through tales or through the many jokes that he shared with them. 'Do not fear to put your hand to any type of vocation required by the exigencies of life,' he added when they returned from their swim. The children were not listening this morning. They were far too excited and hungry.

Neither the Ramayana, nor the Mahabharata formed part of the endless stories and folk tales he enjoyed reciting each evening to his children. His stories did not abound with gods and goddesses. Not with Krishna and his 16,000 gopis (milkmaids), nor of Shiva and his consort Parvati. His stories were those of the land, of nature. Sometimes, they included superhuman beings, but his heroic and extraordinary beings were never in the nature of God. Liberal, non-conformist and unconventional, he was obviously not the traditional, stereotypic image of an Indian father of the early 1900s. He did not discriminate amongst people of different religions either.

'Do good work; this is the only religion that I know,' he insisted repeatedly. These were people to whom holidays had little meaning. It was work, worship, or religious festivals. Clearly, his worship lay in the dignity of labour. 'No profusion of labour or work is ignoble.' But wasn't this just the secret that Krishna had tried to divulge to Arjuna in the battlefield when Arjuna had lost the nerve to fight? Yashoda knew instinctively. '*Karma kar.*' Yes, those were the words. How often she had heard this injunction on the lips of her mother, of her teachers! As for Kirparam, the lessons from the Bhagavad Gita he had learnt as a child from his parents had probably receded to the depths of his subconscious.

6

Unholy wars

In Africa when an old man dies,
It is as if a library has burnt.

—Amadou Hampate Ba

It was August 1914. The German army had invaded Belgium. The protectorate was caught with its defences down. News arrived that England was at war with Germany. British East Africa and German East Africa became enemies. At first, they thought it would be over by Christmas, and the mood was patriotic but not grim. The handful of German nationals in British East Africa were placed under house arrest. The sale of ammunition was halted. Rumours were rife, martial law was proclaimed.

Bereft of radio, with weekly newspapers taking time to reach the farms, settlers in British East Africa were taken by surprise by the outbreak of war. When the news spread, many settlers rushed to Nairobi; a recruiting office was opened. Hundreds volunteered, armed with shotguns, revolvers and knives. Enlistment fever took over: they looked at war as a glorious adventure. The German side was no better prepared. When General Paul Lettow Vorbeck arrived, however, he led the British forces a macabre dance.

Military activity was stepped up: the first reinforcement of Punjabi troops from India reached Mombasa as early as September. Between 1914 and 1918, about 1,60,000 Africans served in the British army. The British sought the assistance of the South African army in British East Africa. Under the command of Generals Smutts and

Botha, soldiers from different parts of the world—Britain, India, South, West and Central Africa—invaded German East Africa. The South African air force built a base in Garba Tula to fight the Italians in Abyssinia.

The warfront military force had come into existence embracing all forces—African, Indian and British. When General Smutts landed at Mombasa in February, high-ranking officers from India were sacked. The settler community was dissatisfied with the Indian troops, especially over the question of volunteers. The campaign went into a pattern of guerilla warfare with confessed stories of defeats at Voi, of General Smutts' victory in German East Africa, of the arrival of more British troops.

In any case, the troops were ill-prepared for the African terrain during the war. Jiggers, dysentery, gangrene, lions (as had been the case with the coolies eighteen years ago) and thirst depleted their energies. None knew native languages or the customs of those whom they were leading, beside whom they marched and those they fought. Many were lost, killed or wounded as they marched through unknown, ill-mapped country in the Kilimanjaro area. Desperately short of food, African porters carried on in the most appalling conditions, day and night, rain or shine: 44,000 of them died in active service, while Germans continued their raids on British territory. Often neither side really gained any advantage.

Baluchi soldiers in turbans and loose-kneed trousers, Punjabi regiments, battalions of South African artillery and the King's African Rifles, khaki-clad like the rest, became visible progressively. The King's African Rifles were deployed along the German border. The Uganda Railway had acquired strategic importance and became vulnerable to attack by raiding parties from German East Africa.

An armoured train patrolled the railway line along the vulnerable section of the rift where the Germans held the southern boundary. Between Nairobi and Mombasa, 480 km of track needed to be defended. Just by destroying a few bridges, the Germans could cut off supplies between the coast and the highlands. German raiders frequently managed to breach the line. On one occasion the bridge was captured 30 km from Nairobi, at Athi River. Two trains were destroyed that night. The onset of the first world war put an end to all political bickering—temporarily. The status of the Indian was at an all-time low.

Martial law was declared throughout British East Africa. Nairobi as a town saw little enemy action, but German soldiers bombed the line along the Uganda Railway. The situation was tense. Suspected of being allies of the Germans, some Indians from British East Africa were jailed, deported, hanged or shot—as the generals thought fit.

A fiery political worker, L.M. Savle, was arrested and sentenced to be shot for being 'disloyal'. Sardar Bishen Singh, a fuel contractor for the Uganda Railway, and Lalchand Sharma were arrested in Tsavo and imprisoned in Fort Jesus jail. Bishen Singh was hanged in public, without a fair trial, in Mombasa market. Lalchand Sharma's sentence was reduced to ten years' penal service. A British military staff officer had made false charges against them for assisting and harbouring the enemy coming from Moshi in German East Africa to bomb the Uganda Railway.

It was not uncommon for British military officers to entice Luo labourers to give evidence against Indians in connection with bombing along the railway line. The Luos were often bribed, sometimes forced, to bear false witness before military courts. Proceedings were short. Some detainees could afford lawyers, but their lawyers were not allowed to submit a defence. The Indians had very little political protection.

At Mile 129 fuel camp, sub-contractors Ganeshidas and Yog Raj Bali were similarly wrongly indicted. A court verdict by the British military in Voi was given at 4 a.m. 'You will be shot at 7.30 this morning,' Major Lazal informed them in a cold voice. All the other detainees were asked to attend the executions. The public of Voi was also invited.

Ganeshidas and Yog Raj Bali went to their death clad in *dhotis*, their feet bare. It was almost as if they were going for prayers. The killing of a Brahmin belonging to the highest caste in the traditional

Hindu social system was considered one of the most heinous crimes. The Indian soldiers refused to shoot. Eighteen English soldiers took up their rifles and fired mercilessly. The Brahmins were executed in an ignominious manner, even denied the necessary Hindu cremation rites. They were buried in 'unmarked' graves dug previously.

Designed to strike terror among political minded non-Europeans, such executions were carried out on the flimsiest evidence. The attempt was to crush Indian demands for equal rights in British East Africa. Dwivedi, a Supreme Court interpreter, was arrested simply because he attended meetings of the Theosophical Society. *The Secret Doctrine*, a theosophical book, had been found in his possession. He was repatriated to India. Station master Sita Ram was tried by the military court and convicted of being in possession of seditious literature. He too was deported to India. Swami Dayanand's nationalistic and reformist echoes had been heard by Indians outside India. In San Francisco and Vancouver they had brought out a journal in Hindi, Punjabi and Urdu. The *Ghadr* had found its way to the jungles of Kenya.

The military also pounced upon the Arya Samaj in Mombasa. Some officials and a number of devotees were arrested. Charged with waging an anti-British campaign in the guise of worship, they were deported to Voi detention camp to await judgement. Arya Samaj, Mombasa, was proscribed and its property confiscated by the army. The closure sent shock waves among the adherents, who on every occasion continued to vouch for the non-political nature of their organization.

Despite the war, and despite the attack on the Arya Samaj in Mombasa, another Punjabi Hindu association in Nairobi was making plans to build a temple on a massive scale. The war may have dominated their lifestyles, yet these men went about discussing plans for the place of worship as if circumstances were normal. Construction work would commence in the very near future. Fear was thick in the air, but they got together with architects to design a cultural centre of sorts, where believers could meet and worship various idols of their choice, hold festivals or marriages. They were even to include a school and a library—all this, regardless of the insecurity that reigned in town.

At the beginning of the war, Nairobi had only been a military depot. By 1916, it had also become a centre for staging, training and recruiting soldiers. Troops and officers swarmed the town. They flocked to the Norfolk, the oldest hotel in town; they crowded into the New Stanley. Often, they got drunk and rowdy. It became 'improper' for elite ladies to expose their faces to the gaze of these soldiers. Indian women—Muslim and Hindu—of some social standing started going about clad in *burqas*.

A white *dupatta* covered her head as it had always done, but other than that Hardei did not wear the *purdah*. She had no time to fear the soldiers, nor did she consider herself elite. The demands of her growing family were paramount for the moment. Many families decided to send their women and children back, to be with families in India. Neither Kirparam nor Hardei had any strong family ties left in India and they decided to stay put and continue with their lives as normally as possible under the circumstances.

In any case, by now they were more at home in Nairobi. They were acquainted with its people. They were accustomed to different ways. If that meant being at home, they were at home here. They hardly ever talked about India with any special sentimental attachment. In fact, their little conversation rarely made mention of India, much less of return to India. Home was where work was. Different in many ways, both Hardei and Kirparam had this one thing in common. In this regard, they were perhaps way ahead of their time; they had toughened. Their frugal habits and rugged experiences had stood them in good stead.

Plans for the new temple progressed as scheduled. Whatever his religious convictions may or may not have been at the time, Kirparam agreed to preside over the finances of the building committee. On paper, the temple began to take shape. Donations began to pour in. Believers were encouraged to give generously. Those with thriving businesses donated significant sums; others happily parted with their tithe. Volunteers gave of their time, despite uncertainty and anxiety that the war provoked. Meetings were held and Kirparam made himself available for service. It was difficult to plan a budget at various stages of construction as prices were escalating without much notice, sometimes rising by as much as 50 per cent. Credit facilities were blocked; the famous 'IOU' chits were not, for the moment, being honoured. But Kirparam and his team persevered under the trying conditions.

At some point, irregularities in the financial situation became obvious. Kirparam was worried. As was his habit, he checked and double-checked. But no, the mistake was not in his calculations. There was no doubt about it: there was definitely a huge deficit. The whole night he slept badly, tossing and turning. For a few days he did not say anything, but made inquiries on his own. Pretty soon, it became obvious that funds were being embezzled by certain members of the temple committee. It was easy and it was tempting; their shallow play and pretentiousness disgusted him.

Once he had reached a stage of fury, he denounced them openly. In his now fluent English, he wrote a letter to the managing committee. He even had the names of the offenders, but did not reveal them. Later, he was to think that perhaps he should have done so. However, not one of the committee members was ready to bring the issue out into the open. Incessant arguments were of no avail; they pretended that it had not happened. Yet, Kirparam could not keep quiet about the whole affair; he stuck to his guns and did not repeat any of their untruths, nor listen to advice to hush up the matter. To say that he was annoyed and nonplussed at their behaviour was an understatement. He was visibly shaken. He tried to stay calm, but the incident brought about a great change in him.

Publicly and boldly he renounced this way of worship. He, who at one time had been at the receiving end of criticism of religious bigots, now gave it back to them. Moreover, their denial that anything of that kind had taken place caused him much consternation. Any excitement that he may have felt in becoming religious soon changed to a badly bruised faith. The voluntary position ended in a bad way. He walked out of that yet-to-be constructed house of God, never to enter another again. This was in 1917.

Kirparam became a rebel—he broke bonds and came to regard nature as the sole god. They looked at him as a renegade. Neither temple nor idol was for him. Gods have become mere instruments in the hands of the greedy, he started saying. God is not an external being waiting to be met; it is a state of consciousness to be realized. Kirparam announced himself a *nastik*, agnostic, unbeliever—a term inviting grave religious reproach. It caused a small scandal in the community. But he was beyond caring about his place in society. Of what use was such society to him, when it was so full of hypocrisy? The administrators, committee members, the little men and the big men—all those who controlled the functioning of the religious institutions—Kirparam had seen them at close quarters. It was all a question of power and its use and abuse.

That night, he was still burning with rage. His peace of mind had disappeared when he walked out of the board meeting. I don't need religion to teach me the rules of modern conduct, he thought. He picked up his pen and started writing in Urdu, the language he was most familiar with. The Arabic characters flowed with ease and beauty. Why did it have to be like this he wondered? Why did they use the excuse of god to make money, to cheat, to tell lies. He continued to write. The ink flowed freely. He knew instantly what he would call it. *Jihad*. Yes, I feel like one. A *jihadi*. This will be my revolution. My holy war. The light was very dim; the kerosene lamp had started flickering. He did not have more oil, and tried to manage with the little that was left. It was throwing shadows, flickering in the wind, threatening to blow out any minute.

In the end he gave up and just snuffed it out. He curled up to sleep, but his mind was still agitated and sleep did not come for a long time. Eventually, he fell into a troubled slumber, and started dreaming. A man astride a huge lion came past him once. Then again, and again. The lion was roaring ferociously. He was screaming, and with the silent cries, he almost fell off the bed.

It woke him up. He sighed deeply, picked up his pen and began once again.

It was a tortuous exercise, for he was trying to explain to the world, but more to himself, why he chose to remove religion from his life. The revolution was as much within himself as his relationship with his social circle. He questioned time-honoured values and customs. He talked about the unity of life, of solidarity and emotional sympathy at various levels of nature.

Several copies were published in Urdu in Nairobi sometime later, boldly declaring to the small Punjabi Hindu community to which he belonged why he chose to ostracize himself. The little red booklet did not increase his popularity; people thought he was just plain crazy. His *Jihad* was not fired with a missionary zeal to try to convert the others to his way of thinking—far from it. It just seemed a way to clarify himself and his responsibility to society. As a result of having written it a tremendous change took place within him. His outlook, in matters both spiritual and mundane, was further liberalized and he was freed from any commitments that he might have felt towards his community. Knowing that the petty politics and the smallness of their minds would engulf him, Kirparam quit the association without a minute's hesitation. Any leaning he may have had towards ritualism and orthodoxy receded even further.

Some people claimed to have read his *Jihad*, but soon after not a single copy could be found anywhere. The disappearance of this book was a mystery like certain other aspects of Kirparam's life. Kirparam's conscious decision, his wayward lifestyle and strong pronouncements seemed to be tolerated, for not a word was said against them. No one threw stones at him. He was not beaten, nor was abusive language showered on him. Not one person came forward to challenge his convictions, nor were opinions shared with him. They did not even say that he was excommunicated from the community, or barred from participating in Hindu ceremonies at the temple. Nothing was clearly defined, but from then on, there was a distinct difference in attitude towards him.

7

River of life

Njira ndiraga mugendi 'huruka'
(The road never says to the traveller: 'take rest')
— Kikuyu proverb

The war brought opportunities, and there were many. There were those who lost, but there were many who thrived and began a journey to prosperity during the war years. Constructors, uniform suppliers, drivers, mechanics and food suppliers opened up the country to the material, commercial world.

For those who were willing to open up businesses in the interior, government contracts were not hard to obtain. Kirparam contracted to carry groceries and mail to ensure regular supplies of grain and tea for the army in the interior. When he had arrived, he could barely speak English, but with time, he had learnt to write his name. Eventually, he composed elaborate letters. Until then, Swahili was a language more or less restricted to the coastal peoples. Business in the interior also meant that one should be able to communicate in the necessary local languages—Kikamba, KiMasaai, or Kikuyu.

The war altered many facets of life in Kenya. It opened up the country to the outside world. It somewhat breached the north–south divide in the country. It further exposed the interior to the so-called modernizing influences of the 'civilized' world. Consumerism found its way to virgin ground. Airplanes flew in the skies. Model-T Fords soon stopped being the big novelty on the roads. Even though the age of motor transport had come very early to this part of Africa (the first motorized vehicle, the Dion-Bouton six horsepower had arrived as early as November 1903), their presence during the war was tremendous. Roads were constructed. Many still remained dirt tracks, but they were motorable. The fragile balance of nature was wrecked even more; the bush, hitherto untouched by engine sounds, would be affected permanently.

Even before the end of the war, the rapid frenzy for motor transport was significant; it changed the pace of Kenyan lifestyles forever. Otherwise inaccessible areas became accessible. The days of easy transport had arrived: Fords, Chevrolets and Morrises. Kirparam shared resources with a partner and bought a lorry—a Chevrolet. They taught themselves to drive. They got themselves contracts to run dukas for the army, the prisons, and police personnel in camps.

Soap, tea, flour, sugar, rice, spices from India, enamelware, brass wire, tinned provisions, beads, hurricane lamps, matches, cigarettes, looking glasses—they supplied them with all kinds of daily necessities. Travelling in a remote area was like going to a different planet. Where there were no roads, they wound their way through earth tracks cleared through bush. At the most they covered 16–25 km, carrying goods to scattered stores. But it was better than the bullock cart, or the ox-cart, or even caravans and porters—various stages that they had already passed through.

Kirparam was soon dreaming of another adventure, this time into the interior. His idea was to venture up north as far as possible, past the Rift valley and the Mt Kenya region, and return via the Indian Ocean island of Lamu. The timing was perfect. It was a chance for him to get away from the shackles of society. It was no wonder then that he got restless in Nairobi. The urban life was not for him. He found excuses to escape.

Kirparam was equipped with the typical emotional identity of the migrant. Fundamentally, he was a true nomad. His journeys took him vast distances, enabling him to get a real feel of the country and its nervous system: from the shores of the Indian Ocean to the foothills of snow-capped Mt Kenya and to the deserts beyond. Long journeys made on the dirt road, with a few violent and rib-shaking miles. Through grasslands and woods, across the Rift valley, around mineral lakes and volcano fields, life was a constant adventure. He could not be tied down; he refused to lead a life of routine monotony.

As soon as he left the town, the outskirts of Nairobi gave way to vast open spaces, forest lands, jungle; it teemed with wildlife. When he had arrived in Meru for the very first time, the area was mostly forest land; not even a local market existed. Urbanization and all the other evils that went with it had yet to penetrate and change people's way of living. Lots of elephants, zebras, lions and other wild animals abounded. Surprisingly, there was no malaria and the water was good. A government *boma* (an administrative centre) had been installed when he put up a duka in a tent, soon to be replaced by a mud hut with a grass roof. For days this was both shop and home.

Meru was important: geographically, and as a food-producing district, it was a key to the unknown north—a long way away on the north-eastern side of Mt Kenya. The trip could take four to five days from Nairobi, but Kirparam soon knew the whole area on the eastern side of Mt Kenya. When he arrived in Meru, the snow-capped tops of Kilimanjaro, over 220 km away in the then German territory, and Mt Kenya, approximately 120 km north, were clearly visible. Atmospheric pollution was minimal, the forests abounded with animal life. Overlooking the North Frontier District to the north and Embu to the south, the site was central. Little kiosk-like dukas soon sprang up. Besides Meru, Kirparam soon opened branches at Thika, Embu, Chogoria, Nanyuki and Nyeri. More contracts for the railways and road construction had been secured.

Nyeri-ri-ri-ri. It was the sound of water falling down the hill. Kirparam chose Nyeri, the land of the Kikuyus, to build a second home. This ultimately became the place where he would spend much of his time, and where he would be laid to rest at the end of his life. Nyeri town, which takes its name from the hill, lies approximately 50 km south of the equator, 150 km north of Nairobi, at the edge of the fertile Kikuyu plateau, next to the Rift valley. It is dominated by the Aberdares range rising to over 12,000 feet to the west.

The town itself was a colonial creation, founded as a result of a punitive expedition sent from Fort Hall to subjugate the people of Tetu. A fort was built, gradually growing to a *boma* with four Indian shops in 1904. Many settlers had come to the highlands; here the heat of the sun was seldom oppressive. In spite of being so close to the equator, it was temperate because of its altitude of 5,943 feet above sea level. The climate was perfect, cool nights and equally fresh mornings. And the mountain, rising over 19,000 feet, was a sight to behold. The beauty of the place was so complete that it was not difficult to understand why Mt Kenya was considered to be the throne of god, made of a very fine powder called *ira* (snow). By now Kirparam was familiar with the legend he had heard often.

Long ago, Mwene Nyaga appeared to Gikuyu several times. Nyaga or Ngai was the all-powerful, all-encompassing force of the Kikuyu people. Invisible, beyond shape, *Ngai* literally meant 'rain', a good steady fall of rain, a caring moderate rain that people could depend on for their lives. Ngai took Gikuyu, the first man, on the crystalline Kikuyu plateau, and atop the snow-covered peaks of the great mountain Kere Nyaga, the mountain of brightness, where no man had yet set foot. He showed him the magnificent landscape with its silvery rivers and profound valleys and numerous animals grazing on the green grasslands, and he told Gikuyu, 'This is all yours . . .' Lifting up his arms in joy, Gikuyu said, 'You are the Great Wisdom, the Master of the Sky, and of the Earth, accept me as your warrior standing at your orders.' And, God gave Gikuyu a wife, whom he called Mumbi. 'May your children multiply in these lands!' Mwene Nyaga said as he blessed them.

The hills and mountains became sacred. Gikuyu and Mumbi lived happily; they had nine daughters. Kikuyu old-timers say that their father Gikuyu came from the direction of Kere Nyaga (Mt Kenya) with his young wife Mumbi. Historians claim that the Kenyan Bantu (the Kikuyu, Meru and Akamba tribes) first migrated from their ancestral area in what is now Zaire, about a thousand years ago.

With their hands raised in prayer, the devotees turned towards Kere Nyaga and offered sacrifices. Up there, at 17,000 feet above sea level, lay the gates of the supernatural, while deep in its forests, witchdoctors looked for healing herbs and plants. Kere Nyaga became the official resting place of the creator who lives in the sky, but has a temporary home on the mountain. Kere Nyaga, had been named after the ostrich, predominantly black with white splashes—just like the snow-capped mountain. When the German explorer Ludwig Krapf saw it from Ukamba Province for the first time in 1849, the Akamba tribe, having no 'r' in their dialect, told him it was '*Kee Nyaa*'—hence it became Kenya, and the country got named after it.

The Kikuyu land was progressively hilly. On roads such as these, they probably did not clock more than 30 km. A few patches of cultivation appeared on the edges of the valleys, amidst the red earth, steep paths and clusters of huts—grass-roof huts and grain stores raised off the ground on platforms.

Cultivating sweet potatoes, groundnuts, banana, arrowroot, maize, millet, cassava, beans and peas, many women laboured in *shambas*. Pineapples and peppers had arrived thanks to the Portuguese. Exotic foods from newly discovered lands that grew easily in Kenya's climate and its fertile soil were introduced.

A young woman struggled up the steep hill with a *debe* of water delicately balanced on her head. A once-bright orange with a contrasting black *kitenge*, now muddy brown, shriveled and drenched, covered her thin body. She wore a cautious and tired look—perhaps exhausted by the countless hardships of life. Other Kikuyu women carried heavy loads of firewood on their backs, big gourds filled with water at the stream. These women worked long hours. Traditionally, among the Kikuyu, work was done by the women. The Europeans thought this all wrong and argued that farm work ought to be done by the young men. Introducing them to 'civilization and industrious ways', they began to preach the gospel of labour, to show the African the 'dignity of labour'.

Sermonizing was easy; conversion to their culture was another story. 'Africans don't understand discipline,' they complained constantly. The Africans had their own rhythm and pattern of life, but the Europeans expected them to adhere to a different culture immediately. When absenteeism from work entailed excuses like, 'My mother died' for the third or fourth time, the white men would explode in anger. But Africans did have more than one mother. All of his father's co-wives were his mothers. The European didn't understand polygamy and other African customary laws. Sudden disciplining was totally incomprehensible and threw the Africans off balance; it was undeserved.

His truck forever full of goods of every kind that one could imagine—from tinned provisions to soap, padlocks and safety pins to boots, Kirparam had since long been driving a lorry now. Tea, flour, sugar, rice, spices from India, umbrellas from Germany, looking glasses and cigarettes from France, watches from Switzerland, calico from the US: Kirparam continued travelling and looking for new outlets, supplying his various canteens right up to Maralal in the north.

It was the month of April. Kirparam had already been in Kikuyu land several days, but he was in no hurry to move just yet. It was heavenly to be in forest lands. Black and white colobus monkeys with enormous tails leapt from branch to branch, almost never descending to the ground. He looked up and felt great to be alive under the blue sky with its pink and gold clouds. The early morning light was startlingly clear, the stillness almost hypnotic. The crackling log fire broke the silence; a silence which had come to be identified with his personality. The only thing lacking in the picture was a pipe. But he had never smoked. He reflected alone, in his own space.

In fact, Kirparam's silence had varied nuances, reflecting his many moods. Hardei had never understood his moods. When he was angry, the silence lay heavy and cold, the atmosphere became charged and uncomfortable; no words were necessary to convey his displeasure or disapproval. The appreciative, meditative silences of love brought about warmth and security.

He was up at the crack of dawn. It had rained much of the night. An enormous rainbow covered the sky. Walls of torrential water lasting a very short spell quickly gave way to the sun with great ceremony. Some years, the April rains could last for three months. Rain could come any time: there were no hard and fast rules. No month was totally wet or dry. However, from March to May, and October to December, the precipitation was usually significant. The total quantity, season of fall and effectiveness were far more important than variations in temperature—further complicated by the monsoons, which could produce a total reversal of wind direction over the country.

This was the domain of the Indian Ocean. Warmer than the Atlantic, the play of the rain-bearing monsoon winds ruled the roost. There were long spells and short spells, the 'rains of French beans', or the 'rains of millet'. The least delay to the fall of the waters, or a very short season of rains meant a miserable harvest, or even worse, a famine in the land. Too much rain, and the largest river leaping down the slopes of Mt Kenya and the Aberdares 700 km to the Indian Ocean—the Tana—was sure to flood.

The Tana flowed, and the Tana flooded. At awkward bends it changed course, at others the colour turned to muddy brown. Seasonal floods raged down the Tana washing away entire villages; people along lower reaches could be marooned for weeks; immense surfaces were transformed into lakes. Yet the Tana gave life to many generations. It was a fishing river; a river for cultivation, for irrigation. The silt-laden waters carried away the fertile topsoil of the highlands.

He walked along the muddy brown waters of the Tana. Once

again, Kirparam's mind went back in time to more than twenty years before. How like the Jhelum, he thought. The Jhelum, the river of his childhood days, where he had grown up, bathed and played. He smiled at the memories of those good and carefree moments. However, the Jhelum could also ravage with its seasonal flooding, and in one such catastrophe, the Jhelum had taken away his brother. Kirparam became pensive and a little sad. Just as he was about to leave, the sound of bells could be heard approaching from the distance.

They made a circle. In the middle stood a man singing solo; the rest accompanied him in chorus. Their bodies began to move slowly, the feet rising alternatively. Towards the end, all the dancers beat the earth and the sentiment of rhythm was so well pronounced that the 200 or so ankles sounded like one. Little by little, the voice rose, the circle was filled with the energy of the dancing bodies. They lowered themselves, touched the soil and bounced back with a new lease of life. The group got closer, the voice rose again, the movement accelerated. Suddenly, the song stopped and the dancers began to laugh and threw themselves on the ground to regain their breath. The elders watched the show with profound admiration, reliving their own times; they were far too emotionally moved to say anything. Filling their mouths with millet brew, they sprayed it on the youngsters in greeting. 'Go in peace,' they said.

'Kikuyu and Akamba dances are too erotic; they leave nothing to the imagination, they must be banned', said the *wazungu's* men of God. European officials with a Victorian prudishness supported the mission's ban on such displays. The settler community was convinced that it was bringing civilization to the 'dark continent'. One in which the dead were not even accorded burial rites, but were left to die by themselves. According to Kikuyu custom, a person must not die in the home, nor was a corpse to be handled. The sick, the elderly or the mortally wounded were carried out into the bush as they neared death. The early European pioneers were appalled.

Writing on Kikuyu mythology in his book *Facing Mt Kenya*, Jomo Kenyatta—eventually to become independent Kenya's first President—mentions some of the successful magical ceremonies performed by his grandfather. Referring to rainmaking rites, he says, 'Our prayers were answered. Even before the sacred fires had ceased to burn, torrential rain came upon us. We were soaked. But the white man, when he came, laughed, and said: Your prayers do not reach God in Heaven. These are pagan acts. You have not been born again through baptism.'

Soon, churches of the white man sprung up everywhere. The black man was encouraged to christen himself and his children. New names were born: Ngugi and Mumbi became James and Mary. Together with the settlers came the missionaries with the zeal to reform and convert—and to farm. Large coffee farms were set up around Nyeri, and the neighbouring town of Nanyuki. The railway reached Nyeri in 1928, Nanyuki in 1931; the towns began to develop.

The Kikuyu kept their heads shaven—both men and women; sharp edges of broken bottles were used for the ritual. The brightness of their completely shaven heads contrasted with innumerable beads decorating various parts of the body—neck, arms, feet, ankles. With long distended earlobes, many women had also started stringing small coins in bundles of ten around their neck—the small cent with the famous hole in the middle, introduced to eventually replace subdivisions of the rupee (the *anna* and *paisa*). Other women wore cowries in strings of fifty. One needed at least a thousand of them to make the rupee. A blanket loosely wrapped around themselves, their feet bare, heads bent, bowed under heavy loads, the women marched towards different areas to dance and hold their *sokoni* (market).

Each day of the week, the market was held in a particular place; women were delegated the duty of carrying huge loads on their backs held in place by a leather strap which went up round their foreheads. By middle age, most women had a permanent deep depression round the forehead, and were stooped and pigeon-toed from the heavy loads.

Around heaps of bananas, sweet potatoes and maize, they sat long hours to barter their wares. Kirparam wandered around the vegetable market and looked at the various piles. He stopped in front of the sweet potatoes. They certainly looked inviting. He picked up one to feel its texture for freshness. The quality was certainly better than what he would get in Nairobi—and cheaper. 'Ngapi (How much)?' he asked the vendor. They bargained and bantered for a few minutes until each party was satisfied.

Cash was not often used in these parts yet. In fact, the exchange of money was a new evil arriving with the introduction of the hut tax. The African was forced to take up employment to pay the compulsory annual hut tax of twenty shillings, in rupees or in florins.

It got dark very suddenly. The *sokoni* was closing down. The vendors were packing the last of their wares before trekking back over the hill to their reserves. Kirparam continued walking towards the forest. He was not afraid to stay in the bush. He had grown so used to the quiet and the solitude that he never really could readjust to urban life. Whenever he went 'home' to Nairobi, he would rarely stay more than a few days. For him 'real life' was in the bush, amongst the big acacia, in the flight of the vulture up in the blue skies, in the stretching movements of the waking leopard. He would often be away from the family for long periods—days, weeks, sometimes a month on the road. There was not much money in the business, but he enjoyed it—the adventure, the travel and the risk. It was a country that was to grip him for life.

A lone eagle was perched on the summit of the tallest tree. It flew and soared over its territory. With its extremely keen eyesight, it spotted its prey far away and then struck with such unerring accuracy, that the solitary splendour made it the emblem of victory. The area was a part of the forest reserve of mostly eucalyptus trees. One could not see the sky at all in this mysterious region, but when sunlight fell through the foliage, it seemed as if angels were ready to dance. 'We must carry on tomorrow—rain or no rain,' Kirparam thought.

The sky remained overcast with clouds; it drizzled often. Wild animals had made huge footprints in the soggy mud everywhere. The road got messier than ever. Elephants had not yet bothered his lorry, but Kirparam was concerned about rhinos who certainly could get aggressive. The fog and rain lasted many days and nights. Driving became mostly pushing; painfully slow and tiring. With his two boys—a Pokomo called Geti, and a KiMeru called Mutua, he drove on further to the north, transporting supplies to different government and private organizations. On these long trips, they slept in the lorry.

The distance seemed endless. There was a world of difference between the forested regions of the highlands and the semi-desert of northern Kenya. It was another world, much of it scrub desert. It was easy to lose oneself here. An area in which small forces could be ambushed and cut up, larger ones could suffer hunger and thirst; both could lose their way.

Kenya's north was simply described as the NFD, the Northern Frontier District—just like Pakistan's North West Frontier Province (NWFP), from where Kirparam's father had migrated to Mardana. Somehow, the NFD was not regarded as a part of Kenya. The NFD was dangerous—uncharted and unexplored. Only the army, the colonial administration, some missionaries and suppliers were permitted to enter the area. Even then, one had to sign in at the police post, and rescue parties were sent if one did not return on schedule. It was a region where blood-money, fines and compensation for murder and stock-theft were in accordance with the *Shariat*, the Muslim code, and also tribal custom.

The frontier plains stretching out towards Ethiopia and Somalia swarmed with military camps, for it was disputed territory. They called it 'Greater Somalia', refusing to accept it as Kenyan territory. The initial British policy isolated the northern pastoral peoples from participation in the wider Kenyan economy. After Kenya's independence in 1963, the Borana (a semi-nomadic tribe of the region, close to the Ethiopians) would join with pan-Somali guerillas—later to be known as *shiftas* (bandits)—wanting the NFD to unite with Somalia instead of with Kenya. Just as Afghanistan was to lay claim to NWFP, calling it Pashtunistan.

It had been an exceptionally long day. They had spent the night somewhere near Lake Baringo. Awake before daybreak, that morning they drove to Samburu land, and on towards Archer's Post and Maralal. Here they camped for another night. The district capital consisted of a single main street flanked by shady pepper trees on either side. Maralal, which means 'the shining' or 'the glittering', had been named after the corrugated tin roofs of the dukas that shone in the noonday sun.

Somali men sauntered past in their traditional loincloths towards the two Indian dukas. Samburu and Turkana warriors stood proud in their traditional finery, their majestic backs straight—spear in hand, the right leg crossed over the left. A cultural paradise with a drastic change of landscape.

Taramattwa rushed to greet the lorry. Named after the cow that was being milked when she was born, the young Samburu woman stopped suddenly to stare at the newcomers. Decked in all her wedding finery, she presented a beautiful picture. Endless strands of colourful beads decorated her small neck. She couldn't be more than fifteen, Kirparam thought. Her tiny frame presented a child-like beauty, with small, firm breasts, and a tight body marked with tribal scars, especially on the stomach. Taramattwa's one-year-old daughter looked up at her mother and smiled. A pearl girdle hung loose on her hips, necklaces and bangles on her tiny hands. The baby watched Kirparam with curiosity. He must have seemed a strange creature to her.

She touched his hairy arms. '*Mwarabu* (Arab)?' asked Taramattwa. '*Muhindi* (Indian),' said Kirparam. That was the end of their short conversation. He would have liked to talk to her, but it was difficult to communicate: Taramattwa did not speak Swahili. Mother and child sat themselves on a goatskin mat. Far in the distance, clouds were beginning to shimmer above Uaso Nyiro, the big blue mountain—the mountain of Samburu gods. The wind was blowing in his face, the trees began to sway to and fro. They returned to their lorry and moved on.

The climate, the vegetation and the landscape changed drastically. It was undoubtedly the hottest, driest and remotest route in the country. They bumped down dusty tracks and were instantly consumed by clouds of dust. The more they ventured up north, the further they got away from the stereotypical image of Kenya. The menacing desert and the monotony seemed to enclose them. It felt like the end of time. The test of the sun and the overheated air pushed by a wind that burnt all the way, the eyes that became reddened by the sun-scorched savannah . . . in this situation, the morale sometimes sank to its lowest ebb. The road seemed to stretch for hours with no end in sight of sand, gravel and meagre scrub. A mirage shimmered further out on the horizon. Hardly a blade of grass peeped through the unproductive soil. The terrain was flat and almost featureless.

The mid-day sun was strong and they stopped for a short rest under the shade of a lone tree. Kirparam looked up with half-closed eyes. The heat of the ground was terrifying. The way was deserted, sad, devoid of visible animal life—almost. Suddenly a dik-dik appeared as if from nowhere. Extremely swiftly it stretched its long neck and stood on its toes to reach for some greenery. The elegant antelope of the desert appeared to spend a lot of time on its hind legs searching for leaves of the acacia thorn. The sight was refreshing.

Garba Tula was well developed; it was the gateway to the north. The increased frequency of dispersed bushes put them in a better frame of mind. Progressively, the landscape was showing more signs of life. A vulture at first. Then a big black crow with a hideous caw that seemed to tear open the skies. Some lone Indian stores—bags of grain and pulses and an array of cheap goods for sale. Here the Indians lived with their families amongst the tribesmen. Morans, Somalis, and Abyssinians, a few Gabra women. Rendille and Borana with their big cattle and many goats, en route to auctions and barter. Only a chief was posted here, never a district officer. Chiefs in all districts were appointed by the colonial administration.

When Archer, an Englishman, founded a post and his little shop in this part sometime in 1909, he became the first district commissioner of the NFD, and the town was named after him. Archer's Post was a dull windy town in the middle of barren plains, with tiny shops—shacks of tin and cement. It was the last outpost before one reached the Abyssinian highlands

In 1920, the town of Isiolo was born not far from Archer's Post in the arid lands towards the north and the east of Mt Kenya. Fifteen thousand feet below on the plains, dusty, windy, with cluttered tin-roof brick houses and police huts, it became the headquarters of the NFD. Through the district flows a small river. Every three or four years, when the rains were good, the river flooded, leaving the plains full of lush green pasture. Otherwise the area was generally dry. Here again, one found some Indian stores selling groceries, but visitors to the area, especially women, were not encouraged. Bandits from Abyssinia often raided the neighbouring region of Marsabit.

A group of young Boranas and Somali nomads in sarongs and turbans—tall, slim women in long robes, an air of confidence in their stature—thronged the mid-day market to buy bushels of the mild narcotic *khat*. The women went their way while the men bolstered themselves for a long afternoon of chatting and chewing of this drug, *Catha edulis*. The narcotic leaves of the *khat* were popularly called *miraa*. Some women and children hung around to listen to the talk of the men without actually participating.

Miraa, in any case, was not to be taken in solitude; it was almost ritualistic in aspect, partaken around an afternoon or evening of stimulating talk between friends. It was as if the plant tied the community together. It kept them going on their long travels, without food or rest. A drug that won friends or made sworn enemies, one for which you could be killed. It was jealously guarded, just like their water wells.

Kirparam crouched on the ground and watched them from a distance. The men plucked out the softest leaves and pushed them to the back of the cheek. Some of them made a gesture of invitation, but Kirparam waved back without moving. He didn't particularly like the aftertaste of the bitter green and reddish brown leaves and the dryness of mouth that left him thoroughly dehydrated. As it was, water was a luxury in the region.

With his cheeks bulging and a hand supporting his head, the older man lounging on the palm mat was already preparing himself to be part of another world. The conversation turned lively and much laughter was heard. After several hours of chewing, juices of the leaves would transport them into a state of heightened perception and emotion. With an effect similar to that of amphetamines, it released adrenalin and raised their body temperature and blood pressure.

Over 1,000 km from Nairobi, Mandera rests uncomfortably between Ethiopia and Somalia. Kiraparam and his crew travelled tirelessly, supplying the dukas in the army camps around the area. Here too, his managers ran canteens for the military. Army and police personnel and other workers in the surrounding area often came to deposit their wages, or ask for credit facilities or loans. Little 'IOU' chits were written out, despite continuous bad debts. The unlimited credit facility was extended by small dukawallahs. What started off as a friendly service became a norm—banking and financial services, postal facilities and a message bureau.

The Indian lorry driver had already been stamped with a reputation in the colony: 'seen without lights, sometimes with a hurricane lamp stuck on the ramp, without brakes, or driving an engine which looked like conking out at any moment—pushing trade through the most inaccessible places'. When Kirparam's gear lever got stuck in the middle of nowhere, he knew that he would have to improvise a way out of the situation. The territory was hostile; it was a nest of ivory poachers. Without much choice, he crawled underneath the lorry and lay flat on his back to look for the problem. The position was uncomfortable, yet he carried on fumbling with the machine for some time. But neither he nor the two boys could trace the fault.

It was dangerous to sit by the wayside and wait. A quick decision had to be made. Kirparam went back into the driver's seat and started the engine. The lorry started in reverse gear. It was the only gear working. Kirparam drove all the way to Isiolo, 100 km away—backwards. The solution was unique. Keeping his foot stamped on the clutch pedal for a very long time, his neck strained in the wrong direction, he was completely exhausted by the time they returned.

For several days afterward, he continued to suffer severe pain in the neck and back. The pain in the neck was never to go away entirely; it stayed with him like a dull ache. He had obviously driven himself into an osteo-arthritic condition. However, as a result of reverse driving, he built up some kind of reverse philosophy; this was to further influence his life in more ways than one.

He had not returned home in months. But he knew that when he did, Hardei was sure to show her displeasure. But he would remain silent, a man of few words, with her. More often than not, speech would only divide them as Hardei insisted on having the last word. The resignation was perhaps, under the circumstances, a form of dignified resistance.

In his home life, the man exuded an air of quietness. His movements were of silence, of a controlled stillness. Perhaps he was a little overshadowed by his forceful, high-spirited and outspoken wife. The relationship was tense and obtuse. No wonder, instead of returning to Nairobi, Kirparam decided to take the coastal route. Sending his two boys homeward, he headed off towards Lamu for another long trip.

Little dhows shone in the noon sun far in the distance. The Indian Ocean lay tranquil. The island's calm and lazy air was infectious. Small palm-thatched houses, some with solid walls, clustered the town. Lamu is an old Arab town on an offshore island. Two- or three-storey Arab houses with huge brass-studded doors opened onto streets so narrow that a man leaning out of a window was seen shaking hands across the street with a friend opposite. They greeted each other in a heavily accented Swahili. Consisting largely of Arab words, the Bantu language has words incorporated from many other sources. There are words introduced by Arab and Indian settlers and traders, a few Portuguese and German colonists, and a large number by the English. The Swahili language thus kept growing. But the one spoken on the island, the inhabitants were proud to say, was the 'purest'. It comprised a huge lexicon of Arab words, as most of the inhabitants were Muslim.

The huge figure of his manager appeared from behind a palm-hut. Quite tall for a coastal person, especially for a Lamuiite, Kadiri cut an impressive figure. He had a grey beard, and an old *kikoi* covered his legs. His faded half-sleeved shirt was haphazardly buttoned. But he seemed comfortable. He was obviously quite appropriately dressed to combat the heat and humidity.

'*Madafu?*' he asked, not waiting for a reply, because he already knew that Kirparam liked the juice of the coco-palm. Broken fresh and drunk before noon, when the sun blared at its hottest, it was available only in the morning. The sweet milky water tricked down his throat, some down his shirt. He gave a short laugh and wiped his mouth with the sleeve of his shirt. Tricky business, drinking directly from the large hard-shelled seed. With the air of an expert, Kadiri made a small spoon out of the palm frond, scooped out the creamy contents and offered them to Kirparam.

Kadiri was a Mshihiri. His grandfather had arrived on the island from Hadhramudt, a small town of Yemen. He had married a local girl, and stayed on. All his children and grandchildren had been born here. Great-grandchildren were on the way. Lamu was the only home that Kadiri had known.

Kirparam looked at Kadiri, trying to assess whether he had changed since the last time he saw him. Kadiri had been managing his duka for several years now, and he had always found him reliable. Kadiri had aged; he was walking slower. 'How are your knees?' Kirparam asked. They communicated in Swahili. '*Sawasawa*. They hurt, but I manage somehow', Kadiri answered. They discussed the duka's accounts for a while, but before long, Kadiri made his excuses to leave, promising to continue later in the day.

The beginning of the azan pierced loud and clear, '*Allahu Akbar* . . . God is great'. It was time for *al-zuhr*, the noon prayers. From the heights of the minaret, the haunting voice of the muezzin called the faithful to prayer. The voice continued with the *Shahaada*, '*La illaha illa Allah wa Muhammed rasul Allah* . . . there is only one God, and Mohammed is his Prophet'.

Believers responded to the call and rushed to accomplish the sacred task. Kadiri went through the prescribed ritual ablutions, washed himself with water, posed his small prayer mat on the floor and prostrated—a fluid assembly of movements. He was a firm believer and adhered to the obligations five times a day. Here, the day was not divided according to hours and minutes of the occident, but according to the *salaat*—the five prayer timings. Commencing with *al-subh*, the dawn prayers, the day ended with *al-isha*, the night prayers.

The fierce noon sun gave way to a sweet heat. Lethargy set in with the mid-day sun. Inadvertently, Kirparam had fallen into a short but deep slumber, one quite difficult to awaken from. Slowly, he got up, washed himself with cold water, and, grabbing a scalding cup of syrupy *chai,* made his way to the duka to continue the business *shauris* with Kadiri. As soon as the big orb of the sun sank into the sea at 6.30 p.m., the heat became more bearable. Kirparam looked at the fading light for a long moment; it brought about strong emotions of spirituality.

The tall palms made a wonderful swishy sound, in tune with the sea in full tide. The strong scent of jasmine was high in the air, as was the sound of excited cackling. Swahili women covered from head to toe in black *bui-buis*—their heavily kohled-eyes clearly made up to attract attention, hennaed hands and feet impossible to ignore through their excited gestures—emerged all over the town in little groups. Little white crabs danced on the equally white sands, soon to be washed away with new waves of sea coming in.

The town was soon a hub of activity, the favourite being walking by the seafront, eating a maize cob or a piece of roasted cassava. Cut in the middle and filled with salt, red chilli powder and drops of lemon juice, it tasted heavenly. Some sat on the edges of the shore, looking towards the mangrove swamps, or they gossiped about who was with whom. Once married, usually at a young age, the Swahili woman found herself freer than before. The social network was such that the women protected each others' love lives, getting together at a common friend's place, and making a detour from there. Moreover, the common *bui-bui* served a very useful purpose in secret rendezvous, done effectively and simply by exchanging each others' shoes!

On the southern side, the narrow lanes of the old stone town from the thirteenth century were riddled with stubborn donkeys. The paths were covered with their droppings, the green blobs a nuisance to pedestrians everywhere. A strong aroma of freshly brewed coffee and charcoal-roasted meat pervaded the streets. Their business ended, Kirparam bought some sticky Swahili cakes and enjoyed the heavily sugared coffee in a small cup. Yes, Lamu is paradise, he thought to himself. But it was time to go home.

The family business soon diversified. His son Chunilal had joined him as partner. They spread out in different directions. Together, they pioneered the opening of saw-milling, building and quarrying. 'Kirparam and Son' became a long chain of grocery stores across the country. There were *posho* (maize flour) mills and wheat flour mills.

Plots were leased from European farmers for milling alongside rivers and streams; here they built little dukas for selling supplies to Africans working on the farms. Grinding by the river, powered by the fast-flowing water, their mills worked on a similar principle to the *chakki*, the hand-grinder, where grain was crushed between an upper and lower millstone. Their flour mills turned out white flour until the passing of the wheat pool ordinance. They were forced to close down.

The young Kirparam who had travelled penniless across the ocean a long time ago acquired status over the years and came to be known as Lala Kirparam Ramchand Wason—a merchant of some repute. He was no longer a petty dukawalla. His small duka on the banks of the railroad had grown into a sprawling enterprise. The time had come to acquire more workers. He decided to get them from India.

8

Going with the flow

Khao man ponda, pao jag ponda
(Eat to your heart's content, dress to societal norms)
— Punjabi proverb

The river Jhelum has its source in the deep blue waters of Kashmir, with Bhera and Miani as its principal towns. Bracing in winter and annoying in summer, the Jhelum often threatened its towns with periodic floods. However, considerable trade was carried on up and down the river. Salt mined from the nearby Khewra mines, brass and copper ware, silk, cotton goods, blankets, shoes, cereal, indigo, sugar, rice and wool were carried downstream. Spices and European goods came upstream from Karachi. Miani and Bhera became centres of trade.

This was the area of the five rivers: Ravi, Chenab, Beas, Sutlej and Jhelum. *Panj ab*, in Persian. These were the tributaries of the Indus that gave India its name. The *panj ab* became the lifeline of the state of Punjab in the northwest part of India. The rivers witnessed flourishing of culture and civilization.

In the forests around the rivers were born the rishis, whose thoughts produced the Vedas. Panini, the great grammarian of the Sanskrit language; Charak, founder of the Ayurvedic system of medicine; Bharata, the author of the Natya Shastra, the classical art of the dramatics—they all belonged to Punjab. It was here in the land of the five rivers that the historic battles of the Mahabharata were fought over 3,000 years ago. And here on the banks of the

Jhelum, the Indian prince Porus was defeated by Alexander 2,000 years ago.

But this is not their story. Not that of Alexander, nor of the many ancestors before Porus. This is the story of a boy born many centuries later, somewhere around 1876, on the banks of the same Jhelum. Here he grew up, here he played marbles and walked alongside the river bank with his friends. Here he saw the early death of his parents. Here his brother had drowned. Kirparam, son of Ramchand, would leave these shores as a penniless young man, to return only to recruit other such men.

It was not in his karma that he continue to live and die here along the banks of the Jhelum. Possessed with a restless spirit, he was drawn to a life beyond the banks. His adulthood was written along another river in faraway Africa where he was to see the birth of new towns and cities. He was to taste freedom for the first time. He was to learn what it meant to be independent. He was to make his own future and to build upon the good and bad aspects of urbanization. To feel the direct effects of racism that would leave a mark upon him, to renounce the corrupting influences of society. But most of all, he was to fall in love with the vast open skies and deep jungles of Africa.

Nearly twenty years had elapsed since he had left the land of his birth, the land of his ancestors, and found himself in British East Africa. The first world war was not yet over when he decided to return to Punjab. By now he had merited the title of Lala, a designation generally reserved for Khatri merchants. Lala Kirparam brought his eldest son along with him; the one who had left with his mother all those years before to look for the father who had abandoned them. Yes, the same Chunilal. Kirparam now took it upon himself to take charge of Chunilal's *vivah samskar*, marriage.

Their hometown Miani welcomed them. However, according to tradition, they could not look for a wife in the ancestral town. Word went around and soon the neighbouring town of Bhera stamped Chunilal's future. Chunilal accepted Bhiranwali (one who has brothers), his bride-to-be, without any of his own views being taken into consideration. Bhiranwali had had no say in the matter either. This was the way of the elders.

Bhera had once been an important town. 'A miniature model of Lahore,' it was said. The *Baburnama* records Babur regarding himself as the rightful owner of Bhera, his Mughal empire stretching from Bhera to Bihar. On their way to the mouth of the Indus via the Jhelum, Alexander and his men had pitched camp near the capital of Sophytes—at Bhera. Protected by a river that flows the year round, a jungle, and a mountain to the northwest, Bhera became an abode of peace. Just as was implied by its name, 'free from anger and fear'. It was also a sanctuary from enemy raids and the salt kingdom of Lavania. It had been a flourishing economy, a centre of arts and crafts. Rich Hindu merchants—bankers, moneylenders, traders, shopkeepers—were the backbone of the economy.

Some of the finest examples of urban architecture—brick and timber—were in evidence. Door and window frames were elaborately carved in deodhar wood. Entire surfaces of large doorways were covered with boldly outlined forms of foliage and geometric diaper made out for the most part with a V-section cut. A rich museum of woodcarving, much of the wood felled in Kashmir was brought down via the Jhelum. Its Sheesh Mahal, the princely palace of mirrors, was truly a work of art. Here lived many rich Hindus—mostly Khatris. Bankers, moneylenders, traders and shopkeepers: trade and industry remained in their hands. The largest number of Hindus who went abroad for higher education came from Bhera. The women of Bhera were even rumoured to stretch their legs in the direction of Vilayat while in labour. One day my child will go beyond the seas to England, and all the lands ahead, they prayed.

Narrow irregular streets, deep in mud during the rains, flanked by two- to three-storey-high structures provided the streets much needed shade throughout during hot summer days. The town was more or less divided into *mohallahs*—Hindu areas and Muslim neighbourhoods, with some pockets where the two communities lived together. A *mohallah* with a honeycomb of lanes formed a little world by itself and provided for the residents a sense of togetherness.

Bhera society was very closely interlocked. Everybody knew everybody else. Soon after his arrival, Kirparam joined the men in the common chowk (square) of the quarter to discuss day-to-day affairs. However, he could not recognize most people. It had been too long. Many of those whom he knew had left or were no more. He felt totally out of place and wanted to escape as fast as possible to the jungles of Africa. But not before he had attended to the important business which had brought him here in the first place.

Depending on one's family, profession or religious group, one was a resident of a particular *mohallah*—Sahni, Sethi, Anand, Bhasin and Chadda. Some of these, known as the Khokharan *biradari*, traced their origins to Khorasan, present-day Iran. Others swore that their names had Greek origins—from the time that Alexander and his men passed through the land. The Bharochi Khatris of Bhera, Multan and Peshawar insisted that theirs was one of the most ancient territorial groups of the uplands in north-western Punjab. The Khoja, or Khawja *mohallah* was the area where wealthy traders, converts to Islam, mainly from the Kapur clan lived. About ninety such *mohallahs*—more or less caste-based—each equipped with its own well, *mishar* (water carriers), *mochi*, tailor, *vaid* doctor, mosque, and temple. Some even had their own *akhara* where young and old gathered together for physical exercises and *kushti*: wrestling was an important sport. Urban and modern, Bhera was an example to less-advanced villages, such as its neighbour Miani.

While far away in the germinating future town of Nairobi, Kirparam had been selling his *pakoras* and other snacks to the coolies on the railway site, Lajpat Rai was born to a certain Gurdei on 15 December 1898 in Loharanmori Mohallah of Bhera. This was not a prestigious quarter of the town. Here lived the mixed population of Hindus and Muslims—the poorer section of society. Here worked the artisans who made Bhera's famous cutlery, especially the beautiful knives and daggers. They spent long hours carving the handles, polishing them and then making a beautiful leather box for a cover. When he was still a child, little Lajpat often crouched on the floor, admiring the intricate designs of handles decorated in mother of pearl. Sometimes, the artisans even allowed him to caress the precious handles.

A year later, Gurdei gave birth to a girl. She called her Ramlubayi, beloved of Rama. For Gurdei, her new daughter was a find, a treasure, so the little girl came to be called Labi. They had their little niche near the *chakki* in this humble quarter of the town. There was never much peace since the sound of the flourmill could be heard all hours of the day. But at least their small brick house had the usual *thurra* at the entrance. The extended platform was a rendezvous in the evening hours, when Gurdei and her friends sat in sunlit verandahs to relax and gossip. Hardly ever idle, when free from household chores, they sat together with spinning wheels, singing folk songs. Like all the others, their house too was planned around a courtyard. As the weather grew warmer, the women moved to the verandah to sleep and to work. When the heat became intense, the whole set-up shifted to the terrace.

Gurdei's day started early and ended at sunset. Right until the months of October and November she, together with other women, went to bathe in the Jhelum at 4 a.m., especially during the fasting days of Navaratri. Carrying little brass pots on their heads, or on their waists, they began their ablutions by the riverbank. Rinsing, gargling, brushing their teeth with frayed twigs of the neem tree, and performing transformational rituals to maintain personal relationships with the universe. Hardly anyone in the village had a watch, yet somehow they coordinated their tasks of the day effectively. Nature was their guide: the call of the birds, the first light of day and twilight hours for prayer.

The town had its own rhythm and its own way of life. Except on moonlit nights, there was little movement outside the courtyards after dark. Though there was constant traffic between villages, few strangers were seen. Not many had kerosene lamps: Gurdei burnt oil in little clay lamps. Dung cakes for fuel were left out to dry in the sun. Extra bedding and clothes were kept in big wooden boxes. Money and jewellery were hidden away in the least expected of places—in a hole, behind a loose brick in the wall, in a bin of grain.

Many years later, when Lajpat was a young man, one afternoon, as the pale light of the sun was losing its warmth and there was a nip in the air, Gurdei came out of her little shack to enjoy the last rays of the sun. She sat on the *thurra*, running the little wooden comb with teeth on both sides through her hair when Lajpat arrived. She quickly braided her hair and covered her head with the thick dupatta before starting to lay out the hand-made *dhurrie* on the floor. Lajpat made his appearance and went inside without looking at his mother. 'Wash your hands and come out to eat', she shouted after him. He came and sat down beside his mother, but for some time continued to ignore her.

'Any luck job-hunting?' she asked at last. She could see that he was disturbed and did not wish to talk, but she could not contain herself any longer. 'Obviously he has had no luck again,' she thought to herself. It had gone on for so long that she just expected him to nod his head in negation. For once, Lajpat flared up. 'They all want to know my family background first . . . where I come from . . . who was my father. Why should all this make any difference? Who was my father anyway? What exactly did he do for a living?' Gurdei could not face her son. She knew that it must be strained with pain, but she had no answers for him. Most of all, she did not want to talk about her husband, not even to her own son; it only brought painful memories. The man remained anonymous, a nameless enigma.

Lajpat had no recollection of his father; the latter had died when Lajpat was just two. 'Cirrhosis of the liver' is all that he had been told. Unlike many Hindus in the village, his father had not been a businessman. Not a farmer, nor a professional craftsman. 'Strange,' thought Lajpat to himself, 'for here almost everyone is at least one of these.' The days of craftsmanship were however very slowly going out of vogue, even though the town of Bhera had for long been renowned for its artisanal works—woodwork, dhurries, *khusa jooties*, baskets, intricate gold jewellery. Lajpat did not in fact want to produce any of these—not unlike the father whom he had not known.

Later he learnt that his old man had not been much of anything in particular—in fact, most of the time he had just lain around drunk. Doing odd jobs here and there, the meagre amount he earned was just enough to support his alcohol needs, which meant that there was hardly ever enough to eat in the house: *jau di roti* was their daily meal. The barley meal was a poor man's food as compared to *genhu*, wheat, considered the rich man's grain. 'Barley gives me flatulence,' Lajpat complained to his mother, 'I have had enough of it!' But his mother pretended not to hear. Even this meal came with difficulty. 'My son, how I wish to make *phaini* in milk with lots of sugar and almonds, raisins and cardamom seeds for you . . .' she wanted to tell him; tears welled up in her eyes instead.

Lajpat felt frustrated. Not even two rupees jingled in his trousers. He strolled around the old ruins, hands in empty pockets, brooding over the whole scene. The ancient, but still very much intact mill thrust against their little *kuccha* house. 'The ruin has been in the same state even when I was a child,' he muttered to no one in particular. 'The rest of the town is beginning to take the shape of modernity, but not our ruin; it still stands as it must have since the time of Babur!' He felt trapped in the gullies through which his father had wasted his way.

He wandered around the whole afternoon. He lay under *ber* (jujuba) trees and played about with the wild plums. He sauntered through the hundreds of acres of cultivated henna fields. He knocked about *kikar* (*Acacia arabica*) and wild olive trees. He walked through the Kabuli and Chirri gates of the town. A new temple had just been built near the Chitti Puli Gate. It was small but beautiful. Lajpat liked to come here and be inspired by its beauty. An octagonal space with a canopy-like porch, its architecture stood out for the mélange of Islamic style with a Hindu décor. The facade bore pictures of mythological figures, of birds and floral patterns in striking green, orange and blue.

Its beauty took him away from the ugliness of the surroundings of their home. He would admire the intricately carved doors built during Jehangir's time. Or he would walk through Sethi Mohallah or Sahni Mohallah—here lived the very highly educated, the rich merchants, Khatris mostly. The Kapurs lived behind them. There was the Chidiya Chowk *ka mandir* close by. Near the Hazirnath darwaza lived the Mehras and Behls. Magons and Vohras also lived here. The Lalluwalla darwaza bisected the city into two. All Hindu traders were on this side of the road. Pir ka Darwaza was the Muslim area.

At other times he walked along the Jhelum, ending up in the bazaar by evening. It was a day like any other in his life when he knocked about aimlessly, like a leaf tossing on a windy day. 'Just a small-time graduate without a job,' he swore to himself, as he kicked up the dusty path with his feet. Even though his stomach was never full and he couldn't stop belching, it did not stop him from having some fancy dreams. Every evening, before finally dropping off to sleep, he dreamt of the day when he could leave town. It may have once had a flourishing economy, but it was now almost a ghost of its former glory.

'Guests from across the waters—all the way from Afreeka! Jobs on offer! Jobs on offer!' Men came out from their workshops, women peeped from behind their half-shut doors, children followed him wherever Kirparam went; a crowd collected under the big banyan tree where he advertised jobs in distant Africa. The patron-client system was widely prevalent among Indians. Workers from India were sought out as apprentices. 'All travel expenses will be borne by me,' Kirparam was explaining. 'As apprentices for work in my shops, your board and lodging will also be taken care of in the beginning. Once you acquire sufficient skill and experience, you will be put in charge of a new shop. I will eventually even encourage you to start your own business.'

Their whispering turned into triumphant cries. Lala Kirparam's search for stalwart young men willing to put their thumbprint on a contract bidding them to work in distant Africa sounded like a treat. The would-be future managers of canteens all over central and northern Kenya queued up in a hurry. With tales of adventure doing the rounds, many a young man was excited. Board, lodging and a small salary to boot, what more could they ask for? The fear of crossing the black waters and defiling your caste had already lost its hold in these parts, judging from the numbers who turned up to sign a three-year apprenticeship agreement on the King George V rupee note, hand-written in Urdu. Those who could not write—and there were many of these in Miani—had put their thumbprints as signatures under their full names.

Ever since the *firangi* raj had taken over, news had spread that contracts for employment had to be made. Moreover, they were to be signed by the person concerned. All sorts of surmises had already been made about the shape of things to come: *Kalyug* has arrived. What is wrong with just saying yes? Time-honoured verbal agreements had been acceptable in the past. The words '*Dharam nal*' used to be sufficient. 'My word is dharam. It is truthful and respectful. My word is the duty of my worth. An absolute authority, my word carries weight—it is almost religious in aspect. It is my most cherished possession. But, come the western administration, it has changed the face of the old dharam with one stroke. My oral agreement is worthless. The written word is to supersede the trust of my self. The pen will now become the magical symbol. "Touch the pen," they now tell me.'

The Bharochis of Bhera were more or less literate and were quickly learning to sign their names. The young men were quite impressed by the ceremony of signatures. New recruits put in their required worth in writing on the fancily written document contract for employment: Name? Lalluprasad. Father's name? Durgaprasad. Surname? Family name? The man fumbled a bit, not understanding. Your *jat*? Your *gotra*? Your *qaum*, what is it? Gandhi. *Zila*? (district) Jhelum.

Next.

Name? Moolraj. Father? Anokhamal. *Qaum*? Bhasin.

Next.

Gur-Baksh. Ram-Ghulam. Sohan-Shah.

Many of the names were a mixture of Sanskrit, Persian and even Greek. Lal, Ram, Pal, Rai, Baksh, Ghulam, Shah (cherished, God, protector, prince, granted, slave, king). Dei and Devi (granted, goddess) were for women. Persian, Mohammedan and Sanskrit-based adjectives were often added to elaborate first names and to show a distinction between higher and lower castes. The lower caste—the Shudras—were prohibited from using any such ornamentation.

Some of the prospective candidates only answered to first names, even though by now the surname had become a requirement. The inscription of a name under a constant and particular form to affirm its exactitude, the surname was supposed to carry and assume a responsibility. And be accountable to a family or to a clan name. Surnames have a history behind them and a story to relate. British rule in India, and the subsequent bureaucracy that they introduced, led to a whole new set of surnames; the last name could pin you to your caste, village, or trade.

They began by adding a parental or caste name, some took the name of their village as surname. The idea of surname as such was alien, but Indians had their own complex ways of identification— occupation, caste and *gotra* being some traditional methods of classification. Generally, a caste was identified with a profession, the sub-caste with territory or region. The lineage, the joint family system or the family line that existed before the caste system belonged to a larger clan (*gotra*). Intermarriage was forbidden within this *gotra*, but encouraged within the sub-caste of which it formed a part. The *gotra*, the Sanskrit word for cowpen (each *gotra* had its own branding mark for cattle held in common) traced a family line to a mythical or a historical ancestor. Regardless of religion and caste, the *gotra* system cut across all Hindu society, with ancestors associated to one of the many Vedic rishis.

Some names had ancient military affiliations. Bhalla was associated to a spear; Bhasin to brilliance. Mahendra was a chief, while the Bhel was strong and steady, a chariot of war pulled by bulls. Kapur, for camphor, used in lighting the sacred fire, was an upper class Khatri from the moonline. The most territorial group appeared to be the Uchhandi Khatris of the uplands in the north-west—the Multani, Peshawaria, and Bharochi of Bhera. Some gave themselves the honorific title of Mehta, a respected, educated master or clerk, or a Dalal, a broker, manager, treasurer, as a surname; these were not Sanskrit-based. They were derived from Persian titles, ranks or functions during Mughal rule. Others took the father's first name for a surname; even a respected elder brother's. The Shankardasses took the name of their elder brother Shamdass, as a source for their surname.

Many boys had already signed up, but Lajpat's widowed mother didn't want him to go. 'Others have been recruited, why are you making a fuss about me?' he asked. Lajpat wanted to leave without a moment's hesitation. 'He will be well looked after,' Kirparam said, trying to assure the poor woman that there was nothing to fear. Friends and relatives persuaded Gurdei to let him go. 'It is time the boy earns something,' they told her. 'Let him seek a better life elsewhere.' Bebe heaved a sigh. 'What is happening in the world, I don't know,' she whispered. She looked above at the heavens and said '*Khudani marzi*', Let God's will be done.

With great reluctance she let her son leave. She prayed fervently, and the merchant left with the boys of the town. Together with others, the young men boarded a train bound for Lahore to get their passports. It was a big city. The colours and sights of Lahore were legendary. According to one, Lahore was founded by Lav, a twin son of the mythological hero king Rama. At last they were going to see it.

Anarkali was the most fashionable shopping centre of Punjab. Anarkali meant 'pomegranate bud', and it was named after a renowned court dancer in Akbar's time. The boys boasted of making purchases here, even if all they had done was just walk the length and breadth of the bazaar, entering and exiting row after row of displays. The Lahore of the day spelt romance and golden dreams, a capital of fashion and style. It was the heartbeat of the land. Endless bazaars, including the reputed Hira Mandi—gem market—of singing girls and courtesans, the city revealed itself to their longing eyes. The boys looked down at their poor attire and were sure that they were easily recognizable as hailing from a small town; when they spoke, their accents gave them away.

The principal immigration officer conferred upon them the rights of citizens of 'British East Africa, Uganda, Zanzibar and conquered territory'. Lajpat was considered a 'fit person to be received as an immigrant in British East Africa'. His new identity card number conferred upon him the status of a subject of British rule in India. Of course, all the politics did not make sense, but for the moment he was just glad to look forward to a more fruitful life with a guaranteed job. The first world war was not yet over when Lajpat Rai, together with many other boys, left for British East Africa with Lala Kirparam Ramchand.

9

Alliances

God save the king
Gracious king,
God save the king . . .

A procession was winding through town: from the railway station, round Victoria Street, along River Road and back to the station. The all-African Kenya African Rifles band was playing military music; soldiers of varied ranks walked behind. They were followed by families in rickshaws. The purpose was to create a sense of nostalgia, a sense of victory in the onlookers. The first world war had ended. German East Africa became British territory and was renamed Tanganyika. It had been paid for with over 50,000 lives—many of them African. They had died in the name of King George and the German Kaiser.

Kenya became a colony. From a 'protected' status, the people became colonized, subject to all that went with it. However, the 'white man's war' had brought a change in the Africans. They had travelled far. They had seen white men shoot each other. They understood that even the white man could be vulnerable. And they banded together with their own, encouraging the strengthening of African nationalism. The various Indian communities, also in a rare display of solidarity, said in a unified voice that they would not accept discrimination. Over the next decade, the clash between Europeans and Indians was to reach its highest point.

Soon after Lajpat arrived in British East Africa, an Economic Report was sent out: 'It is our firm conviction that the justification of our occupation of this country lies in our ability to adapt the native to our own civilization. If we further complicate this task by continuing to expose the African to antagonistic influence of the Asiatic, as distinct from European philosophy, we shall be guilty of a breach of trust.'

Thus, it became 'a duty' to protect the helpless native from the rapaciousness of the Asiatic. This set a match to the powder of racial feeling. The Indian Association protested vigorously. The community found itself trapped between two fires. Damned if they did, and damned if they didn't. The Europeans made them look 'politically dangerous'. If they sympathized with the Africans, they were 'opportunists'. If they kept aloof, 'they did nothing for the native'.

India had already been stirred by the post-war spirit of self-determination. In distant colonial Kenya, there was an echo. Politically conscious people like M.A. Desai arrived from India. Soon after his arrival, he started the E.A. Chronicle. It was to become the platform for Indian views. Desai transformed the 'Indian question' into a major political issue of imperial importance. The struggle stimulated much political action. It most certainly put a stop to settler ambition by arresting the move towards the South African system of complete aparthied.

For long, the 'Indian question' continued to be a major issue. At one point, it almost seemed that the fate of India depended upon its outcome. The settlers almost rebelled against the king's government. Skin colour became a primary determinant of social status and all aspects of life. It was offensive for a coloured person to smoke a cigarette near a white person. Service was rendered to people according to their colour. Whites did not have to queue anywhere because they were 'busy' people. No 'coloureds' were appointed to higher posts in the civil services, the military, the police force, or the railways. Nor were professional degrees from Indian universities recognized. Churchill affirmed the highlands for 'Whites only' and restricted Indian immigration—despite what he wrote in his African diary fifteen years earlier. In 1907 he had given assurances of fair play. Extremists in India only welcomed this speech. It supplied them with further anti-British ammunition. The rupee as Kenya's currency was finally abolished in 1920, and the last official links with India were severed as the protectorate was transformed into a colony.

The daily routine in the Indian bazaar had not changed much, although a totally new world was opening up. An introverted and withdrawn child found herself slowly drawn into the mysterious world of the word, the magic that would be her last refuge in her ageing years. Yashoda was now being led into a new realm that she had not known before—one that allowed her to express the labyrinth of her dreamy self in new ways. The exposure to literacy, to reading and writing began to give her some confidence, and to give her the much needed sense of security. It was a way to relate to the world.

Yashoda was just considering herself lucky to have the opportunity, when her school closed down, yet again. The first time, the pandit teaching them had lost control when one of the girls had a recitation problem. He slapped her, the parents protested strongly, the pandit was dismissed, and the school closed down. The next teacher was young, and could not resist making a pass at one of the girls. The school shut its doors once again. 'Married with wife living in house' were the requirements for the next recruit.

The closure of the school became quite traumatic for Yashoda. As it is, many in the community did not consider it necessary to educate their girls. Marriage came early, soon after the start of menstruation. Kirparam was quite aware of all this. And yet, he just couldn't brush aside the look of yearning on his daughter's tender face. He would not shirk his responsibility to educate her. Not particularly demonstrative, Kirparam was however very fond of children. He was especially sensitive to Yashoda, and to her needs. Perhaps the impact on Yashoda was measurable.

Mnemonically, it coloured her thoughts and actions throughout her life.

'I must look for a tutor,' Kirparam mused for a long while before he found one right under his nose, in his own house in fact. 'But, of course, the young man who came with me from India,' Kirparam sighed with relief, 'he can read and write!' That is how Lajpat came to be Yashoda's tutor.

A few years after he had arrived with Kirparam from Bhera, Lajpat Rai was tasked with teaching Lalaji's daughter for a few hours each week, besides carrying out his duties at the shop in Nairobi. Lajpat Rai taught Yashoda Urdu, the little English that he knew, and basic accounts. Each time, somehow, the hour allotted to them seemed shorter. It was as if they weren't spending enough time together in the little room where Kirparam let them study.

Yashoda loved every minute of it, but she hardly uttered a word. She listened and made notes—all the time fascinated by the young man. She raised her head with expectant eyes. Anticipation and eagerness was written all over her face. She stared at him transfixed. 'He knows so much,' she gazed thoughtfully at him. His little moustache was barely an inch long and much in vogue. How she liked it, and his curly hair. At night in the privacy of her bed, she dreamt sometimes of just a slight caress, or a touch of his hair. Too timid and modest to let even her dreams get more colourful.

Lajpat was not particularly good-looking, a little apish in fact. He was short, with a head too big for his body, and a broad nose. You could call him stubby. An unassuming and modest air hung about him. To Yashoda, he was divine. At times she stared at him without having heard a word. She smiled to herself, all alone in her room. What was happening to her? She had never felt like this before. Nobody had been able to arouse such passions in her being before. She shuddered. What were these new changes that she was perceiving in herself? They frightened her a little. She did not really know how to handle them.

Whether it was happiness, or excitement, she wasn't too sure.

Perhaps it was wrong. Some guilt crept in. She wasn't able to analyze it. Nobody had ever talked about these things to her. All she knew was that she suddenly felt a little uneasy with herself, and concurrently a little too conscious of her own body. Of course, she dare not mention it to anyone, least of all to her mother. The shy and as yet unformed curves of her breasts were giving rise to an uncontrollable awareness. The pangs of the first ache of love. She was perhaps ready for the transition to womanhood.

The rains had started with vigour. Hurling themselves violently against the tin roof, the drops appeared to melt on coming in contact with the small glass window. In their decaying wood and iron classroom Lajpat was shouting, but his voice was barely audible to Yashoda. In any case, she was in a dream world. The lesson did not make much headway. Thunder and lightening enveloped the town. Shyly they looked at each other, yet pretended not to look. Something passed between them. Lajpat opened his mouth as if to say her name softly, but not a word came out. In that pregnant moment, they both knew.

Yashoda's face went red, Lajpat felt himself burning, utterly confused. His heart was beating so fast, he thought it would burst. He did not have the courage to speak to her directly, and quietly walked out. They came out into the storm, soared above it, madly and passionately in love. Lajpat looked back. Yashoda was still standing at the door. Raindrops glistened on her face. She rested her weight on one leg. The slight asymmetry highlighted the deflection of her pelvis, giving her a mildly erotic look.

He became restless, tormented by his feelings. He had to talk to Yashoda's father somehow, but was too nervous to go up to him. He scolded himself for this inappropriate feeling, 'I dare not defy my class,' he muttered miserably—conscious of his own position, or the lack of it. Here he was, Lajpat Rai, a poor contractual labourer, asking for the hand in marriage of his boss' daughter. A socially unacceptable impulse. 'The daughter of Lala Kirparam, merchant.' Lajpat could not summon the guts. 'No, I dare not talk to him. It is sure to offend him. I am aiming too high. Better forget about the whole episode,' and he blew out the little kerosene lamp next to his bed.

That night Lajpat Rai tossed in bed for a long time. In the seclusion of his room, he began to brood over Yashoda. Her image flitted repeatedly into his mind. The soft beige sari that she wore the last time that they saw each other became a regular replay. He screamed her name out loud, not once, but over and over, until his voice went almost hoarse. He longed to caress the nape of her neck, as he felt his own ablaze with fever. He felt guilty, as if caught, in a crime. Neither rebellious, nor normally bold, here we are with the audacity to fall in love and daring to proclaim it, Lajpat thought to himself.

As the days coalesced into nights, and the nights into days, the guilt decreased, and ultimately vanished. The dilemma evaporated. Yashoda became a *junoon*, an obsession. By now, he was even beyond being bothered about his lower social status. He only longed to hold Yashoda in his arms. He wanted to have her before his eyes all the time. And then one day, when he could bear it no more, when he was absolutely sure that there was no existence apart from her, he built up his courage, and unburdened himself to a respected elder of the community.

Kirparam got the message. Days passed without any feedback. A worried and sleepless Lajpat contemplated his next move.

Yashoda was barely sixteen, tender and frail. Hardei was anxious about their daughter. What she saw in this man, Lajpat Rai, Hardei couldn't for the life of her understand. The man had no money, no position, not even a modest business to proclaim his worth. Just a small-time worker in one of her husband's dukas—*naukar* she called him, a servant. Yashoda was being an impractical romantic, and Hardei was going to have none of it. Marrying a man with no money, did she realize what this would mean? It would mean suffering and hard times. It would mean having to sacrifice all the time, or having to go without food when necessary. I should know.

Haven't I suffered enough? What does my child know—she has not seen the pain that I have had to go through.

Hardei reacted with hostility. She had tried to impress, without any effect whatsoever, upon the girl's father, that 'all this education phase that you are encouraging her to go through is nonsense, only an invitation to trouble. Moreover, leaving the young couple all by themselves is dangerous'. But, as usual, Kirparam had let their daughter have her way. Hardei could not understand why her husband had to listen to the whims of a naïve girl without any worldly experience.

'Marriage is no play,' she tried to argue with her daughter. 'You think this folly can sustain and endure the long journey?' Hardei did not use the 'love'. 'Money, position, power, these are important,' she added. 'Whoever heard of a girl having her own way? This is scandalous. Are these the fruits of my karma?' With these crisp words she left the room in a huff, banging the door behind her. Yashoda stood rooted to the spot, not saying a word. She too had suffered many sleepless nights; the torment of indecision had passed, there was now no question of choosing. In her mind, she was already married to Lajpat Rai. For once, her face reflected a strong resolution, a firmness of purpose. 'How can I even think of another,' she thought to herself, 'that would be defilement.' Anger, rage and hysteria—these did not form part of her disposition, but she could not understand her mother. What she did not realize was that Hardei herself had never really known love. How could Yashoda have known? Her mother had rarely, if ever, shared her dark past with her daughter.

They could not escape the web of society and of words unspoken, threatening to engulf them all. When still too young to remember, Hardei had lost her mother. Her father's new wife had brought her neither happiness, nor love. Only pain, and more struggle. Marriage to Kirparam had added some colour, and new desires had entered her bleak existence. But that too had been short-lived when he had run away to Africa. Left alone once more to fend for herself, hardened by all that life had offered, Hardei had learnt to rely on the power of money—that through years of lone survival had slowly given her the much-needed security. Her small business of lending money on commission was giving her a prestigious position in society—and the necessary additional confidence.

Hardei's own proposal for marriage had come when she had not even begun to menstruate. No one had asked for her opinion. She had only seen the man she was to spend the rest of her life with after all the ceremonies were long over. Face to face with a new partner in a strange house, and a village that she was familiar with only by name. Anger swelled up within Hardei's breast as she thought of her daughter. 'Idealistic, vulnerable, romantic, impractical—values sure to bring her pain and depression,' she was convinced. Little did Hardei realize how true her prophecy would ring towards the end of her daughter's life.

Kirparam knew the new look on his daughter's face. His heart softened somewhat. Stroking her head, he tried to dissuade her. Yashoda was suddenly becoming conscious of herself. She felt his troubled gaze and would not meet her father's eyes. Hands held in front of her, she carried on looking down towards her bare feet. So innocent, he thought to himself. She does not even know how to say 'yes' or 'no'. 'Does she really know her mind?' he wondered.

Yashoda's young man was neither well established, nor rich. Kirparam did not approve of it either. He knew that it would be a difficult start. He stared at his daughter for a long while, feeling a little let down. Then he shook his head before speaking. He too dismissed Lajpat as a *naukar*. From all that one knew about his unconventional thinking, it was ironical that he too endorsed it in the traditional way. 'A servant in one of my small dukas; just a young boy I had picked up from the poorer areas of Bhera. How can I agree to it?' he said, trying to talk his daughter out of it. He reasoned with her. But Yashoda ignored her father's wishes.

For once she seemed to know her mind. Or, was it that she

could only listen to the beats of her heart, but not see the sense of his logic? Suddenly, she spoke up. Yashoda did not shout back at her father, in fact she hardly said much. But, the little that she did say was enough to show both of them that somewhere a steel-like determination lurked in their child. She was adamant, and she told them quite firmly, 'I will marry Lajpat Rai or no one at all.' To avert any further embarassment, she quietly slipped inside to change her sari.

Hardei and Kirparam were taken aback, quite surprised at the strength in their daughter's voice. They had done their best at *palan–poshan*: their duty to nurture, protect and develop their child. To see her in this new light came as a shock. To them, she had always seemed weak and fragile, well-mannered, and quiet.

They felt their strength drain away in front of their frail child. Her new-found independence was so unexpected that for a long while they stood dumbfounded. And then, most reluctantly, Kirparam gave in. This was perhaps the only time in her life that Yashoda stood her ground and had her way. As for Hardei, something snapped within her. She never forgave her daughter. She shrugged her shoulders and started preparations for the wedding in a half-hearted celebratory spirit.

Hardei did not keep a shrine in her own home, but continued to offer prayers at Lala Prasad's small Radha-Krishna temple. Religious in her own understated way, she went only when a need arose—when the situation got out of hand, when things did not go her way. She always went alone. None of her children accompanied her; perhaps this is how she preferred it. That evening Hardei was most upset over her daughter's behaviour. The feeling of bitterness increased in her breast. She wanted to pour it out, give vent to her frustration. She knew she must talk to someone who would hear her. So she fought with her god.

The new temple that had recently been built on Duke Street was big and housed many gods. It was not far from her house, but Hardei did not like going there. Perhaps it lacked the appropriate aura: the idols had not yet been impregnated by the holy spirit. Whatever it was, she felt more comfortable worshipping her Radha-Krishna in the little temple of the bazaar. The small *diya* in her hand created a magical effect; it left deep shadows. She placed it in front of the statues. The partial light challenged the imagination of the devotee to seek a likeness of the image of god—just enough to capture it, then to recreate the likeness with her own inner light. Her Krishna was utterly incomparable. His face never looked sad, serious or tearful. Soon a smile came to Hardei's lips.

Ever since his *Jihad* and the temple incident, Lala Kirparam had become increasingly cynical and sarcastic about her holy visits. He would tease his wife when she got back. 'Come children, come and kiss your mother's hands. She returns from the temple. There her hands have touched God.' Clearly, Kirparam was embarrassed at the thought that his wife went before the idol of Krishna and anointed it with ghee. Eventually, Hardei stopped giving Kirparam the *prasad*, the sacred food that had been offered to the deities. She would not even tell him that she had gone to the temple.

Kirparam had never worn the sacred thread according him the status of the twice-born. Neither had any of his sons gone through any purification rites of *dvija*. Even for Diwali, no prayer ceremony was held in the house—perhaps the only Hindu household not to do so. This did not mean that he deprived his children of the fun and spirit of the festival. On the contrary, they spent a long day touring various shops full of colour and aromas. Here, each of them would be treated to gifts. And at home, he would have spent many days prior to the festival making all kinds of sweets and pastries. *Gulab jamuns, barfi, jalebis*, he was adept at them all. After all, he had started off as a *halwai*.

* * *

The political scene was less celebratory. It was the year leading to the white paper on the 'Indian Question in Kenya'. It would discuss the provision of separate social services for different races—separate and inferior hospitals, schools, prisons, transport facilities were to be set up.

Coloureds would not be served in European hotels, or in their clubs. Public toilets would be appropriately marked—European, Asian, African. The rupee had already been abolished three years before. A law requiring the rendering of accounts in English, or in Kiswahili written in the Roman script was passed. Traders had been submitting their accounts in the Persian script or in Gujarati. Most of these traders in British East Africa could neither read nor write English, while many white officers were familiar with some Indian language. It aroused strong Indian protests. For six weeks Indian shops remained closed. Kirparam was already fluent in English so he did not panic.

The wedding of a first girl in the family was a big affair and required much preparation. Especially as Lala Kirparam had become a merchant of some renown. Not that he particularly cared about defending a reputation.

Her youthful body was prepared for its ultimate destiny, washed and anointed in gramflour paste. *Jhoomar, chownk, pase, sringar patti, band, paunchi, gajra,* her hair fully decked up, *jhumkian* in the ears, and *tika* on the forehead, Yashoda sat in all her finery. The ladies of the house had taken pains to wave her hair on the sides of the forehead, as was the fashion of the day. A long blouse with slits on the sides revealed nothing of her youthful body. From head to right shoulder, where it was held in place with a big Parsi brooch, the *pallu* covered it entirely. The innocent look of naïvete—totally devoid of make-up, except for the *surma*, black sulphuret of antimony pencilled to beautify her eyes, a spot of *kajal* added at the base of her chin to ward off the evil eye. The red dot in the centre of the forehead, the *bindi*, was not applied, but her hands were dyed red with henna. Where the family came from in the north of Punjab, the Hindu attire was culturally closer to the Muslim, although the younger generation of these Punjabi Hindu women in British East Africa had taken to the sari in preference to the earlier salwar kameez.

The family had gathered together. Tents were erected. Part of the road had been blocked off. The street was decorated with marigold. The mango-leaf garlands were a sure sign that a special ceremony was being celebrated.

But perhaps there was to be no celebration after all. The temple priest refused to come. He would not conduct the sacred rituals in the house of a non-believer. 'There is no way I will go to plead with him,' Kirparam snapped. The women of the household panicked; embers flared up once again and he was confronted with mounting pressure. For a while Kirparam felt himself at a loss. He refused to succumb to the mood of desperation. The family was large, as were most—brothers and sisters, cousins, *bhabhis* (sisters-in-law) and mothers-in-law—amongst others. The house was buzzing with noise and activity. There was simply no room for privacy. And Kirparam needed to think. Leaving them in the hullabaloo under the tent, he started walking down the street. It was the only way he knew of getting his thoughts into a clearer framework.

The religious ceremony was not important for Kirparam. This was public knowledge by now. However, he reflected that perhaps his young daughter would not be accepted in a social milieu unless she had gone round the sacred fire. He would have been perfectly satisfied with the ancient practice of *gandharva vivah*—marriage by a simple exchange of flower garlands, bereft of ceremony. As for what he knew about Lajpat Rai, Kirparam was quite confident that the rituals were not necessary for the young man either, the blessings of the gathering being enough. But would it have convinced the rest of the family? Perhaps not. The quarrel was Kirparam's, and he did not want to deny them their place in society. He saw himself as a deviant, but he neither condemned, nor praised any other lifestyles.

Before he reached the end of the road, Kirparam met a friend, and he could hardly believe his luck. It was perfect, just the person who could be of help. The man Kirparam came face to face with at that moment was not another priest used to reading marriage rituals (a marriage was supposed to be read rather than conducted), but someone who had some knowledge of sanctified mantras. Kirparam asked, and the young man agreed; the two hurried back together.

Sacred verses from the Vedas were chanted. Kirparam was quite confident that few present understood the meaning or the importance of the hymns being chanted. No one present could have said for sure that they were the appropriate mantras for the occasion, but apparently everyone seemed satisfied. At least they had not lost face in society. The holy fire was lit. With every piece of wood that she fed into the fire, Yashoda's anxiety mounted. The glow in the *havan kund* grew. Sacrificial substances poured into the fire reaching up to the gods.

Yashoda was trembling while circumambulating it the prescribed seven times. As the flames heightened, two hands came to her rescue, and she felt saved—another rite over! She was not sure whether her legs would support her. Her heart was pounding very fast, her hands trembling. Anxious and afraid of her decision and the new life that now lay in front of her, quite unsure of what she had got herself into. She suddenly realized that she hardly knew anything about the young man. They hadn't exchanged any private conversation so far at all. Where did he come from? What was his background? Have I done the right thing? With a mind in turmoil, she went through the motions.

Yashoda was susceptible and extremely fragile, brought up by a father with tender loving care. Unlike her mother, she was neither strong, nor aggressive. As if woken out of a daze, she suddenly felt flower petals on her face. The blessings of the congregation were upon them. The ceremony was over. She no more belonged to her father's house! She was being led forward to touch the feet of elders for their blessings.

Yashoda and Lajpat Rai soon after their wedding

'I give you as a gift my daughter whom I have looked after with love and affection. Look after her, that is your duty,' recited Kirparam in Sanskrit. 'She is half my body; I will look after her,' replied Lajpat Rai in holy acceptance. Kirparam gave away his girl to Lajpat Rai as *kanyadaan* together with an offering of a necklace made out of guineas. The government had been minting twenty-one carat gold guineas. It had become a fashion to offer a guinea for an engagement ceremony to the bride or to the groom, or to make an entire necklace and earrings with these guineas to offer to the bride.

10

Changing values

Ghadiyon pa na dendi pani
Chikyon la na dendi roti
Pedi kaudi to vi khoti

(She will not offer you water from her pots,
Nor serve you with chapatis from her baskets;
Worse than a bad cowrie she is)

      —Bhera woman about Miani woman

Even before Lala Kirparam had given his blessings to the young couple, Lajpat had returned to Bhera to get his mother. He had been uncomfortable at having left her alone. With the passage of time, his anxiety had only increased. Her travelling alone was unthinkable—he knew that she would not come. As it was, Gurdei had not wanted to leave. Any form of transport other than the bullock-cart frightened her. She had always preferred to walk. In fact, she rarely left her village. Crossing the black waters was unthinkable. Lajpat was quite aware of her deep-rooted fears, and did not divulge any part of the journey to his mother until the very end.

The first hurdle had been the innoculation. When Gurdei saw the huge needles, she screamed. They had to literally tie her up with ropes. Keeping her eyes shut tight and looking the other way, she kept on screaming 'The *teeka* will kill me. The *teeka* will kill me.' As soon as the prick was over, she asked, 'Is that all?'

Gurdei had never seen the sea. The big expanse of the ocean caused her to panic. A deep fear of the unknown half killed her. 'I will not get into the *bedi* (boat),' she repeated incessantly. Ropes came in handy again. She was tied up and hauled on board. Gurdei's last glimpse of her land did not even hold the emotion that she strongly felt afterward; her whole being felt only one sensation for the moment, 'I will die.' Obviously, Punjabis were not people of the sea.

Perhaps it was a little cruel, but Lajpat preferred to have his mother next to him, rather than let her be, all alone, so far away. Gurdei prayed fervently. All through the voyage her mind was concentrated on her gods. She vowed that if she arrived safely, she would not cross the black waters again. And, she didn't. Gurdei never returned to her hometown in India. She missed it for a long while. But nothing would make her repeat the sea journey. It was with great relief that she finally sighted land.

'You know I was very fond of *ber*', Gurdei was telling Chachi. She was thoroughly enjoying herself sharing her stories with Bhagwanti. The two women had become very fond of each other. They were so alike. 'One day while climbing up one of these yellow fruit trees, my salwar got caught in the thorns. Ascending higher up, I heard a big rip; of course, it was my salwar, torn up by that much,' she indicated 'that much' by her hand to elbow length. 'I let out a scream. What will my mother-in-law say? I was terrified, so afraid that I even peed in my *salwar!*' Gurdei carried on with a chuckle, 'Somehow, I got past the door of the house, and lo behold it was my father-in-law whom I first encountered. I did not have to say anything. He knew immediately from the way I held on to my torn *salwar* and the fear on my face. Without questioning me or scolding me, he handed me a needle and thread. But do you know what?' chuckled Gurdei, holding her friend hard by the right shoulder, 'I did not know how to stitch! So, of course my mother-in-law found out. I was given a nice scolding, and barred from climbing trees again.' Their sides were splitting with laughter. At the end, Gurdei sighed, as if relinquishing all joys of life: 'That was the last time I ate *ber*!'

It was impossible to spend a few moments with her and not know her immediately. Nothing could disguise her real self. What she was in appearance, she was in reality. Gurdei had hit it off with Bhagwanti almost spontaneously. It was as if they had always known each other, chatting away late into the night in their high-pitched excitable voices. Intimacy of language, custom, and convention brought them close together. No sooner had they wished 'Ram-Ram' to each other, each knew without doubt that the other must hail from the same town. Not only did they have a common dialect, even the way they dressed was similar: huge *salwar* and *kameez* akin to the Muslim attire of their regions—in preference to the sari.

Names, clothes, food, ways of eating, outlook in life, everything coincided. The women exchanged their veils, men turbans—this was their way of swearing a friendship. The fact that they were from the same town—with the peculiarly accented Punjabi of the Bharochis—had already set a common ground for a long-term association to flourish.

Bhagwanti, daughter of Sadhu Singh, was Chachi to all. Older women were generally called so. The men were Chacha, whether they were the father's brother or not—it didn't matter, for these were terms of affection and respect. Chachi had become a matriarch of a certain standing to those who knew her. She had a soft corner for children. '*Pairi pona* Chachiji,' they touched her feet in respect, and ran away. '*Jiyo, jiyo!*' she shouted after them, showering her blessings of long lives for them.

It was Bhagwanti Chachi who had accommodated Gurdei when she had first arrived. Lajpat Rai and his mother had for a short time shared space with Chachi—a room to each family, the kitchen had been common. Chachi prepared her meals in one corner, while Gurdei sat in the opposite corner. Often, they exchanged dishes. A bowl of lentils passed hands, or a bowl of vegetables.

Other than gossip of the day, their favourite topics of conversation were the alimentary system, the ailments they suffered from and the best herbs for cure, or the number of children in the family. 'Tenth or eleventh?' they laughed, and the charpoys moved under their weights.

'One day when he is old, the Pupli will pay him for doing nothing,' one of the women, beaming with pride, told Chachi and Gurdei. 'Pupli' was the public works department, and the fact that the husband would get pension after retirement was a source of honour. How happy she was to discuss the well-paid job of her husband as a clerk with the Uganda Railways. '*Oy haramzadiye, ren de, ren de!*' said another, 'Don't pull our legs!' The women hurled abuses at each other in a typical Punjabi display of affection, of closeness—in a manner that tended to shock the Gujaratis, or those from other Indian states. Women of Chakwal, a town not far from Behra, often joined their group. Sometimes, they brought their work over—cutting vegetables, weaving, embroidering or knitting. Charpoys leaning against the walls were brought down immediately for the Bebes and the Chachis to sit on, their legs tucked underneath.

Properly maintained, these charpoys were simple but wonderful. They served multiple purposes. During the night and the afternoon siesta the charpoy became the bed. The rest of the day, it served as a sofa on which one received one's friends. It was also a worktable on which one sat to clean vegetables, sift rice, or remove husk from wheat. The rope strings, however, needed constant tightening. Once, Bhagwanti Chachi's friend—of considerable weight—had almost fallen through! How they had laughed. Every once in a while the women put in new ropes to avoid mites getting in. The last time Chachi had all the strings replaced by cotton ribbons. Chachi, like all her other friends, spent long hours on the charpoy.

Gurdei had not been more than six, perhaps seven years old, when they had come for her. 'Come my little one, we have to make you beautiful,' her mother had said as she had rushed to pick her up. 'You will wear a lovely red salwar and a *dupatta* with little gold dots.' And when Gurdei had asked her mother whether they were going for a festival, she had been told, 'It will be your very own festival. We are going to make you into a little *dulhan*. You will make such a lovely bride, my child.' Gurdei had been happy to be fussed over and decorated, 'I will tell all my friends,' she thought to herself. It was not every day that she could wear lovely clothes; in fact it happened only sometimes when they went to the fair.

With that, a real bridegroom was brought for her. A boy dressed in a white kurta and pyjama, with a red turban too big for his head, that kept falling off. He would hold it in place, but when his hand got tired, it would fall off again. When the boy came close to her, and the little ones were asked to garland each other, Gurdei had let out a scream. Why, he was the same boy she was playing with not long ago! 'He has stolen my marbles. He has cheated me at play,' Gurdei had screamed, and she had cried, 'He cannot be my *dulha*, he's not my groom. I don't want him.' But the ceremony could not be interrupted; the auspicious moment selected by the astrologers had to be adhered to. Nobody paid much attention to their tantrums. Their initial excitement over, the little couple reconciled, immediately wanting to get back to their marble play. But the mantra chanting carried on in the same drone, at the same pitch. By the time it was finally over, the newly married couple had cried themselves to sleep.

Years later, when her menses had finally commenced, *murkian* were pierced in her ears. Gold rings, perhaps a dozen or so for each of her small ears. For seven days, they had teased her as '*mendiyan wali*', the virgin, with her hair braided in three parts: from a parting in the centre, down each side of the forehead, the braids were pinned above her small ears. The ritual of '*mendiyan kholna*' was a grand affair. Female relatives of the groom came with offerings of sweetmeats. The eldest woman came over to undo Gurdei's plaits.

They sang songs comparing her to *'mendiyan kanak'*. 'O beardless wheat, your grain is tightly packed like the braid of a woman's hair . . . the virgin has the glory of her braids.' On the first day of the ceremonies, only sweets were served to the *barat*. Mountains of *laddus, shakkarparey* and *balushiyan* were placed in front of the groom's family and other guests. The next day was salt day. Only on the third day could they partake of a full meal. Gurdei had stayed with her mother until her menstruation. When *muklawa* arrived finally, she was taken to her in-laws as a true bride. With the onset of her first period, the Sikh bride was prepared for consummation of her marriage to the Hindu boy to whom she had been wed a few years earlier.

Married couples avoided any show of interest in each other when in public. It would be regarded as highly improper if a man showed any sort of affection for his wife in the community, or even in front of his own kin; he would be characterised as a weakling. Lajpat Rai did not suffer any such apprehensions, and displayed due concern for his young bride. He was tender with her. It was an unusual relationship. They sometimes even held hands when going for a walk. People smiled; others passed comments. Some said of them, 'There goes the Ram-Sita couple.'

When Yashoda was expecting her first child, Lajpat prepared all kinds of nutritous foods to help her body regain its strength. *Panjiri*, with its five main ingredients of dry dates—Arabic gum, seeds, coconut and ginger were mixed with semolina and fried in ghee. Carrot *halwa* full of almonds and sunflower seeds, apple and mango *murabba*, iron fortifying liquids—and he made sure that she ate them too.

It was Krishna Janamashtami, the birthday of Lord Krishna. That same cold night in the month of August, their son was born. Unlike the god, he was not born at midnight. Nor was he their eighth child. But it seemed only natural that Yashoda, who had already been named after the foster mother of Krishna, should want to name her son after the god. So they called him Krishen.

Oil was immediately thrown on the ground and under her bed, beneath which green grass had been placed. Bebe Gurdei spat on the baby's little palm and put a blob of black kajal on his forehead. To protect against any evil or harm coming to the child or to the mother, the *dai* (midwife) who had assisted in the actual birth hung an iron bangle to Yashoda's bed. She insisted on being gifted a gold bangle for herself. It was an auspicious occasion, for a male child had been born. Yashoda looked at the iron scissors that her mother-in-law had placed under the pillow to protect the grandson from fear. For her these rituals were not meaningful—the Arya Samaji educational background had ensured that. But, she went through the motions because they were important to her mother-in-law, who still clung to orthodox Hindu mixed with some Sikh beliefs—having had a Hindu mother and a Sikh father.

Chura women, the lowest of the low, the outcastes, the cleaners of the night soil, ornamented the bedroom door with a *sehra*. Fresh mango leaves were tied with red *mauli* (sacred thread) on top of the door. *Churas* were not invited; they didn't have to be. Somehow, they just seemed to appear wherever there was a festive occasion in the family—an engagement, a wedding or childbirth—trotting from one Punjabi house to another. Singing, playing the *dholaki*, dancing and finally demanding a reward according to the status of the family. Barging their way into the house, they refused to leave until given something. Employing all kinds of bargaining tactics, they had their way in the end.

'Having given birth to a child, a son at that, is not a joke. Your new grandson will guarantee the continuation of generations. He will perform the last rites after the father's death to ensure a peacable departure to the world of ancestors. Your status has increased, you have become a proud woman; a grandson has been born. Come Bebe, have a big heart,' they taunted in turns from the crowd. For once, Gurdei happily dished out some coins. Another sang in praise of each member of the family, and for the long life and prosperity of the newborn. No one dared to criticize the *churas* for, once enraged, they would shower abuses and curses on one and all. They had however been rewarded to their satisfaction. They sang and danced, mimicking professional dance girls. Their presence on such occasions was tolerated and even considered auspicious.

Shakkarparey was distributed according to the number of turbans (representing male members) in each family. Two for each pugree. The whole house was cleaned. For the first few days of birth, mother and child remained secluded in the inner room in a state of ritual impurity. No contact with the rest of the family was permitted until the ritual ablution had been completed.

At sunset of the third day, the *dai* washed Yashoda's breasts with water using blades of *kusa* grass as a brush to symbolically prepare her to give milk to her child. Jaggery was applied to the child's lips before giving him the breast. Bebe Gurdei showered her blessings upon the new-born, adding a wee bit of gold leaf, 'If its taste of the new world is auspicious, its whole life will be auspicious.' *Gurhuti*, the first liquid food given to the child, was supposed to determine the future formation of character, therefore the choice of person administering the jaggery or drop of honey was important. You selected a person who in your view was ideal in character, whom you wanted the child to take after.

Her well-oiled and massaged abdomen was bound tightly with a cloth to support her internal organs and encourage her uterus to involute. Finally, on the fifth day, the *dai* helped Yashoda have a bath. She pared her nails for the first time since her confinement; washed her hair in milk. On the thirteenth day when Yashoda could finally leave the room with her son, she offered clothes to her Gujarati *dai*. Nursing, midwifery was not considered a respectable profession amongst the Punjabis; it was polluting. The very few

Punjabi women forced into the trade refused to cut the umbilical cord, or to clean the child or the new mother.

A bonfire was lit, old furniture burnt. It was a time for renewal. The baby was showered with gifts. Lala Kirparam and Bebe Hardei came loaded with clothes. These are for Nairobilal, Bebe Hardei said laughing. They danced and sang folk songs around the fire throwing in sweets made of sesame, groundnuts and puffed rice. The baby was witnessing its first Lohri, the darkest night of Indian winter. Makar Sankranti, the harbinger of more light and sunshine, while reducing the darker aspects, was popular—even more than Diwali. *Til-gur*, sesame seeds brimming with fragrant and delicious oil, and jaggery were distributed.

They produced a baby a year. Barely a year after the birth of their first child, when Yashoda was expecting a second child, her mother, Bebe Hardei was carrying her last. It was not rare to see mothers and daughters pregnant at the same time, going through the pains of delivery consecutively. However, Bebe Hardei and Yashoda were not to share their pains, nor would they celebrate the pleasures of child-bearing. The strains in their relationship had not yet eased. Besides, Yashoda and Lajpat had moved to Thika, despite the fact that the small town had a reputation of being terrorized by hippos. In nearby Ruiru, a small dam had been constructed. By 1906, it was sufficiently powerful to supply the electricity needs of Nairobi. However, with hippos getting jammed in the connections, powercuts were always common. The dam was a pleasant place, and Lajpat sometimes came for a walk with Yashoda here.

Soon after their marriage, Lajpat had decided to end the contract that he had once signed with Lala Kirparam. Their relationship was still uncomfortable, and the salary hardly sufficient to accommodate the needs of a growing family. He found a job as postmaster in Thika. Her heavy stomach could scarcely undertake the strains of travelling, but Bebe Hardei came all the way to Thika, 41 km north of Nairobi, to see her daughter and the new grandson. In her condition, she braved the day-long journey—what would now take less than an hour. Laden with the customary gifts, she baptized her new grandson as Thikalal. Yashoda saw him as Baldev, the younger brother of Krishen. Just as in the mythology. A few weeks later, Bebe Hardei gave birth to a girl. The daughter would be a few weeks younger than her grandson Thikalal, and twenty-five years younger than her eldest son Chunilal.

* * *

Despite the racist attitude of the British towards Indians, more and more Indian women began arriving to join their husbands, which meant that they were beginning to regard as permanent their homes in the Kenyan colony. In addition, the friction between Hindus and Muslims, so pronounced in India, was virtually absent here, although intra-community competition could erupt even here.

The Arya Samaj followed undeterrred policies of distinction between itself and the Sanatan Dharam. It continued to create opportunities to advocate the strong differences between them— despite the fact that they were both Punjabis and of the Hindu fold. How their religious and cultural traditions were differentiated was vague. There was, however, a fine line between religion and culture. The basic disparity lay between being an idol worshipper or not. In this period of transition, opinions carried weight and such differences could reach fundamentalist proportions. Open confrontation was rare, but when it did take place, it remained ingrained for a long time to come.

Sometime in the Nairobi of 1928, the Arya Samaj invited two pandits for a debate. Pandit Madhavacharya was from the Sanatan Dharam camp and Pandit Buddhev Mirpuri from the Arya Samaj. The debate was to be held in the Arya Samaj School. They called it the 'Shastraarth'. The intention was to discuss the meaning behind the Shastras, the books of Hindu knowledge. They planned it with much aplomb, but the contest would be barred to women. Controversial, sexually oriented, dirty, unfit for the ears of the weaker sex, and therefore taboo. Not a single woman would question, or openly defy the ban. In any case, discussions of sexual nature were not encouraged, not even between the women themselves. But the subject was to become an exhaust valve for an overheated debate.

The highly contentious topic 'unsuitable to women' was none other than the god Shiva. It was the same Shiva over whom a question mark had been placed by Swami Dayanand, founder of the Arya Samaj many years earlier. Dayanand had then discredited the power of Shiva, and the incident had led to the birth of the Arya Samaj. The same Shiva who was worshipped by millions of men and women through the ages with fervent zeal. Women prayed to Shiva to make them fertile, to give them strength. To them, Shiva was god. A god with a double identity. And a notorious nature. Shiva was seen as the symbol of sexuality. He was also seen as an ascetic, a yogi.

Shiva the androgynous. Genderless? Sexless? Hermaphrodite? Or a controller of senses. Of desire. Who was Shiva? What did the Shastras have to say about him? How did the Sanatan Dharam and the Arya Samaj differ in their interpretations? In many ways, Shiva was the most uniquely Indian god. With an ambiguity as the great ascetic, while at the same time recognized as the erotic force of the universe. Phallus and *yoni* on the one hand symbolizing energy, fertility, potency. On the other hand, he stood in a yogic posture, with a power of sexual abstinence, penance, strength and unity. Shiva was propitious. It was left to the adept to choose the momentary profile for worship, for meditation.

They were seated on wooden chairs. The small classroom was packed. Over 300 young and not-so-young men sat on either side of the camp. They were mostly Arya Samajis. Was this going to be a one-sided affair? It remained to be seen. Up front, a small dais had been constructed, with two chairs for the contestants, Pandit

Madhavacharya and Pandit Buddhev Mirpuri. Both in their early forties and highly read in the Shastras, they looked ambitious, anticulate and ready to defend their version or aversion for Shiva as they made their entry.

Buddhev Mirapuri showed up in an ordinary *kurta* and a loose white pajama. The perhaps more arrogant Madhavacharya came clad in an elegant *kurta* and *dhot*i. A big red *tilak* mark covered his forehead. Dilating his lynx-like eyes, he paused in a theatrical manner and looked around. You knew that he was on forbidden territory. But, yes, they were all there—the big and the small, the influential and the ordinary. Then in an equally dramatic fashion, he turned his head and walked towards the podium. A trunk held in the right hand provoked suspicion. 'Books', he said in a haughty tone. All eyes followed the junior member who had been asked to put the small black trunk aside. However, a senior Arya Samaji was not convinced. Taking the trunk from the young man, he locked it away, beyond reach. The contents were later revealed to be knives of all kinds and sizes. Why the arms? The question lingered for long without any adequate response. Was it in preparation for physical combat if pushed over the edge in the intellectual defeat? They left it at that. However, the whole incident transmitted shock waves that reverberated for long, both within the Arya Samaj and the Sanatan Dharam.

The windows were small. The room was stuffy, bereft of light. In a cold and stark room, they faced each other. The contestants were not garlanded ceremoniously; the ritual orange marigold of temples was missing. Prayers were not said. The debate was launched with few formal procedures. And the tactic was one of attack and defence. It was initiated by the Arya Samaj priest, Pandit Buddhev Mirapuri.

'Your Shiva is just a sexual being. He is not a god!' Silence overtook the mutterings in the hall. The attack was offensive. 'His phallus is in constant erection; he's purely and merely a symbol of virility.' Madhavacharya fumed with rage and interrupted, digressing from the topic under discussion, 'Your *Satyarthprakash* written by your Dayanand Saraswati says that if a man stays away from home for two years, his wife is allowed to have children from another man . . . perhaps your wife also goes to others while you are away . . .'

It was a personal insult and felt like a physical injury. Buddhev swallowed the bitter words but was not going to let the Sanatani get away with it. He continued from where he had been interrupted. 'Have you read the *Shiva Purana* . . . or the *Matsya Purana*? What is the meaning of the *Shiva lingam*?' Not waiting for a reply, he continued, 'I will tell you. When a devotee enters one of your numerous temples, what is one of the first things he does? He pours water or even milk on the *lingam* of Shiva. Enter another devotee, a woman this time. She too pours water on it . . . and a third . . . and a fourth. And the process continues for as long as the doors are open and the faithful keep coming to worship. Why do they do this to Shiva's *lingam*? To keep him cool! To keep his phallus in check, for that is what the *lingam* is—Shiva's phallus in constant erection!'

There was great shock at such open discussion but the Aryan youth were clearly satisfied. They smiled smugly and shifted their chairs noisily. It was going to be better than they had expected. There was much enthusiasm, apprehension, curiosity and suspicion. The debate, more or less one-sided, heightened in its intensity. It caused varied reactions: the elderly were clearly appalled.

Buddhev was in no hurry to stop. 'Let's take a closer look at the Shiva-Parvati incident. For the benefit of those of you who don't know it, let me summarize the story. Shiva is so charged that he never leaves the poor Parvati alone, not even when she takes a bath—so much so that to protect herself from his constant advances, she creates a guardian from the dirty foam of her body'. Here his face contorted with disgust. continued. 'She names him Ganesh. To prevent intrusion, this new creature, called Ganesh, is put on guard outside the door leading to her bathroom. Shiva arrives, his *lingam* erect and in full view—as usual—ready to take Parvati. He pushes the door open. When Ganesh tries to stop him: Who are you to stop me, Shiva says, and with one stroke, he cuts off the head of Ganesh!'

To the audience, these histrionics were riveting. Doubtless, Buddhev was the more forceful contestant, in his oratory at least. But what was supposedly an academic activity had already turned nasty. 'But Mahadeva had great strength,' Madhavacharya tried to put in weakly. 'Don't blurt out whatever comes to your head,' Buddhev was in form and let it be known, 'better think carefully,' he said. He remained quiet for some time trying to make out what he might say next, and then Madhavacharya continued, 'Shiva is auspicious—without beginning or end. Undecaying, supreme, self-resplendent, He is all that has been or that shall ever be. He is eternal. Knowing him, a man overcomes death. Mahadeva is an all pervading god. He is the reproductive power, perpetually restoring that which has been dissolved. As a restorer he is represented by the *lingam,* the phallus. He is Mahadeva. He is the great god.'

Madhavacharya's explanation was totally unacceptable to the Aryan Buddhev. 'Hocus-pocus, mystifying jargon,' he spat out. Unable to defend *murti puja* (idol worship) on this scholastic level, Madhavacharya became diffident in the face of the Arya Samaj argument. It was a very tricky situation. It looked like the debate was already coming to a close. Buddhev had beaten him. Madhavacharya asked for water, but he did not drink it. Instead he threw both the glass and its contents onto his opponent. Fortunately, young Ramarakha who was sitting in the first row, caught it mid-way with the deftness of youth.

Immediately, pandemonium broke out. Someone tried to stab Ramarakha in the stomach, but he got away with minor scratches. There were loud shouts from all quarters. There were

Sanatan Dharam band in 1929

those who wanted to run away, but the doors had been quickly closed. The *dhoti-tika* Sanatanis tried to climb over the walls. But the young Aryans would not let them get away so quickly. Pulling them by their *dhotis,* they brought them down. There was much kicking and slapping. 'We are Aryans, we are Aryans . . .' the Sanatanis were heard shouting in fear for their lives, rubbing trident symbols and three-lined Shiva *chandan tikas* off their foreheads.

Suddenly, there was heavy banging on the doors from the outside. Someone had called the police. They came on horses. Silence reined once again, but this time it was different. Now they were all afraid, Sanatanis and Samajis alike. The Arya Samajis were asked to remain behind. The Sanatanis ran away, leaving their Panditji behind. The head of the Arya Samaj, Badrinath Arya, was flabbergasted. 'Is this how we treat people?' he shouted at the younger members of his congregation. They remained silent in defence. 'Go and drop Madhavacharyaji at his home, and make sure he reaches safely,' he exhorted them. Madhavacharya quietly picked up his turban and tied it round his head in total humiliation. On the way home, the boys made sure that his suffering was complete. They teased him about his *dhoti*, his *tika*, his slippers. But Madhavacharya did not utter a word. He left the country the very next day.

11

Setting up shop

You herbs, born at the birth of time, more ancient than the gods themselves
O plants, with this hymn I sing to you
Our mothers and our gods
Unharmed be he who digs you up, unharmed the man for whom I dig
Let no malady destroy the lives within your guardianship.

— Hymn in praise of herbs, Rig Veda

They swore that when the small black bug was put on the skin, it would suck out some blood and cleanse the body of all impurities. At the end of its body, a suction extractor permitted it to attach itself to the skin. Its mouth was armed with three teeth with which it made an incision. And then it sucked upto sixty grams of blood. Meet the sucker—a big, black leech to get rid of inflammation of the veins. Each morning, a few men carrying gunny sacks on their right shoulders were seen making the rounds of streets in the Indian bazaar, especially near the *pansari* shops. Their huge *sisal* sacks contained leeches. They were renowned as 'great cures of phlebitis'.

While these men were doing their rounds, Mama Radha was called upon to get rid of tonsilitis. It was said that when she took a little ash and salt between her thumb and two fingers and applied at it the back of the throat, within three days, the pus was vomited out and the pain was gone. Whoever had heard of antibiotics then? Chunibari was also adept at the same treatment. A little further on in the bazaar, sat Lall Singh. He would rub a lead pencil beneath the ears of the patient to get rid of mumps. There were many such small-time freelance healers in the Indian Bazaar; they were held in high regard. Mama Radha and Lall Singh did not even charge any fee; they did it for free. Other freelancers, *hakims* and *vaids* included, generally asked for a nominal amount—something within the reach of all.

Isher Singh Pansari, Chunibari, Chuni Sethi—the choice of *pansaris*, of herbalists and of grocers was not limited, but many years ago, Diwanchand Pansari had found himself in a compromised situation. His clientele had been forcing him to revert to his Sikh roots. Ever since Diwanchand, Kishenchand Chawla's father, had shorn his hair, his Sikh clientele began to boycott his business. Word had gone around that the once proud Diwanchand had given in to their pressure. Once again he donned his turban, the Sikh way. Diwanchand became Diwan Singh. Diwan Singh's shop started prospering once again. On retirement, he passed it on to his son Kishenchand—better known as Kicha.

Whether it was because he did not follow his father's example in changing from Kishenchand to Kishen Singh, one will never know, but the truth was that Kicha seemed less favoured by the gods where the shop was concerned. One night, much screaming was heard from inside the shop. It was in flames. By the time help arrived, the sounds had subsided. All that was left were ashes—herbs, medicines, roots, firecrackers were all gone, as was Gandamal, the servant who had no home of his own. The verandah of the shop had been the only home he had known. He worked there during the day, slept on the bare hearth at night. Gandamal perished with the rest that night. They said that his body was found near the mortar of potash as if still in the action of pounding it to make the firecrackers. The mystery would never be solved. Kicha's shop was hastily rebuilt, a few provisions were added therein and it was put up for sale immediately.

Word went around that Kicha's 'Indian Herbs and Ayurvedic Medicines' was going cheap. Kicha was in a hurry to sell his little duka with all the provisions in it. The deal looked too attractive to be ignored, and when a friend of the family, a commission agent, heard about it, she contacted Lajpat Rai, Lala Kirparam's son-in-law, straight away. 'I have saved a little money, but the shop is still way beyond my reach,' Lajpat confessed. The agent insisted on loaning him the money at a very low rate of interest. That is how Lajpat got himself a duka and became a dukawallah. Lajpat Rai left the postmaster's job in Thika and the family returned to Nairobi.

A small *puja* was held in the shop before it was opened to customers. The usual mango-leaf garlands, together with small limes and green chilli were hung outside for fertility and prosperity. And for protection against evil spirits. The priest sanctified the space with prayers and chanting; the holy fire purified the atmosphere. Relatives and friends came forward to congratulate him, but Lajpat was in a dilemma, 'Where do I start from?' he thought to himself. With a shop in hand, he suddenly realized his limitations. 'What do I know about Ayurvedic medicine? Meat heats the body, cucumber cools it, too much meat is bad in summer, dates heat the body in winter—just the few tips which most other Indians know for their day-to-day healthcare!'

Taking a deep breath, he sat down all by himself in a corner. His legs crossed one over the other, he placed his head upon his hand and looked down at the floor, deep in thought. 'Are you all right, Bauji?' someone came and touched his shoulder from behind. Lajpat looked up and brushed the man's ministrations aside with a quick, 'Yes. Yes, of course, thanks,' but cursed under his breath, 'This is certainly not like selling potatoes, or sugar. Perhaps, I have made a mistake. How can I give advice on products I know nothing about?' His thoughts depressed him even more. Slowly, however, he took courage and began considering his next step.

Little did Lajpat realize at that moment what a breakthrough this was to be—the venture would bring a new element to his life and to that of his family. It would lead them to a discovery of the world of plants and herbs. An entrance into the realms of the body, a disclosure of the effect of the seasons and temperature on physical and mental well-being, a whole new cosmos would open up before them. Books on Ayurvedic medicine were quickly ordered. *Vaids* and *unani* experts were contacted; *hakims* were engaged to read the pulse for diagnosis and proper medication.

This was when their fourth child arrived amid much colour. The noise all around quickly drowned the sounds of the newcomer. When the girl was born in their home, the rest of the *biradari* was spraying each other with coloured water. It was Holi, the first day of the Indian spring. Red and yellow powders were being thrown around. Ochre and earthern browns were being smeared on faces when the child's first cries were heard. And so most appropriately, she had come to be called Krishnaa. It was the feminine form of Krishna, the god who was very much related to spring. Some swore afterward that they could actually picture the god Krishna dancing the *raas-lila* with his *gopis*. It was a celestial symphony indeed. The god Krishna had become so much a part of the family.

The baby could have been born on 4, 10 or 13 March—no one knew for sure. Neither was it noted whether the year was 1932 or 1933. All they could remember were the festivities, the colour and the noise. And that many members of the household were fittingly dressed in the sacred yellow or orange colours. Not because Yashoda brought forth a girl into the world—on the contrary. The birth of a girl was not supposed to be an event calling for celebration. Sweets were not supposed to be distributed among the *biradari*. Even the *dai* bringing the girl into the world had refused money. 'How can you even think of offering me money?' she had exclaimed in surprise. 'Better leave it for the next time, when God willing you will have a son,' she had told Lajpat. He hadn't insisted and had just put the five shillings back into his pocket. These were the rules of the society he lived in and Lajpat did not give it a second thought.

But he did remember Hira-Mani, a girl of their neighbourhood in Bhera. She must have been younger than me, he thought. According to legend, *mani* is a jewel more precious than the diamond—a rare produce of the snake. And, when a snake does bring it into creation, it protects it ferociously, letting no harm come to it from anywhere.

In their small *mohallah* of Bhera, when Hira-Mani's mother had given birth to her—a third daughter in succession—people had mocked and made fun of the family. She's produced a girl again, they had said. But the grandmother of the newborn was a strong woman and would have none of it. Not under my roof, not while I am still alive will I allow this teasing to continue, she had said rather courageously. And she had stuck to her word. Until the day she died, she protected her granddaughter from harm, ferociously. She sheltered her from their savage taunts. I will protect her, whatever it takes, she had said. Of course, she had named her granddaughter Hira-Mani, my most precious jewel.

A paternal instinct crept on him. Lajpat felt a little bit like Hira-Mani's grandmother. From the moment he first took her in his arms, his first daughter was his favourite, and boys who complained about her were beaten instead. When he saw her smile, Lajpat's spirits immediately lifted. His drooping shoulders relaxed, as if a heavy burden had suddenly dropped off, and he began to breathe lightly. He started calling her Mani. Mani quickly got distorted to Muni, my little girl, and the name stuck. Muniye, to Bebe Gurdei, but Gogdi to her friends, 'O what a lovely little paunch has our Gogdi,' they teased. Pinching her by the cheek as hard as they could, they cajoled her but at the same time left the poor child screaming and red in the face.

Lajpat had watched with much admiration English couples promenading their young ones in prams. 'What a fantastic idea!' he had thought to himself, 'our children are always carried on hips, which is so tiring for the mother.' With the help of his two sons, they made a beautiful wooden wheelbarrow for Muni. Discarded tyres from old cars came in handy. What fun the three of them had carting her around! Yashoda would be pleading, 'It is feeding time,' but the trio took their own time. She looked at the paste of *moong dal* and *haldi*—green lentil and curcuma paste—and shouted again, 'The paste will dry up, Muni's legs must be massaged', but they were already out of view. Lajpat was happy, so excited to have a girl, that new ways to celebrate had to be devised. He even distributed coconut and *mishri*. Something hailed as scandalous for the birth of a girl, and a cause of much gossip for days on end.

Soon after, Lala Kirparam paid a princely sum—40,000 shillings, in cash—to buy a new house. He was talked about again: they sat up in awe. Lalaji is certainly a rich man, they said in admiration, having obviously forgotton by now how he had been talked about all those years ago. Kirparam was able to pay all that money in one go. For a new house on Fort Hall Road. And in a new location. Fort Hall was a recent allocation to Indians—upper class Indians.

The road marked the boundary between European and non-European residential areas. Up until 1926, the over 9,000 Indians—a third of the population—had been squashed onto 300 acres, or 4.7 per cent of the available land in the centre of Nairobi. In a struggle to get out of the ghetto of River Road and Canal Road, of the bazaar and its immediate vicinity, they challenged the political system. The lower Parklands area was largely undeveloped, and the Europeans pacified the upper class Indians with this land—at a good profit to themselves, of course. Kirparam felt happy with his new acquisition; he had correctly assessed the mood of the times.

The house was situated on the main road. On the right, the way pointed to Thika. On the left, you drove towards the main town of Nairobi. Towards River Road and Grogan Road. Towards the Bazaar. Towards Duke Street and the house that they would soon leave. Bebe Hardei's jubilance was total. She had no regrets about the move from their house on Duke Street, although even this house had its own separate garden with a huge *jamun* tree full of black berries. She felt a surge within her that she had not felt for a long time. Just the decision to move into a new area and a new house rejuvenated her.

She left the old house without any remorse, although her daughter, nearly ten years now, would continue to wax nostalgic about the *jamun* tree, even when she was well into her eighties.

Bebe Hardei demonstrated her sense of joy in ways that were possible for a woman of her times. She was definitely more relaxed, for one. She taunted less, showed more generosity. The house became Hardei's longed for luxury, one that she allowed herself. The first one, a barrack-like accommodation for railway staff, had been in the *landhis*. The next move was to Grogan Road. It had been a brick structure with corrugated iron sheeting for a roof. The house on Duke Street had been more comfortable. But this one on Fort Hall Road was better and bigger; it was special. Kirparam was never around very often, and the house soon became Hardei's own space. With it her identity emerged in full confidence. Bebe Hardei's social position rose a few notches; her esteem grew.

The front rooms served as sleeping rooms for family members. Those at the back, on the other side of the *veda* (compound), were soon rented out. Hardei's business mind had been at work once more. There was no one to question her or object to her decision. A Sikh family, a Gujarati family, Hindu Punjabi family, even a *mochi*—every tenant of Bebe Hardei belonged to a different community. When alone she did not hesitate to pass the word around; one or more of her tenants would send her a part of their meal. Sometimes, Hardei broke her fast with her Muslim friends during the month of Ramzaan. Of a careless person it was said, '*Pani pi ke jat puchhni*—asks their caste after having drunk their water.' But she had no apprehensions about dealing with various castes, or of sharing their food.

As she explained years later, 'I was not even twelve years old when things changed in our house. My maternal grandmother was very *vehmi* (superstitious). After the *churi*'s visit, she would take a bath. Even if she smelt or saw raw meat, she would take a bath. One day she fell down from the second floor of her house. A *chamar* rescued her, picked her up and brought her into the house. Since then, taboos associated with pollution and accepting food and water from different castes stopped being an issue in the family.'

In fact, Bebe Hardei did not have the time to indulge in superstitions, nor of long-drawn out conversations—so much a hallmark of the women of her generation. She did not sit around waiting for you to slowly finish your sentence. Independent, loud and clear, this was a woman in a hurry with no time to waste in any sort of useless gossip. She had a job, many jobs to handle. And she managed them fast. One marvelled at her aptitude. The speed with which she learnt to do mental accounting soon increased with ease. Even when she asked one of her children to do the calculations, in the end she relied on her own methods of computation. She was too impatient even to learn Kirparam's self-taught accounting methods that had enabled him to keep his books up to date. He had picked up the script from other traders very early, to keep account books safe from prying eyes. With an infinite possibility to multiply or divide crazy numbers, the traders' abstruse mental calculations made many heads dizzy.

Wearing a long white shirt with collars and buttons, a small-bottomed *salwar* and the white starched *dupatta* rinsed with Ricketts blue—Hardei did not present a fashionable picture. Yet, she soon saw the possibility of indulging in another business— that of haute couture. No, she did not change overnight into a fairytale princess. She remained unconcerned with aesthetic sensibilities for her own self. Perhaps her simple attire only added to her no-nonsense personality. Luxury for herself, she continued to frown upon. Why, earlier, had she not used gunny sacks as curtains?

She started dealing in bales of material for *salwar kameez*, for saris, for *dupattas*, for blouses and for petticoats. Actually, her Muslim friends had given her the idea. They themselves did not dare go out to shop. Hardei, however, had no problems being seen alone on the streets. 'Why don't you bring the bales of material to us instead so we can choose the materials ourselves,' they told her. At first she acted as an agent between the merchant and her friends. Soon she found it more convenient, lucrative especially, to set up shop herself. Bebe's confidence knew no bounds. Within no time, one of the bedrooms in the house had been converted into a duka.

White bedsheets covered mattresses; they were laid out on the floor; bolsters were stacked on the sides for comfort. It was quickly fitted out with mirrors, shelves, and little cupboards that could be locked. The new room resembled a mise-en-scene laid out for a *mushaira* session, a poetry recital, or a music concert. Her customers were only women. They were mostly Muslim women, Punjabis and Somalis. Removing their shoes before entering, the women were quickly transported to the beauty of the East. Satins and georgettes, silks and crepes adorned the whitewashed room. Colourful textiles arrived from India; they also came from China. Sequins and beads gave an added lustre. Bales of brilliantly hued *sisal* silk and satins made in Japan. In a very professional way, Hardei took out her tape to measure out the yards—five, six or even seven. She appeared to be in constant motion, exuding energy. The lady paid up. Hardei quickly put the notes into the pocket of her *kameez*. She accepted sale on credit; moreover she even took to loaning money—on commission, of course. Hardei remained a Diwan to the core, continuing to earn more money. What she did with it, one never knew.

The customers left, one by one. It was closing time. When the last one was gone, Hardei closed the door behind her. The younger children peeped from the outside, standing at the door, not daring to enter. Hardei had that authoritarian look and a heavy accented voice that sounded very definite. Her will was so physically imposing that she got others to work along as well. They were in awe of her, and perhaps a little afraid. 'Bebe *aaaiiii . . .*' the grandchildren shouted and ran away, as soon as she turned her head in their direction. She didn't even have to raise her voice at them. Double-checking that no one was about, she went towards the bales of cloth searching for her treasure box. She opened it with a little key, took out the sales of the day from her *kameez* pocket and put the money securely inside. She replaced the money box under a different bale of cloth. This was Hardei's security measure. Her step-mother in Haranpur used to hide her guineas in a gunny sack; Chachi hid her notes in a different pillowcase each time. They did not trust banks with their money.

She carried neither list nor paper; she did not know how to read or write. Details of every material in her little duka were confined to memory. Hers became a world of numbers. What she could not do in the beginning, she learnt to perfect—the art of adding and subtracting, multiplying and dividing. She educated herself in mental calculations. She learnt how to calculate cost and returns. She acquired the faculty to compound difficult calculations without the aid of pen or paper. The numbers spoke to her; they jumped or they fell. Their motions in infinite speed excited her, and gave her the sense of worth that she had once badly needed. Hardei handled and maintained the sale of her tissues all by herself. Moreover, she took care to understand the needs of her customers and fashion of the day. But she never acquired expensive habits. Content with simplicity, she simply got on with her life.

Lala Kirparam had nothing to say in the matter. He just accepted his wife's new venture as a matter of fact. He hardly ever interfered with her independence, or that of anyone else, for that matter. In any case, criticism would have only led to irritation. A 'tamarind tongue', Bebe had also earned the title of 'Mama Kali'. She commanded respect, if not downright fear. She threw out taunts, slighting remarks, not always fully understood by the younger members of the family. Not many had the strength to withstand the fury of Hardei's unleashed tongue, not even Kirparam. In any case power inside the family, even if it was paternal and patriarchal, could often be maternal in application. All that he had endured in his early years—the dependent life of an orphan at first, and later, the superhuman effort to establish himself in business—had made him a quiet, determined and taciturn man. His compact frame of five feet four inches kept within its limits of patience.

By 6 p.m. she had not returned. Kirparam would have known if she had, even without turning to look in the direction. It would have been the sound of her slippers dragging, but sure step. He got ready to cook. Sitting on a low *pidi,* a small wooden rectangular stool that he had made himself, he bent over the open charcoal fire, an iron spatula in his hand to check the status of the casserole. Invariably, the aroma of *khichri* simmering on the *jiko* drifted out all the way into the verandah. The staple food of rice and lentils, *sarson da saag* and *makki di roti*—spinach with cornflour chappatis—invited the children to join their father. *Pakoras* were reserved for cold, rainy, foggy nights. Vegetables deep-fried in a batter of gram flour with garlic chutney—no meal was quite complete without garlic. 'Your mother will not return until she has collected all her money,' he told the children, urging them to begin the meal.

Saturday was the money-collection day. Those who had not yet paid up knew that a visit from her was assured on this day. She always went on foot. From River Road up to Eastleigh, a distance of 12 km or so—even as far as the public works department *landhis,* behind the railways. She never took the bus. Why take a bus when you have two legs, and the energy to walk? Hardei considered taking the bus a waste of money. She exhibited a rare blend of rigidity and resilience in an interesting combination, fortified with a strong work ethic that was almost unmatched. In some manner, she was way beyond her time, possessing the attributes of a modern working woman. Advancing, creating or looking for avenues with upward mobility. Her strong ideas about how a business should be run—wasting nothing, not even time engaged in useless conversation—stood her in good stead.

But in equal measure, she could be downright stubborn and niggardly. Beyond being just parsimonious, she could even be stingy, with herself to begin with. Despite financial independence, Hardei was still seen in her usual white cotton *kameez* and coloured *salwar.* Her cuisine never pretended to be anything but simple. She did not take a holiday to travel to exotic destinations. She never joined her husband on his safaris into the interior. She did not even give herself a break to return to her hometown in India every once in a while. She had been back only once since her arrival in British East Africa. Hardei stayed put and worked. Day in and day out she carried on a disciplined routine.

In the end perhaps it was only business that gave her real pleasure. Every inch of Hardei's being was cut out for business. Gifted with down-to-earth shrewdness and savoir faire, possessing a strong build and a hard look—the woman had energy, lots of it. She rushed about with a passion for prosperity. It did not matter what kind of business. Even selling spare parts for a motorcar—she could have done it efficiently. Hardei had found a niche of security that she so badly needed; she had found a way in the world. Earning, dictating, creating, she had gained a strong quality of strength—like refined steel—that once eluded her. The small business became her source of freedom. It gave her a stability within; a centredness. It stopped her from thinking: 'He still has not returned'.

12

Innocence of youth

Panda pandariya kitnaka paar
Ik moothi chuk lai
Dooji tayaar

(Clenched fists on top of each other,
How weighty they are!
Like burdens and responsibilities in life,
Unending . . .
Lift one and the other is ready).

— Punjabi childhood game

'*Ingel mingel tali talingel sawa pila dakara dakare ute janj khaloti janjo uthaya tera rah pein di sawari veere de vya . . . yellow festive colours, departure of newly wedded sister, wedding of a brother, yellow festive colours . . .*' '*Kabaddikabaddikabaddi . . . .*' The long and breathless moment carried on for what seemed like ages, but what fun they were having in testing who could make it last! They were still playing in the *gullies* as the *veda* (interior courtyard) was not spacious enough. But even in the narrow by-lanes, the children always felt a little squeezed. It was okay with games like *gadam gada* when they chased around with home-made wooden bats. Before long, however, they could hear Bebe Gurdei calling from the back door, '*Sham wele hath pair nai marde! Chalo andar!*' The light of day was fading out. Evening was a time for prayers, for telling stories.

'Come my children I will tell you a story,' she repeated, entreating them to enter the house. They obeyed. They were quite fond of her, and even felt free to throw tantrums, or to tease her. '*Agle wele hik patsha aha. Usna tra puttar aha* . . . Once upon a time there was a king. He had three sons . . .' Bebe Gurdei began in Lehnda, the dialect of the Salt Range whence she came. The children were already giggling away. Her dialect sounded funny to their ears. 'Neither Bauji nor Amma speak like this,' they thought. Having grown up in Africa among Punjabis who hailed from all over the land of five rivers, Yashoda did not speak the dialect. Lajpat had lost his very early at school.

When Bebe Gurdei went visiting friends, they knew she would not return until late. Led by their elder brother, they felt free to escape beyond the confines of the *gullies* surrounding the home in the bazaar. They would play *gulli danda* in the fields. The flat piece of stick placed on a sharper one was struck far in the distance, and then hit again before letting it land on the ground. They played a bit but soon looked for other diversions and decided to play *meru danda* instead. 'Go collect flat pieces of stones of different sizes,' Krishen ordered his younger brothers and sisters, 'let us play our favourite version of cricket.' He selected the right sizes from what they had brought and laid before him, and then Krishen made a stable pyramid in the middle of the field.

'Let me start,' Baldev insisted and began by throwing the ball at the pile with full force. Instead of losing its kinetic energy, the ball whizzed through the fields to the shrubs, totally out of view. Off they all went in their rubber slippers, into the long grass and swamps in search of the missing ball. 'It couldn't have disappeared just like that,' said Baldev, feeling very guilty; he was clearly upset. 'Don't worry, we will not tell Bauji, not just yet anyway. We will continue to play with maize cobs instead,' said Krishen. It was clear though that he too was troubled. The ball was one of the few toys that Lajpat shopped for in the bazaar.

They continued long and far, but the ball was not found. It was getting quite late and Krishen marched his entourage back towards home. Suddenly, Muni jumped up with a cry, 'I have been bitten by a *dudu* (bug),' she screamed. Soon they were all scratching away. The tall grass was full of all kinds of bugs, big and small. Tears streaming down their hot, dirty cheeks, they walked on with much difficulty. The older ones braved the misery, but they too were limping.

By the time they returned home, they all looked miserable and were in obvious pain. Their feet were swollen up; parasites and jiggers had quickly burrowed a nice little colony for themselves in their bare feet. As it is, Yashoda had begun to feel anxious and had already called for Meru to go in search. Meru and Kamau, Kikuyu boys, were their two faithful servants; they had been with the family for many years. When she saw the children's state, she was appalled. A usually composed woman, Yashoda panicked. She ran looking for Kamau as well. 'They will know just what to do,' she was confident. And sure enough, with steady hands, very carefully—most torturous for the children of course—the beasts were removed with needles sterilized in the candle flame.

More children were born to Yashoda and Lajpat. Some died in childbirth, others in infancy. The children were happy in themselves, and without the burden of homework from school, it seemed as if childhood was a time for play. They had little need to look for friends outside the numerous cousins, nephews and nieces, uncles and aunts in the family—who visited often, each weekend, in fact.

Lajpat looked at the long plaits of his adolescent sons, a little shocked. As if he was seeing them for the first time. About time they were shorn, he decided. Between them, Lajpat and Yashoda finally agreed on a date.

Krishen and his younger brother only learnt about the decision a few days prior to the event. As the day drew closer, their anxiety increased. How would they go to school? Other boys were sure to make fun of them, tease them to death. When the day finally dawned, they hid themselves in the fields. The *nai* had already arrived for the head shaving ceremony. The *muhurat* was passing. 'I must begin the rites soon,' the waiting Sanatani pandit said

The extended family in 1948: Seated, L to R: Ramlubhayi, newly weds Padma and Krishen, Lajpat Rai, Yashoda, Gurdei. Muni stands behind her father Lajpat.

anxiously. But the boys were nowhere to be seen. Relatives of the family began to take their places around the *havan kund*. The priest started arranging the small pieces of wood to light the sacred fire. The entire house was searched. Under the beds, behind the cupboards, amongst the sacks of lentils and rice—but they were still missing. The family was in a frenzy. When they were finally discovered, they were happily playing cricket far out in the fields, their fear forgotton. They were brought back by force, bound and tethered.

Thence onto the ceremony they were desperately trying to avoid. The *mundan samskar*, removal of the hair connected with the womb. The last trace of impurity connected with birth that had to go. Usually performed during the first five years of childhood, the ritual could only be executed at an auspicious time, decided by the priest according to astrological charts. Somehow, every favourable time seemed to arrive at a wrong time for the family; there were always other more urgent issues at hand—death of a relative, a visit to Nyeri—and so it went on for many years. Actually, neither Yashoda nor Lajpat were scrupulous about these rituals. But Bebe Gurdei was, especially so—what with her very networked social linkages, it would have been too shameful otherwise. She would surely lose face.

Prayers were said, Vedic mantras chanted. The ceremony had to be quickened, cut short because the auspicious time was almost over. Planets were worshipped to obtain favourable omens. The *nai* held the young boy's head between his knees. Thick long plaited tresses fell on the ground as he knelt in front of the barber; Yashoda's heart almost missed a beat. She had oiled and braided her son's hair every morning, all these years. Now she blocked off the view with the edge of her sari, it was too painful to look. The barber—who did not cut ladies' hair—went over the head mercilessly, several times; finally the shave was really smooth. Cut for the first time—all of it, the hair was tied in a redcloth and later thrown into the Thika Falls. Yashoda was already imagining her sons' hair flowing into the Tana river—Kenya's longest river—

draining off the slopes of Mt Kenya and the Aberdare Range—
and finally becoming a part of the Indian Ocean north of Malindi.
She would cry herself to sleep that night.

Bathed and dressed in new white clothes offered by Bebe
Hardei and Paya Kirparam, their maternal grandparents, the boys
looked like young monks. Brahmacharis ready for retreat into
the forest. Soon they were turbaned and a red *tilak* applied on
their foreheads. Nairobilal and Thikalal were born anew. Bebe
Hardei looked pleased, as did Bebe Gurdei. The two grandmothers
congratulated each other, but other than that they kept out of
each other's way. The barber was offered clothes and money as
shagun. Bebe Gurdei also blessed her grandsons with gifts and
money. She was a proud woman today. Every traditional ceremony
performed in her house gained her a place of honour, especially
amongst her beloved friends; they all came forward to congratulate
her. The oldest male member present offered everybody little
brown packets of *boondi*—gram flour balls coated in syrup.

The Dawoodi Bohra group. Visa Oshwal community. Bengali
Association. Ramgarhia Board. Konkani Muslim community.
Patel Brotherhood. Parsi Anjuman. Parsi Zoroastrian Association.
Arya Samaj. Aga Khan Foundation. Shree Wanza Union. The list
was endless. They organized themselves around small units of
family or religious associations. Their social connections hovered
around common linguistic-regional-religious groups. The various
Indian sub-communities more or less kept to themselves. Each
separate community and its institution was more significant in the
daily lives of most of its members than the 'Indian community' as
a whole. The crystallization of caste and community in early Kenyan
history was the result of complex interaction between the Indian
cultural tradition, the compartmentalization of colonial society and
conscious British policy. The political party Kenya India Congress
never managed to unite them all.

Each association used its meagre resources to establish separate
services, such as schools, hospitals and burial grounds. Their focus
on commerce enabled them to survive many challenges and crisis,

also contributing greatly to the city's development, but because they didn't have the zeal of the Christian missionary (and also were not allowed), they were unable to share their lifestyles or thinking. With the collapse of the Indian initiative in politics in the Kenya of the 1920s, British officials increasingly dealt with leaders on a communal basis. The government began encouraging the formation of such associations by providing land for communal buildings.

The day the Arya Samaj benefited from a land grant from the government for the construction of a girls school, a great community festival was organized. They all came in their best attire. The mayor of Nairobi was invited to inaugurate the ceremonies. To welcome him, the Arya Samaji *pehelwan*, muscle-man, took up his bow and arrow and shot a garland around the mayor's neck as he was stepping out of his car. During the few seconds before the crown of flowers could embellish his broad torso from the heavens above, as it were, the Lord Mayor's eyes popped out in utter disbelief. He stood traumatized. The shock of the approaching arrow immobilized him completely. It landed. And the man's squat body gave a sigh of relief. Fortunately, he hadn't ducked in the process. The orange flowers that struck his neck, contrasted starkly with the white face that had turned red by this time. The garland had landed just where it was intended—much to the shock of the white man and his entourage. His nose twitched at the unpleasantly bitter odour from the sacred bouquet. The garlanding ceremony was thankfully over.

The Arya Girls School that had sown its seeds very early had taken deep root. By the time Yashoda admitted her daughter to the school, the new building was ready. She was only six at the time. It was here that she received her first lessons. On the very first day, the young girl got to wear her new uniform. How proud she felt of herself in her striking yellow frock! She even had new leather shoes for her little feet, which for several nights she took to placing carefully right next to her pillow. Her mother oiled and plaited her hair into one braid—two was considered too fashionable. A small white handkerchief folded into a neat little triangle hung below the upper right shoulder of her bright yellow frock with a tiny gold pin. Yashoda did not walk her girl to school. At seven in the morning, the teacher came herself. Durga Penji's additional duty was to collect the younger girls living on this side of town, and drop them back at noon.

No special fuss was made over the new venture in the young girl's life. On the contrary, every moment was one filled with play. From River Road to Ngara, Muni ran with the other children while Durga Penji tried to keep up, shouting every now and then '*ahista, ahista* . . . slow down, slow down'. But the girls did not pay heed. The dukawallahs had just begun opening their stores to customers, or were in the process of preparing their wares—*gunias* full of lentils of all colours and shapes, rice, sugar, wheat, dried red chillies, dates, aniseed. As they ran along, the girls splashed the produce from the *gunias* into the air, not daring to look back. Not even when the men shouted back at them: they just ran faster. Holding their shoes in their hands, or the strings tied around their necks, often preferring to walk barefoot. During the rains, the mud was damp and difficult to walk on, and they did not want to be seen arriving at school with dirty shoes.

Muni was made an example of cleanliless and hygiene for all the other girls in the class to see and emulate. Her nails were clean and she had a handkerchief, which of course she never used—not even when her nose ran. Moreover, being a shy child, she was embarassed to even ask for the toilet the first time; she relieved herself behind the school walls! She looked up and saw the older girls looking from the upper floors, laughing down at her. Muni was so ashamed that she never had the courage to look at them again; she walked with her head down. Her slate fell and broke. But she dared not cry.

'*Ek dooni do, do dooni char* . . .', the loud chorus came from one of the classes reciting arithmetic tables in poetic fashion from far. Swaying their heads up and down, reciting their lessons to themselves at the top of their voices, curricular life at school followed the rhythmic pattern—as did their lessons in *pahare*. The multiplication table, the alphabet, literary text, everything was memorized and chanted out aloud. Muni was already familiar with this way. That is how she had seen her brothers pretend to study from their *qaida*. They were even encouraged to cram English lessons.

'Look *dekho*, pigeon *kabutar*, *uran* fly, *asmaan* sky . . .' Hadn't she and her younger sisters often sat cross-legged on the floor, tightly oiled plaits swinging along with their heads, imitating one of them. 'Mother is cooking, child is sleeping, father smoking a pipe, birds are chirping . . .' Muni never felt tired of going through the brothers' *qaida* over and over. They were full of beautiful drawings, she had thought then. How she had admired them! Of mother cooking by the fire while father was working or resting or smoking. A child slept in the cot. In fact the girls spent more time discovering this world than the boys ever did; they only laughed at these silly pictures that they had to learn from.

Cramming, memorizing, learning by heart—that was the way to study. Like Indian poetry, repetition was the rule. Whether they were verses for incantation or lessons for school, the subject had to be circulated in the mind, until it produced an appropriate emotive response. Newspapers were also read out aloud. This culture of sound, with its precision in repetition at exact intervals, over and over, again and again, supposedly permitted the sound to act upon the inner personality, to transform sensibility, way of thinking, the state of the soul, and even moral character. Learning by repetition was supposed to influence the sub-conscious mind from which everything profound and enduring emanates. Before the total entrenchment of western education, Indian children absorbed the learning process through this resonant world of sound—supposed to have metaphysical power. They learnt by looking and listening. By imitating, they were developing a hyper-sensitivity to the dynamism of the auditory world.

Diction was given a special place in Vedic chanting. Reciting the Vedas began almost immediately on entry. As young as six,

Muni was already able to chant complex hymns from the *Rig Veda*. Details of the ritual, and recitation with the right intonation from the Vedas—all these were requisites of the curriculum. The right sounds, in the right combination, uttered in the right sequence and with the right inflection. The hymns when recited properly were supposed to have power. The influence of sound on their consciousness would supposedly help to orient their perceptual centres towards the inner acoustic spaces of the unseen.

The Arya Samaj was a Hindi medium school. The curriculum included Hindi, Indian history, knitting, cookery and painting. English was only introduced after the sixth standard. All classes and instructions were conducted in Hindi. Any other language— Punjabi, Gujarati, and English included—was severely discouraged, except during the special language courses. So strict was the rule that a disobedient student was fined ten cents. The boys who went to the Government Indian Boys School were neither taught the Vedic rituals, nor did they have lessons in Hindi. Their classes were conducted in Urdu. The Punjabis, with no written script of their own—not until the Sikhs invented one for themselves—spoke Punjabi, but wrote in Urdu or Hindi. Like other girls, Muni was not taught the Urdu script at school. Considered a man's language, it was reserved for male students at the boys' school. As the man Muni married many years later could not read a word of Hindi, any written communication between them had to go through others!

Muni arrived at school at 8 a.m., as usual. Havan would begin in a few minutes. The first hour of each morning was reserved for chanting hymns from the Vedas around the fire altar with a priest conducting the ceremony. She sat in the half-lotus position on the *dhurrie,* and learnt the mantras and practice of the rituals by watching the older girls. Neither priest, nor any other teacher was present that day. On Wednesdays, they were left to their own devices. It was a day off from studies, but they had to come especially to perform the *havan.* The older girls were encouraged to conduct the ceremony all by themselves. Sometimes, they decided to have fun instead, even though they were conscious that tampering with the revered rites could land them in trouble, should they ever be caught. Apparently, the risk was worth the pleasure.

One Wednesday morning, as usual, the little girls gathered together in their bright yellow frocks, the older students in yellow saris, at eight in the morning. They lit the sacred fire, closed their eyes, folded their hands and began chanting. In the middle of the *sandhya* mantras, whispering was heard amongst the sari-clad older girls, which quickly gave way to giggles. There was much shifting and changing of places. Sets were made as they paired in partners. The students had been grouped into two parties—the bridal party and the groom party. They were going to have fun enacting a Vedic marriage ceremony amongst themselves. The seniormost student agreed to play the role of a Vedic pundit.

'Repeat after me,' commanded the girl 'priest' to the 'bride', and she did so. '*Om maduparko madhuparko madhuparkaha prati grihyatam*'. The 'bridegroom' accepting the pot of curd and honey from the hand of the 'bride' also repeated after the 'priest', '*Om pratigrihnami.*' Just as the 'groom' took the right palm of his 'bride' in his left hand, and they got up to circumambulate the fire, a strong male voice was heard in the distance. The school inspection team had turned up. You can imagine what punishment the senior students got. They were interrogated individually, and the initiators expelled. It was a harsh punishment.

She was made of brown cloth and stuffed with cotton wool. Her hair was plaited out of black cotton wool. A small red dot for *bindi* cut out from red cloth was stitched in the middle of her forehead. She wore a sari and a blouse. *Guddi* took on the air of an Indian woman. How beautiful, Muni said, ecstatic when Yashoda handed her the doll. Muni loved her the moment she held her in her arms. 'What lovely plaits she has, Amma,' she exclaimed again and again. She had not seen her mother working at it and it came as a surprise. Immediately, she insisted on showing it off to her friends, so she invited them home on Wednesday afternoon when they were all off from school.

'Look what my mother made for me!' A beautiful *guddi*, they all agreed. One of the girls had brought her *gudda* along. Join together the *guddi* and *gudda*, and then a child will be born, Yashoda told them. She enjoyed playing *guddi patola* with her daughters, but since the friends were here, she left them to play on their own. 'Why don't we get *guddi* and *gudda* married?' suggested the girl who had brought her male doll along. 'Yes!' exclaimed Munni excitedly, that way a child can be born. And so preparations began in earnest.

Yashoda had a lot of fun stitching tiny little clothes for *guddi*'s trousseau. She even bought her the dowry—utensils, small furniture, cups and plates—all the items necessary for the wedding. Invitations were sent out for real. Many friends and cousins were invited for lunch. The ceremony, held in the *veda*, went off very well. Without doubt, it was a most colourful occasion. Everybody came dressed in their best clothes. Muni, of course, insisted on wearing a sari, her mother's lovely red one. Yashoda tucked it in here and there, but the *pallu* kept coming off her left shoulder. The little girl wondered how women managed to keep it in place, but she would not complain to her mother. She could hardly walk in it, but kept these small issues to herself, for just then she was all grown up, and had to act the part. She suddenly felt so much older than her six years. And important—after all, she was the mother of the bride.

It was late in the evening. The rituals and the feast were long over. The young girls were preparing to leave. However, the girl who had brought her *gudda* would not leave. She insisted on not only taking away the beautiful doll made by Yashoda, but the dowry as well. Shocked and dismayed, Muni stood, erect against the wall, a silent observer to the pillage of what was so precious to her. She watched her *guddi* being taken away, together with all the clothes that she and her mother had so carefully and lovingly prepared over endless days.

The radiant china set was also going, the white cups with flower designs on them. The small rolling pin, the *karhai* and the frying pan—they were all being taken away right in front of her. And there was nothing she could do to stop it. She could not fight, she was even too numb to cry. Her eyes remained dry; not a drop flowed. Of course, after it had all ended, and they had left, she let it all out. She sat in a corner and cried, shedding precious little tears all by herself. Yashoda looked at her with pain in a corner of her heart. Is this how I will feel when my Muni is taken away from me? she wondered. A teardrop ran down her cheek.

13

Community living

Dab ke wah te raj ke kha
(Work hard and eat to your satisfaction)
—Punjabi proverb

'*T oba, toba*!' (Bad omen, bad omen) Bebe Gurdei exclaimed. Her hands automatically covered her ears; alternatively they went on her mouth—as if to shut away the devil. Some human hair—for one rarely, if ever, found cats or dogs kept as pets in Indian homes—was found lying on the floor of the kitchen. She quickly picked the hair up and turned it around her index finger. She stuffed it into little cracks in the wall and put it out of her sight. 'Who has been in the kitchen?' she screamed. There was no answer. Bebe kept on muttering under her breath for the sight of hair in the kitchen, perhaps entering the food, disturbed her tremendously.

At the far end of the *veda* (compound) stood a small box-like structure with a *mabati* tin roof. This was the kitchen whose back formed part of the compound wall. One did not worry about thieves coming in to steal, even though the wall surronding the *veda* was low enough to jump over easily. In fact many times the children did just that—jump over the wall to enter the house from the back. The kitchen was very small, just a store, actually. *Sufurias* and other cooking utensils lay outside in the verandah. Gleaming brass vessels set out to dry in the noonday sun lay neatly arranged in the small passageway. Each family had a similar kitchen. Bebe Gurdei kept hers very clean—for it was more hers than it was

Yashoda's. Bebe Gurdei ruled the roost in the kitchen. And one dare not enter with their shoes on in Bebe's kitchen, or most other Indian kitchens.

The kitchen was a woman's domain, her area. Here she could have her say. Who ate what and . . . when. Since Gurdei did not go out visiting in the morning, she had made it her privilege to prepare the mid-day meal. It was always black gram, *mungre* (seed-pod of radish) or some very bitter vegetables, cooked in a watery curry. *Karela*, or bitter gourd, was edible, even sweet compared to what Gurdei cooked. They are good for your health, she said. The children abhorred these, but did not complain to Bebe Gurdei, and quietly swallowed the curries with the chapatis which they loved. However, they did grumble to their mother when Bebe Gurdei was not around. 'She never uses onions, not even tomatoes in her cooking—totally bland food!'

Sitting on her *pidi*, Bebe cooked leisurely over the *jiko*. From time to time, she bent down to blow into the charcoal fire, and when the smoke went into eyes, she cursed it as well. How different from Yashoda, who never uttered a word of complaint about getting smoked, or acquiring watery eyes from cutting endless onions. For Bebe Gurdei, every *rasa*, every condition of life, every feeling was given its full expression. When she cried, she gave herself to sorrow in its entirety, when she laughed, she could be heard far away. Even when she sneezed, she opened out her lungs to their maximum capacity.

Bebe Gurdei also sang. And when she did, it was with a voice full of emotion, even when she was out of tune—which was more often than not. She chanted while cooking, walking, waking up in the morning, collecting flowers for her gods, or preparing her *puja* room. Anything, a *bhajan, kodi, tappa*; the voice resounded with a calm passion. Bebe Gurdei had no guru, nor the ability to read. She was certainly not cut off from spiritual tradition—penetrating the receptive mystic as if by osmosis. Devotional songs, religious theatrical representations, especially the *Ramlila*, provided her with a rich background of traditional culture.

Bebe looked up and called out to Annadevi, '*Rijak de*', she said bowing her head a little, 'Annadevi *sabda pala kar*.' She gave thanks to the goddess of grain and harvest. Eating food was not first of all an act of pleasure. It was *anna*. An act of giving energy to the body and Annadevi made it possible. The first small chapati was thrown into the fire. This is for the ancestors, she muttered to herself. Perhaps, it was also to avert the evil eye. May my children eat in peace, she said. Sometimes, Bebe also burnt two red chillies in the open fire to blow away the evil present in the home, especially when someone in the family was ill, or when there were financial problems. She reminded you of a Vedic priest offering substances to the fire. She bent closer to the small opening and blew into the *jiko* to increase the flame. Little sparks flew out and smoke went into the eyes. She cursed the rusting metal burner.

Male members of the family rarely, if ever, entered the kitchen. Lajpat had never gone into this one, neither had the boys. If they needed anything, they just had to ask for it. They could ask Bebe Gurdei. Or they asked their mother, Yashoda. Usually, they ordered their sisters to fetch it for them. The kitchen was so small that only one person could enter at a time. They could obviously not eat inside. Meals were served just outside the small store-like kitchen in the verandah, facing the kitchen door. Even here, there was not enough room for the whole family to sit together. Not unless they covered the common verandah, but this was for all the residents.

The sound of mustard seeds cracking in the hot oil, the aroma of asafoetida and curry leaves brought about an insatiable hunger. Lajpat was the first to be served. Gurdei and Yashoda were usually the last ones to eat. They ate together, but in silence, never having anything to say to each other. Theirs was a quiet meal. The uneasy relationship was not entirely uncommon. Daughter-in-law–mother-in-law affairs, *saas-noo* as they said, with its uptightness and tensions had since time immemorial been a subject of umpteen stories, folk tales, songs and jokes.

Gurdei made hot chapatis for her son and for the rest of the family, but preferred leftover ones from the night before for herself.

'*Bai* roti has a special taste all of its own, it has had time to mature overnight,' she said. Lajpat burped. Bebe offered him another chapati and when he refused, she insisted, 'You have only reached halfway through your meal,' and kept the chapati on his plate. Lajpat ate it, even if he didn't want it. It was a good moment for Gurdei to share her frustrations with her son—to gossip, to complain. Lajpat listened in silence, going mechanically through the motions, nodding his head every now and then. He knew that his mother needed to talk. It did her good psychologically, and eased any tensions in her. Often, he commented generously on the quality of the food, his hands enjoying the texture of the rice grains or the feel of the roti. Even if it was not really to his liking, he did not say a word of disapproval. He got up, Bebe handed him some water from a basin to wash his hands. As soon as he had finished, the children were called to eat.

They were starving, and noisily sat down on the low stools. Brass plates were laid on the floor. Only one plate had a spoon. This was for Muni. Muni could never get used to eating with her fingers like the rest. Bebe didn't understand where she had picked up this custom from. 'We have always eaten with our fingers. Such *nakhra*!' Bebe Gurdei scolded. 'You don't know what you are missing,' she said trying to encourage Muni to change the habit. 'The taste of food changes when you are in direct contact with it, when you can feel its texture. Then its nature is revealed to you.' Muni had heard Bebe say this many times before and didn't pay any attention. She had no problem with eating the dry chapati with her fingers. Like everybody else, she dug into her vegetables with a morsel of the chapati with her hand also—but dipping her fingers into the curried lentils and rice, somehow she couldn't do that. Many years later, the day Muni was married, soon after the wedding ceremonies were over in fact, Bebe Gurdei had warned the bridegroom, 'Make sure Muniye has a spoon at meal times. She has never been used to eating with her fingers.' Muni had almost died with shame then.

Hot lentils and vegetables were served. Bebe made a very big chapati, cut it up into quarters with her hands and put a piece in each *thali*. Chapatis did not take long to puff up, especially when thrown over coals. Then they came out perfect, round, soft, with small black dots all over. The first one was gone even before she had started rolling another. With deft fingers, she picked up the rolled pastry and threw it on to the hot iron pan. It was ready in no time.

They kept eating, she kept cooking. 'Hurry up Bebe, we are still hungry,' Krishen complained. 'You are swallowing your food, chew it properly.' She cursed the lot for eating so many. If ever rice was served for lunch, which was rare, they ate and ate, but never seemed to get satisfied; it was as if they had not eaten anything substantial. These were wheat eaters. Rice was only a side dish, not a part of the main meal. Bebe buttered the chapatis for the adolescent boys, sometimes fried them in ghee, and also added extra butter in their lentils, but completely denied her granddaughters any such indulgence. 'You are *paraya dhan*, the wealth of another. We can't show you much attachment,' she said naively but firmly. 'You must not get spoilt by these luxuries, for when you go to your in-laws and are deprived of them, you will suffer. Moreover, boys work hard, their bodies require more fuel.'

By the time the children left, she had already filled out a huge brass tumbler with milk. You could see that she did not rule out the small luxuries for herself. The tumbler had abstract and floral designs etched on it. The *bilori* (as she called it) remained her constant companion. Brass was already going out of fashion, but Bebe would change neither the brass tumbler, nor brass plates for shiny stainless steel ones. She kept hers—from her Bhera days—till the end. Unevenly curved at the edges and almost malleable with age, she kept her old brass plate and bowl carefully in a corner of the kitchen, out of reach of the others. These she washed carefully herself with the dry leftovers of tamarind husk. Her trunk was stuffed, for she never threw old things away. It was impossible to discuss Bebe without mentioning her eccentricities. She was like a museum of the souvenirs of her time. And nostalgia— which to you or me may seem pathetically unimportant.

Pouring thick cream from yesterday's milk, together with blanched, peeled almonds and three teaspoons of sugar, she drank with infinite pleasure. Often she spoke out aloud to herself, thanking all the gods, especially with the first sip of water. Thanking and cursing in the same breath very often. 'O *haramzada*, why did you go away,' her thoughts went to her younger son. 'You were a good boy, what happened . . .' She would utter small lamentations. 'Why don't you leave me in peace . . . even this wheat and water will not pass through my throat.' She contined to eat and drink in the same breath.

Bebe's second-born had died an alcoholic, just like his father. The grandchildren often remembered how their uncle would buy a whole case of drinking glasses and ask them to be broken. Putting Lajpat's eldest born on his knee, he would say, Krishen, these are for you. Now shatter them to pieces. The children of course found it fun for a while, but often wondered whether their uncle really loved the sound of breaking glass. 'A broken glass is a good omen,' he said, but Yashoda would have none of it—when she could have her way that is.

Yashoda and Lajpat brought up their children—boys and girls— with equal affection. Bebe openly spoilt the boys, although she conjured up a tantrum if any of them wasted food, or left behind morsels on their plates. The girls would cry to their mother, who would quietly, but willingly, yield to their desires, no sooner was Bebe out of the way. So they started looking forward to the afternoons, the time when Bebe went visiting. Amma will surely prepare us some delicacies, they thought.

Muni never made a fuss with Bebe Gurdei over the inequalities of food distribution, but she was not denied her fair share either, nor were the other sisters. Promptly, as the sounds of Bebe's footsteps disappeared, Yashoda in her quiet way took to making peas and potatoes with lots of onion and tomatoes. She kneaded the dough lovingly, put some ghee on it, turned it over to begin again the kneading process. It was nice and soft now. The *paronthas* with lots of ghee would be crisp; the children would love them, she was sure. And she was right. While one wanted Amma's thick fried chapati square in shape, another requested a round one.

Muni's *parontha* had to be triangular. Dipping into the pea and potato curry, she bit off a morsel. 'Crisp and hot, most inviting, just the way I like it.' She hugged her mother. Yashoda looked at her daughter and smiled. One was reminded of the time when god Krishna's mother, Yashoda, saw the whole world in his mouth. Cooking on tirelessly, fulfilling their needs, such was Yashoda's unspoken love. She took a steel pot, filled it with water and soaked lentils and red kidney beans for the next day.

Often called '*Mama Mungu*', woman of god, what Yashoda lacked in the way of a passionate, excitable temperament, she compensated for with compassionate attributes. Her pain would shift from a focus upon herself to a destitute other. *Mama Mungu* was always there in time of need. Kimau knew it, and Meru knew it. All the passers-by in the back lane of the house—the vendors and the toilet cleaners, the house workers—knew they could rely on her for medicines, food, or other small mercies. Clients at dukas came to her, as did near and far relatives; the children of course ran to their mother when they were hurt, when they needed money. *Mama Mungu* never turned away her face, or said 'No'. She went out of her way to help.

She did not go out visiting friends or neighbours. Yashoda was not an exceptionally sociable person. She spoke sparingly, confining herself to the needful. Neither gossip nor irrelevant chatting formed a part of her personality. Besides the daily walk to her mother's house, her days were generally spent in the vicinity of her home, with all the workload that came with it. While she restricted her social life, she expanded her reading repertoire. She enjoyed all kinds of books. Why Lajpat had stopped teaching her after they were married, one could not say for sure, but it is quite probable that married life brought many responsibilities. Of course children were born soon after. However, from the little that she had learnt from Lajpat before they were married, Yashoda continued to expand her Urdu. She taught herself to read and write Gurmukhi and Gujarati. Many years later, when she went to England she could even speak, read and write a smattering of English. Yashoda hid herself behind books. She also started talking to her diary.

The veranda was not lit; it was pitch dark, and Bebe Gurdei had bad eyesight. Therefore Yashoda cooked at night. The sound of the brass plate against the floor announced dinner. Once again, the children ran to eat. Yashoda did not shout out of respect for the other families living in the compound. They were the Pindidasses and the Sharmas, amongst others.

Pindidass soon came to be called 'Harey Coatwallah'. Morning or evening, he was to be seen in his famous green coat. It was parrot green, and shone in the noonday sun. Each morning, he turned out in his green coat. Before stepping into the common courtyard, he would flick the index finger of his right hand with his thumb on his beautiful coat as if to remove a trace of dust. Then he would slightly pat his black hair. Not a single hair on his head was out of place. They were all Perewales (Punjabis tend to soften their 'b' to 'p'), Bharochis from Bhera. Being the oldest Perewali in the compound, Bebe Gurdei was given utmost respect— so much so that the younger women treated her as their *saas*, the common mother-in-law. The Perewaliyan touched her feet in the morning, brought her *prasad* from the temple, the sacred food that had first been offered to the gods. They came to her with their small problems. Bebe Gurdei was a proud woman here. She helped resolve little misunderstandings and disputes that sprang up in the *veda*. However, the interminable, continuous and everlasting clashes between Veerawali and Chunibari, not even the likes of Bebe Gurdei could bring an end to. Not until one of them had finally given up and left the *veda* for good.

These two tenants couldn't stand the sight of each other. As soon as the one glimpsed the other, they were stirred into uncontrollable aggression. Bereft of shame, they were unable to contain themselves, not even in front of the communal matriarch. Endless arguments were heard loud and clear at various times of the day. It was feared that they would come to blows—even if the one was a man, and the other a woman of some respectability. Some tenants enjoyed listening to the nonsense, laughing over it long afterward. Others just smiled; mostly however, they ignored them, leaving them to thrash it out. They had all given up after a few futile tries.

Everybody had by now, it seemed, reconciled to them. The first time that Bebe had tried to dissuade them, another neighbour had intervened. 'Go your way Bebe,' he had told her. 'These are extremely crude people.' It was not like Bebe Gurdei not to intervene, and she didn't like what was going on. The pair looked so stubborn and beyond reach that even she had thrown her hands up at the end. However, each time Bebe heard their audacious battle, she wondered how she could put a stop to the excesses that did not seem to shame one another.

The tiny one-bedroom houses in the compound faced one another. Nasty, loud and unkind remarks were thrown at each other from windows, seemingly protected by the security of their own space. However, the common compound was polluted by their noise when they gave vent to their egos, for the rest of the *vedewallahs* to hear. It was often she who taunted him into it.

One day, the notorious spitfire screamed at Chunibari's window. 'You are just a shameless, naked man. Completely bereft of respect—for yourself or for others.' Veerawali's vicious words came out loud and clear. 'Is that so?' Chunibari straightened up, stimulated by the comment. 'Then come out, and I will show you.' She stormed out of her house—unsuspecting of what was to follow. Chunibari was already there waiting for her in the middle of the compound, his pajama and shirt hanging loose on him. 'If you think that I am shameless, then I will show you.' Immediately, he stripped off his pajamas and shirt; they lay at his feet. Then he removed even his underpants.

Veerawali had overstepped her limits; she was now paying the price. Those who were watching the drama were horrified. Veerawali went red with shame. The look on her face was one of awe. Not only her eyes, but even her mouth lay open, exposed to the horror of the spectacle. For once in her life, she ran out of words. For a whole minute there was total silence. As soon as her senses returned, she ran to her house to narrate the episode to her husband. '*Nak wadta! Nak wadta*! Cut my nose in front of all, disgraced me . . . *Mein kya*, I implore you to remove your underpants in front of Chunibari's wife. The man must be put to as much embarrassment as he has done to me . . .' 'Are you mad?' the husband screamed at his wife. For a few days, Veerawali had literally been 'shut up'; she kept away from Chunibari.

For a long time the compound continued to remain a territory of Perewales. As they prospered, however, they slowly moved out of the River Road compound to other new plots allocated to Indians by the colonial government. With Military Singh and Charchoor Singh's arrival, the atmosphere had already started changing. Then came Polu Singh; he had recently arrived from India and married a 'half-caste' woman from the Meru area. Everybody called her *chotara*. The Indian-African hybrid felt comfortable neither with the Africans, nor was easily accepted by the Indians. But Polu seemed satisfied; he was even proud of her. He had her dressed up as a woman of Punjab in *salwar kameezes* of loud colours, especially red. Or she was seen in shiny gold and silver. She could not, or dared not, out of fear of being ridiculed, speak a word of Punjabi, even though one could sense that she had gained familiarity with the language and was beginning to understand it. For the moment, however, Polu contented himself by communicating with his new wife in the broken Swahili that he knew. Every Sunday Polu put on his white startched *kurta*-pajama. Ready to take his wife to an Indian film, in his *thanda* suit.

At the time of these events, only five families were left in the compound on River Road. Each family had only one, maximum two bedrooms. Lajpat was one of the lucky ones. At least they had two rooms—one for his mother. Muni and her younger sister slept with the parents. The brothers slept outside, on their side of the common courtyard. Here Lajpat had added a small *mabati* roof. Privacy in the courtyard remained minimal; few events escaped the eye of the other. On the tampered earth stage and the walled courtyard were enacted all the major dramas of family life cycles.

Gone were the days of familiarity, or of comradeship. Gone even were the days of a common language. The likes of Military Singh, or Charchoor Singh, or Polu Singh had at least had one thing in common with the Perewales of the previous days; they all spoke Punjabi. It had mattered less that the language was diluted, or enriched—depends on which way they looked at it—with regional variations. At least communication had been possible, they often said. The dwindling tribe of Perewales began to keep to themselves in the compound. Different communities their brought their own rules.

'*Kholo, gusalkhana kholo*! Free up the bathroom!' Bebe yelled several times. She knocked furiously on the door. Obviously, the occupant was intent on taking more than his share of time. 'Bath' and 'Toilet' written on the doors in English were common to all the five families, which meant that one had to queue. The queues often got long and quite unfriendly. At times they ended in mini-battles. For sure, none of the families actually timed the number of minutes the other took in the bath, or in the toilet, but the fuming, the rage, the desperate and incessant knocking on the door and eventually the drama of words and bad-mouthing was warning enough of a denouement being overdue.

The door opened with a slight creak; iron hinges shone red with rust. '*Hain*, so long you took in the bath Rasik . . .' in her heavily accented Punjabi, Bebe Gurdei scolded the emerging young man. A *lungi* hung loose around his slim waist, a dirty old towel over his shoulder. The small bar of Lifebuoy soap in one hand was still dripping; an old tin can, left over from some paint job, was in the other. '*Maaf karna* Bebe, sorry,' Rasikbhai apologised in broken Hindustani, 'today I took longer than usual'. 'Why, going to see someone special', another young man teased him shamelessly in front of Bebe Gurdei. Rasikbhai did not like it, but he did not say anything. He spat and started drying his dripping shoulder.

The spit landed on the feet of an aging and balding man. '*Saala gandhiyo*,' the round man screamed back in Gujarati. '*Arre* who does this *majnu* think he is. First he takes extra time in the bath, now this. Have you taken leave of your senses . . . in search of Laila . . . hehehe . . .', they all burst out in laughter. Rasikbhai rushed off to his quarters, blushing red in the face. Yashoda pretended she had heard nothing. She turned on the common tap in the *veda*. She would rather bathe her small son right here, just outside the bathroom. Handing her mother-in-law the bucket of hot water, she quickly put on another empty *debe* on the coals for the next person. Bebe rushed into the bath.

When women got up very early, they usually bathed outside the bathroom. It was still too dark inside and there was no switch for a light. At least there were stars, or a fading away of darkness at five in the morning. But Yashoda dare not be seen having a bath outside in full view. Moreover, she hated conflicts of any kind, and was usually the first one up and about, sometimes as early as 4 a.m.

It was still dark. The birds had not yet started their chirping. Stretching her limbs to get her body to awaken, she yawned with fatigue; she had not had much sleep. But it was hair-washing day, and she needed extra water. Wood shaves had to be prepared, the fire lit and water heated for the bath. She undid her plait. Long silky black tresses opened and fell down to her waist, she looked at them proudly as she sat down on the *pidi* (the little wooden stool) by the fire, concocting her own shampoo with *harad* and *ritha*—myrobalan and soap nuts. These were also handy for washing her valuable shawls and silk saris for they did not harm the natural dye, or dull the gold and silver threads woven into her expensive brocades.

It had provided them with security; it had also ensured the continuity of rich traditional values, but when the warm and familial atmosphere of the *veda* disappeared, communication among the new residents from various linguistic and cultural backgrounds stopped flowing. A goulash of Hindi-Punjabi-Gujarati words mixed in any order possible was used, or they used another language: 'Kitchen Swahili'.

Moreover, Bebe Gurdei had already lost her status of *saas*. The new women in the *veda* saw her just as another old lady. In the new multi-lingual, multi-communal atmosphere, they were further exposed to each others' capricious minds. The other was always the 'other' and viewed with suspicion. Mental blocks, like huge caricaturized frameworks, grew. Stereotypic images were drawn. They became victims of their own distorted images. The Punjabis, who saw themselves as superior, called all Gujarati-speakers 'Kutchis': weak, inferior, sharp and sly, they were not to be trusted. The latter in turn looked upon the Punjabis as show-offs, and as aggressive.

'Ba, ba, Punjabi *na chokro mareche* . . . mother, the Punjabi boy is beating me . . .' Shantaben often ran crying out to her mother. She did that even when she had not been beaten. And because she took to this cunning and capricious way of getting attention from her mother, one of the Punjabi children had started teasing her. Tucking her sari into her petticoat, Ba would run to complain to the huge *salwar-kameez* clad Punjabi mother. Disputes became ethnicity-oriented. Bitter at times, less easily brushed off, nor as jovial. They were less straightforward and less naïve. Incessant scolding and shouted instructions were heard at all times of the day and night in different languages. It was like the tower of Babel. 'Shantaben *mutri ne suija* . . . Pee before going to bed.' She was noisy and loud. A misunderstanding with her was more likely to lead to boisterous quarrels, and sometimes even fisticuffs. With limited space and only one toilet and bath for them all, it was not always peaceful coexistence, nor was there total neighbourly harmony.

She could not have been more than ten years old, but in the *veda*, they all thought that she was mad. And bad and even possessed. So the family kept her tied to a tree at the far end of the *veda*. Each morning, the poor child was tethered with a chain. Like a dog on a leash. Yet, not one family kept a strapped-up dog here. As soon as the mother tied up her daughter and left her there, the girl's torment would begin. They mocked her, they insulted her. They cheered, booed, applauded and sneered.

The young children of the *veda* led her a cruel, macabre dance. They would run out of their homes as if they had seen a beast safely tied up. One from whom they need not have any fear, but one they could have some fun with. They called her names. Sometimes they threw stones at her. She would get angry. The more they teased her, the angrier she got. She would throw herself on the naked earth. She would kick and beat herself. Hot, thirsty, dirty, dusty, left to her own frustration. At the end of the day she was finally untied, cleaned and fed. To be chained to her bed once again. She died soon after. Unloved, uncared for, and anonymous. She too had been one of the inhabitants of this *veda*.

Each day it happened. All kinds of disciplines were tried. None worked. For nobody respected them. Putting out clothes to dry in the sun was always an issue, sometimes to escalate into one of massive proportions. One day, it went beyond aggravation, leading to a tragic end. As Chhotu was helping his mother put up clothes on the line, the lady on the opposite side of the verandah came running insisting it was her washing day, and the line was rightfully hers to use. A fight ensued between the two women. Chhotu got upset seeing his mother being abused unfairly, he therefore intervened. As soon as he heard Chhotu's loud voice, the lady's husband, who had been watching the whole scene from their window, rushed out and started beating up the young boy. How it happened, nobody could have told you afterward, but soon after poor Chhotu was lying in a pool of blood—dead even before he reached the hospital.

There was also the case of the unhappy father who, for several nights consecutively, watched his daughter get up in the middle of the night at precisely the same hour. 'She needs to relieve herself, perhaps,' he thought at first. However, he felt uneasy within himself, and one night got up to look. A light shone at the far end of the *veda*. It seemed to be coming from the common toilet. Immediately, the light turned off, and was switched on again. 'Some kind of a signal,' he thought instinctively. This game went on for a couple of seconds until he watched his daughter proceed to the toilet. The old man was shaking as he followed his girl. His worst fears were confirmed when he saw them together. He caught his daughter red-handed, very much in the act of passionate love-making with the neighbour's young boy. Delirious with shame, fear, anger, he was badly shaken. That a day would come when his daughter would show him disrespect, bring upon him dishonour, 'blacken' his face in society. Times have changed. *Izzat*, respect, society have no meaning any more, he thought with a stab of pain in his heart.

For a moment, he did not know how to react, he was so shocked, beyond words. And then he beat them up—both of them. The family's *izzat* had been muddied. The parents had lost much face in their society; they knew word would get around very fast. Their daughter had brought disgrace to them all. The scandal was too much to bear. The father's 'nose had been cut'. They could not show their face in their social circle any more. Almost puritanical in its morals and conventions, illicit, premarital love was forbidden; virginity was sacred. Having lost hers, the girl's chances of finding a suitable marriage partner were not good—if not ruled out. However, the family soon found someone willing to marry her. Without verifying the credentials of the boy, they got the couple hurriedly through the mantras, and before the girl had even got over the shock of being found out with a man, she discovered herself with another. Her misfortune was that the man legally given to her turned out to be impotent. Poor girl, punished for the rest of her life!

Thick cream had collected on top of her *bilori* of hot milk. Before drinking the milk, Bebe Gurdei picked up the cream with her fingers and started rubbing it hard on her face. It came off as tiny particles of black grease. Her face looked red and shiny. Bebe beamed with pleasure. Once more she patted her face to feel the heat and pleasure of the smooth texture. This was Bebe's facial lotion and skin toner. Muni was sitting on the small wooden stool, next to her grandmother in the *jikoni*, just watching her. Bebe still had some cream left in her left hand and massaged it on to Muni's face. The ageing hands felt coarse and hard on Muni's baby face. Muni had to stretch her head forward so as not to lose balance. She made a grimace but tolerated her grandmother's way of showering love.

Then Bebe heated some ghee in a brass bowl and went out of the kitchen to apply it in the partings of her hair. She still preferred to use the comb that she had brought back with her from Bhera. The one with teeth carved on both sides. It was made out of *kahu*, wild olive wood from Peshawar. 'Why do you continue to use this strange comb, Bebe, when there are so many other more beautiful ones in the market,' asked Muni. 'I know my child, but this one is very special,' replied Bebe Gurdei. 'I have had it for so many years now. It is also very effective in cleaning out lice,' she continued, while starting to apply ghee on Muni's hair as well.

Muni jumped up and started rubbing off the ghee with her dupatta. '*Chhee, chhee, chhee!*' she screamed, 'the smell is unbearable Bebe'. '*Khasmakhaniyen* (Husband-eater, she called her), it is good for you,' Bebe shouted. 'Girls of today, they want to use soap and Pond's cream, instead of turmeric and green lentils paste. Don't they know how bad it is for the face?' Muni had already run off, but Bebe kept on advocating the effects of time-tested traditional hair and facial treatments that were supposed to heal sores, acne and blemishes, while tightening the skin at the same time.

She took a brief look at herself in the small broken hand mirror. Bebe quickly finished combing her hair without lingering over it—just long enough to see that the parting was in the right place. Sometimes she did not even bother about that. Muni did not have the habit, but her younger sister was routinely caught looking at herself in the mirror. Bebe did not appreciate this tendency at all, but Chhoti Muni (the younger sister) could not help admiring her pretty face. The butterflies and the *tikkiyan*—these, she was secretly learning from her friends, to wave on the sides of her forehead, or satin ribbons that she lovingly wove into her two plaits, instead of the long *paranda* that Bebe offered her. Yes, Chhoti Muni was lovely.

Bebe changed her *dupatta* to a thicker starched one. This was a clear indication that she was going out. She too was fashion-conscious in her own way. Her clothes were starched, all white clothes were blued with the famous Rickett's blue. Her coloured *shaneel salwars* of a velvetty material gave her added stature. The lips were coloured with *dattun*, the bark of the neem. 'Lipstick is only for prostitutes,' she said aloud, making sure her still very young granddaughters had heard her. 'No decent woman would be seen wearing it.'

Bebe Gurdei put on her *jootis* and, depending on where she was going, they were either plain ones with just a small flower embroidered in silver thread. Or, out of her black trunk came the *khussas* heavily embroidered with *tila* (silver thread). Today was a special ceremonial occasion. She put them carefully on her feet. They hurt a little, since she did not wear them very often. Before leaving, her hand went into her shirt pocket. She took out a little box, from which she carefully took a pinch of brown threads, put them into her left palm, and rolled them lovingly with the right thumb, before sniffing the *nuswar*—which she had learnt to call *tambaku*—into each nostril. The whole operation took less than thirty seconds, but the action had the same ritualistic air about it as that of the pipe smoker. Sneezing immediately afterward, she said, opens up my sinuses.

Three hours later, Bebe returned from her bout of visiting. She was exhausted. 'Muniye, bring the *kundi-sota*,' she screamed.

Muni had heard the noisy footsteps of her grandmother and rushed to see what she might have brought for her. Bebe never returned empty-handed, whether she went to the temple or to the gurudwara. Whether she had been visiting friends, or just the neighbours, Bebe always carried something in her hand—*halwa* or *barfi*, sweet pastries made out of semolina or milk and sugar with cardamom, *laddus* or *petha*. Sometimes, she arrived with small sweet bananas. Muni loved these best; they had the flavour of cardamom.

Bebe put a packet on the table, removed her *dupatta* and lay flat on her stomach on her hard charpoy. Muni sat next to her on the edge of the bed and begun to move the brass mortar and pestle on Bebe's back. 'That feels good, my child,' Bebe said with some relief. She had gone far, visited many houses and walked endlessly; her back was now complaining. 'Where did you go, Bebe?' asked Muni. Bebe replied, 'Kammo's daughter had a son. I went to wish her. Here, she sent back some *mishri* and *badam*. Share it with the rest of your brothers and sisters.' Muni jumped off the bed, the small packet of sugar and almonds clutched in her hand, and ran off to the *veda*.

When she had arrived about twenty years or so ago, Bebe Gurdei had not taken long to adjust to the social life of Nairobi. She was one of those people who made friends easily. Many of her friends were from her home town in Behra; Bebe Gurdei never lacked company. She so loved to talk. Soon after lunch, she was off. No, she did not have a siesta. With a bowl of cooked vegetables in her hand, off she went. There was always a reason for her visit, 'Kammo has had a child . . .', or 'The child of Bimbo has diarrhoea . . . the child is teething' . . . 'the friend has a headache and so cannot cook.' She would be back at seven in the evening, looking triumphant and relaxed, full of vigour and enthusiasm. The bowl she had left with was sure to be refilled with something else, even if only a lump of sugar. All her visiting meant that Bebe had to walk, a lot.

Her regular activities ordered her life into a neat time cycle. If her routine was neglected or broken, her frustrations were clearly visible; she retreated into a chaos within herself. Birth, marriage or illness—any excuse would do to go visiting her friends each afternoon. Bebes and chachis met and discussed social problems, match-making, marriage, anything—even the fact that women were more and more fighting shy of breastfeeding their children.

'In our time, were women not breastfeeding their endless children?' they would burst out laughing. To them the breast was a very functional part of the body, rather than a sexual symbol. 'When Bhirawanwali's daughter had found her hands full with so many children, she had not hesitated to feed her grandchildren— one on each breast. And her breasts had flowed with milk!' On parting company, they were sure to say, '*Mein chalan?*' One did not ask permission to enter a house, but one always asked for permission to leave.

There were endless causes for celebration. In fact, life itself was a daily series of festivities in Bebe Gurdei's curriculum. One was forever offering *shagun*—clothes, dry fruits, money. Out would come Bebe's money 'bag'—notes folded over and over, sometimes half torn, ripped at the edges, knotted securely and tightly in a crumpled and overused handkerchief. A marriage, an engagement, even a child cutting his first tooth called for distribution of coconut and sugar. It was not uncommon for young girls and boys to be betrothed for many years. When still in his braids, Krishen had one day insisted that he wanted to be engaged. 'For then, like them, I will receive *shagun*. I too will have lots of money to spend.' This exchange of gifts was a prominent custom that in a way kept them well knit in the social fabric.

'Hai, Hai!' was how the birth of yet another girl in the family was greeted, but since Bitia's birth coincided with a stroke of luck, the women said, 'Look! She came and brought good luck. Lajpat's new shop is prospering.' They called her Bitia, the beloved girl. Just before the second world war began, she came in the form of Goddess Laxmi. Soon after her birth, Lajpat's business actually started to flourish. He made more money than he had ever dreamed of.

Even after Lajpat decided to rename his 'Indian Herbs and Ayurvedic Medicines' as 'Popular Medicine & Industrial Store', for the customer it would always be known by its original name 'Kiche *di* dukan'. The name had stuck, even though Lajpat thought that the new name he had registered sounded more professional. 'Wealth will stay with you so long as your Bitia is in your house; the day your girl leaves, so will Laxmi . . .' a renowned astrologer had predicted to Lajpat. True to his words, Lajpat's luck would end with Bitia's marriage.

Somewhere, in a little corner of his heart, he must have been superstitious, even though he never exhibited it openly. Lajpat started to keep a picture of Lakshmi, the goddess of wealth and prosperity. Almost every Hindu duka had a small *puja* room in a corner—a picture of Krishna, or of Ganesh—for good luck. Each morning as he arrived to open the door of the duka, he found the flower garland wrapped in a banana leaf dangling from the doorknob. It had been left there by Malan, the garden woman. She had passed by as usual in the early hours of the morning.

The marigolds were hung on the photo of Lakshmi with a stick of incence burning by the side. This was Lajpat's prayer. No mantras. No chanting, just a silent salutation. The portrait of Lakshmi brought colour and fragrance in the shop. Lakshmi stood youthful and virginal, like the fresh bud of a lotus, not yet unfurled. Arisen from the foam of the ocean in the dawn of creation, a sensuous and passionate image, Lakshmi stood like a talisman to guard Lajpat's little duka in the bazaar.

The new *hakims* and *vaids* whom Lajpat engaged had no degrees; they had probably learnt the art (it was as much of an art as it was a science) from their fathers or uncles. Or from other relatives with whom they had worked as apprentices. These were freelance physicians who worked for a small fee. Consultation sessions were held in the mornings only. Lajpat picked up the high bar stool and placed it just outside the door. An hour later, precisely at nine, Tausif Hassan came and sat on the stool. Today it was his turn. Chunibari would come tomorrow. A couple of people were waiting for the physician.

The bar stool signified the clinic. 'Salaam *hakim saab*,' said the first patient. Tausif Hassan wished him and took his right hand to check the pulse. The frequency and intensity of the *nabz* was an important indicator of well-being. 'What is the taste on the tongue?' demanded Tausif Hassan. The patient blurted out something. The examination provided him information on the condition of the digestive fire and the load of toxins in the body. Actually it gave him a map of the internal organs. He listed out a series of do's and don'ts. 'The problem is gastric: hyperacidity. No potatoes, tea, rice, fats, oils, or curds, no cauliflower, nor white gram,' he said, patting his patient on the back. The patient had been standing all this while.

Very often, the list would exclude yoghurt at night. It causes phlegm in the chest, one would be told. And he might add: no mangoes, but if you must, soak them in water for a long time to take away the pricks of heat, or they will give you fever. The patient seemed to be in a hurry, which was quite unusual. 'O *hakima*,' said the old man, losing his patience, 'what *dawa-daru* must I take?' But Tausif Hassan had not yet finished with his lecturing. Humming a tune—he was forever singing under his breath—he added, 'Fever is the king of diseases. The body will ache, temperature will rise, but your sweat will be blocked. Ah! But then these will depend on whether you have *vata*, *pitta*, or *kapha* fever in constitution'. Tausif Hassan was unusual; he had knowledge of both the Unani and Ayurvedic systems of medicine.

He was still humming away. At last he indicated a series of pills, decoctions, medicated ghees, paste, powder and infusions to be purchased from the shop. The dose of the medication was never fixed; it depended entirely on the patient's condition. Various types of sherbets were also advocated. Therapy was tailored to the precise needs of the patient. 'As soon as you start sweating, you are on the way to recovery, then your desire for food will return,' he slapped the man again on the back, as if assuring him that he was already halfway to recovery. The man rushed off.

The next patient did not have a high temperature, but was feeling giddy. His joints and bones were aching. He had trouble breathing. 'Do you have a burning sensation? Intense thirst?' asked Tausif Hassan. 'Ah! You have an inward fever . . . hmm . . .' His easy way and calm mood relaxed the man. Tausif Hassan was one of those people whose manner immediately put patients on the path to recovery. 'All living beings come into the world with fever on them, and with fever they die. Heat of desire can cause or cure disease, depending on how it is harnessed . . .'

The *hakim* was singing again, setting legendary Charaka—a noted Ayurdevic physician of the first century—sayings to verse. 'This is tricky and harder to treat . . . but we shall see . . . yoghurt mixed with jaggery helps the fever change its course from inward to outward, which is easier to handle . . . but perhaps fasting is the best treatment for fever . . . better take only sips of hot water.' A diabetic patient was sure to be told, 'Sugar, problem of sugar, *maharaj!* Drink barley. It helps soak up excess moisture. Millet, sorghum, bitter gourd, *mung* beans, garlic and onions—these are all good for you.'

14

Echoes of war

'I am the son who goes up the roof before the mother is born. Who am I?'
'Smoke before fire'.
    —Riddle

Mussolini declared war on the allies in June 1940. To the north of Kenya, the Italians and the *habash* were fighting. His large and well-equipped Abyssinian army captured Moyale. Face to face with a small batallion of the Kenya African Rifles and another one from India, reinforcements soon came from South Africa, Rhodesia, Nigeria and the Gold Coast. The situation which had confronted British East Africa in 1914 was more or less repeated in 1939—it became a staging, recruiting and training centre, as well as a launching pad for the British assault on Abyssinia (Ethiopia), occupied by Italy.

Many *habash* refugees came down to Isiolo. Bombers from Italian Somaliland flew in to drop bombs on the British territory of Kenya. What a melee they involved the world in. The Russians. The Germans. The Dutch. The English. The Americans. Fights and friendships, ad infinitum. Dozens of countries were involved. Most of Europe was drawn in. The Asians and the Americans joined the mess. Parts of Africa became battlegrounds. Fights on land, in the skies and oceans; genocide, war crimes. It was a melancholic record of human madness. Fifty million people died in this war. Cities, forests and agriculture were devastated. International industrial capital looked more and more to the third world to furbish it with raw materials.

Around 6 p.m., curfew was on. A complete blackout was enforced then onward. They hung blankets on their windows, or they covered them with black paper. Cutting off all light from interiors of homes was declared mandatory. Emergency movement in cars necessitated covering the headlights, leaving just enough for a peephole. For a while, food was rationed and coupons were distributed. Trenches were dug; rows of sandbags thrown here and there. Enemy planes meant sirens ringing out loudly all over, warning people to take shelter. The shrill sound, at most unexpected hours, intruded upon their lives.

It was a horrible sound, the sound of the siren. It screeched right into the brain and gave one a constricting headache. Moreover, the sound carried with it a sense of fear. The eyes popped out, narrowed down and shut tight immediately thereafter. Adrenalin pumped up, and the heartbeat increased. One lost one's sense of balance. The boisterous cacophony was in sharp contrast to the silence of uneventful lives. The children learnt to go underground, stand against walls, under sand bags, whatever was possible at the moment.

Hundreds and hundreds of Italian soldiers were captured in Abyssinia by the British army and brought as prisoners to Kenya, where they had better facilities for housing them. A few soldiers managed to escape to Eritrea. Mostly, however, they were distributed all over the British-occupied territory. Camps for prisoners of war were located in Eldoret, Nanyuki and Nyeri at the foot of Mt Kenya. All kinds of persons filled the PoW camps.

They hailed from every part of Italy; their background included every kind of trade. Some spent their time in study, while others exhausted themselves with physical work. They planted vegetables, they worked on wheat farms. They worked as plumbers, gardeners, as construction workers. They taught each other, sketched, drew; their paintings were especially valued. Able to get materials by post from home or through the YMCAs, the Italian prisoner artists became popular and renowned. There were actors, entertainers and musicians amongst them. As architects, road builders and wood carvers, they often had to use scrap material to fashion tools. But they all had to farm, for food was in meagre supply. Even then, there were times when they were found begging for food from trains passing near Kijabe.

Their camps were guarded by African troops—sometimes they managed to bribe the guards with cigarettes, alcohol or a few coins, if they wanted to sneak out for a bit. Two or three of the prisoners even dared risking the escape long enough to embark on a long desired adventure—they managed to go up the sacred mountain. Yes, they actually climbed Mt Kenya and, incredibly enough, rejoined the prison camps as normal detainees on their way down!

Their works included artistic creations—carved knives and figurative oils, the Last Supper painted on the walls and portraits of Kirparam and Hardei amongst their canvases. Exploding with burning colours, details of their output were dazzling. The Italian prisoners even honoured Bebe Hardei, whom they addressed as 'Mama *mia*' with much affection, by painting saris for her—which she never wore. She had never worn a sari in her life. The six yards of crepe material was entirely covered in lovely flower designs and creepers.

'Hah! Hah!' the children exclaimed in admiration when they were exposed to the results of the Italian prisoners working in their grandparents' second home in Nyeri. Muni looked at the sari for a long time. She had never seen anything as beautiful, although she would never have dared ask Bebe Hardei to even let her touch it. She just looked on from a distance as it was being displayed to the rest of the family. However, the orange and pink flowers were etched in her memory for a long time. Long enough to be reproduced on her very own sari for her wedding trousseau many years later. For the moment, she took up a pencil and paper and tried her hand at replicating the motifs. An artistic talent was being tentatively explored.

'*Piccolo . . . Bambino . . .*' the prisoners tried to induce the children to play with them, but Bebe Hardei would have none of it. 'They will cut off your heads with the knives that they produce,' she would say, implanting alarm and suspicion in their little hearts. They reacted by teasing the young soldiers with abusive Punjabi words and running away. Although, 'These *wazungu* seem different from the other ones we normally see,' was the verdict of the older children on the Italian prisoners.

In spite of the war, the children still spent school vacations with their beloved grandfather in Nyeri. The prisoners' camps were not far from Lala Kirparam's small place in the foresty lands. And it was during this time that they stumbled upon the Italians. These encounters with the Italian prisoners were their first direct communication with white people. 'How is it that these *wazungu* are so dirty?' they asked Payaji, for the white people they had seen till then were very polished and wore beautiful clothes. Lala Kirparam laughed it off, finding it difficult to begin to explain why some white people were more equal than others. Why there were wars. Why people were captured. Why they were made prisoners. And why prisoners could be treated unequally.

A young Italian painter by the name of Nino Stano had been recruited in the army during the war. He was captured by the British forces in Abbyssinia, present-day Ethiopia, and brought to the POW camp in Nyeri. Lala Kirparam's youngest son, who had more or less grown up in the area, knew many people around Nyeri, including some of the British wardens of the camps. He would often walk around the camps; the wardens allowed him to 'talk' to the prisoners. At first they communicated via the few words of Kiswahili, English and Italian; very soon they fabricated enough vocabulary to make sense. And Kundanlal managed to get some Italian prisoners to come and work for them at their house in Nyeri. Nino Stano was one of them.

The prisoners were very willing (of course they did not have much choice in the matter) as they could leave the camps during the day to work in a more conducive environment—more importantly,

Painting of Lala Kirparam done by N. Stano,
an Italian prisoner of World War II

get good meals (food was in short supply, especially in the camps). Nino and young Kundanlal became friends. Kundanlal discovered Nino's talent. He bought him paints and canvas . . . and the portrait of Lala Kirparam was commissioned.

Nino Stano painted him the way he saw the rapidly aging Kirparam. In a brown coat and a black tie—the Bangalore topee adorning his head. It is through this portrait that this story was born. I have Nino Stano to thank for that.

All through the war, Lala Kirparam's house in Nyeri overflowed with children and grandchildren during the school holidays. He sent train tickets in advance; at times he booked a whole carriage for them. They grew up in the streets of the Indian Bazaar and the little alleyways of River Road; they lived in duka-houses in the town of Nairobi. But the jungles of Nyeri, Nanyuki and Meru were special. Vacations in grandfather's home upcountry were always a real treat and a retreat that would evoke nostalgia for all time to come. Here, they felt a sense of freedom, away from limitations set by adults. A child's fantasy world, where they ran through rivers and streams, with elephants and sometimes rhinoceros tramping through the garden.

The aroma of *khichri* simmering on the charcoal-fuelled *jiko* had drifted out all the way into the verandah. They rushed inside, knowing that Payaji was around. They would pester their grandfather for exciting stories, puzzles and riddles. Evenings in Nyeri were always cold, but the *jiko* warmed the room. Sitting on a low wooden stool, bending over the open charcoal fire, every now and then stirring the *khichri*, Lala Kirparam had many tales about kings and queens, fairy stories and animal tales for telling around the fire on a cold August evening. And the children imagined the strange incidents happening to them. He was truly an artist par excellence at story telling. This is how Krishen slowly developed his talent. Paya Kirparam's style was mature and naturally more intricate. When he took a deep breath, their voices hushed one by one, and all became quiet. No one dared talk, nor interrupt him.

And then he began, slowly and quietly. 'A fairy goes on a treasure hunt into the forest . . . she weighs five flowers . . .'

He became more fanciful as the night progressed. Time did not seem to matter; the story lasted for as long as there was need for it. And the only sounds that could be heard when he paused were the crackling of the fire, a dog barking on the road, or frogs croaking in the pond nearby. There was always a relationship between the aesthetic and the spiritual. The process continuously changed the children's outlook. Their consciousness was elevated, lifted from the ordinary world into a world of creativity, offering raw material for imagination and consciousness that would awaken with the language. They grew on the stories, devoured them. 'Growth arises from conflict,' he used to say, 'while growing old is all about having more stories to tell on dark nights.'

Stories became real, the way he told them. They abounded with serpents and talking beasts, or restoration of broken limbs. Repeating the same stories handed down through generations, the dead metamorphosed into living beings, ogres into golden deer, gods into boars, serpents into princes. Victims turned to stone, beautiful girls became old women. There seemed to be no steady progression in the narratives. Climaxes were very often at the very beginning, while complications only stimulated new beginnings. Ascending and descending patterns flowed into one another with harmonious ease, undisturbed by antagonistic forces. There were always characters to protect. The patterns created a middle space of profound timeless peace, broken by a deep silent breathing pervading an expectation of things to come. Payaji was totally dependent on the participation of the children, who were invariably vocal and deeply involved in the labyrinthine process of his account of events. The shared experience united them within the world of imagination.

More than love or war, what really set the stories going were curses. Fatal words were pronounced and a curse was cast. A cosmic cataclysm unleashed by a futile gesture that nobody had noticed.

Even gods could do little or nothing against a curse . . . they could only suffer like mortals. Representing the invulnerable supremacy of the mind, the curse was the one mental act striking more swiftly than the sword. A word articulated in the Brahmin's mind (for they were the creatures of the mind) concealed a 'sharp-bladed razor'.

'Payaji, *Shahzadi Mirch*, *Shahzadi Mirch* . . . Princess Pepperina,' insisted Muni, and so Kirparam recounted the inexhaustible tale that they had heard many times at regular intervals. Obviously, they were captivated by his gift for storytelling and wouldn't let him stop. 'Two lovers once had a curse thrown upon them by a Brahmin, for some indiscretion. They were turned into ducks and condemned to pass the night apart from each other on opposite sides of the river. All night long each asked to join the other, but the answer ceaselessly remained a firm No.' Paya Kirparam's eyes took on an amused look as he started to sing the stanzas, '*Chakwa main awan? Na chakwi . . . Chakwi main awan? Na Chakwa.*' The laughter of the children was heard far away, as they excitedly repeated the verses after him. How well they knew them! The evening by the coalfire was indeed magical, while outside was all dark and cold.

Kirparam would begin his stories only in the evenings. 'When idle girls and boys tell stories during the day, a poor traveller will lose his way,' was his explanation. His stories were without beginning or end, imagination gone crazy, unfolding in myriad exciting ways, conjuring all kinds of possibilities in their minds. For was imagination not the very stuff of existence, of *maya*, of illusion itself? Even kings, queens and fairies became foolish earthly beings. His tales did not make children go to sleep; on the contrary, they kept them wide awake every night. They loved ghost stories, especially the one about Churel, the woman who dies in childbirth. Ugly, black, breastless, stomach and navel protruding, feet turned backwards. It did not matter that they later spent endless nights 'seeing' Churel everywhere—under the bed, next to their pillows, flying straight above their heads. Intuitively, however Paya Kirparam knew that a good yarn must have a good moral, a happy ending—preferably both.

And, when it rained, it was time to make *pakoras*. When the mercury fell, and sweaters were worn, it was a *pakora*-story séance. The deep-fried vegetables in a paste of chick-pea flour seemed appropriate for any and every occasion. Brinjal, potato, cauliflower, even onion and carrot, sometimes spinach, it was truly a Punjabi speciality. That was dinner—a lot of *pakoras*. Paya Kirparam, Bebe Gurdei, Bebe Hardei succumbed to these hot, heavy savouries. Of course, only pure ghee was used. *Pakoras, puris*, all eatables were cooked in ghee. Many people made their ghee at home—butter would be heated in *debes* for a long time.

Ghee was almost revered. It was ambrosia, food fit for the gods, with the additional sacredness of being made from cow's milk. The pungent aroma it released when melting was enough to send Pavlovian signals to their taste buds. Lala Kirparam loved cooking. Even when on a trip, or travelling, or when he drove the children in his lorry to Nyeri, or to Nanyuki, he would stop on the way near a river, and say, 'Come, children, let us have some *pakoras*.' The cooking stove, kerosene oil, ghee, vegetables and flour all seemed to appear as if by magic. No food ever tasted as good as that eaten in the open, beside a wood fire, dipped in garlic chutney with red chillies.

* * *

They came in numbers, the old and the young. Some came in their pajamas, others in pants and jackets, in shoes without socks; in pugrees or in hats. They kept coming, until there was no place to sit. The room was full to the brim. Those who could not find seats did not mind aligning their backs against accessible wall spaces; others sat on the floor, or squatted at the entrance of the door—even in the passageway. Each seemed to be breathing in the exhaled breath of the other. It was hot and stuffy. But nobody seemed to mind.

The huge radiogram used up a large part of their small *baithak*, and people covered every inch of available space. The colossal radio made a lot of noise and transmissions were never clear, but attendance was always full. Lajpat switched it on only for news broadcasts. People were naturally keen to get the latest update on events of the day. The only reliable source of information was the BBC. With very few people owning radios, those who possessed one had to handle a big gathering. The fact that hardly any of them could understand more than a few words of English was besides the point. Between four and six each evening, the room gradually filled up.

He already knew the jargon by heart, almost word for word. It would begin with 'tut tut tut . . . this is the BBC. Here is the news read by . . .' Young Krishen was the translator—what he himself could get the gist of, that is. One could never be sure how faithful the translated version in Punjabi was to the original, but Krishen did his best. And he had fun. In many homes, young boys like him with some fluency in English became sources of information, of communication, of a journalism of a special kind. 'The accent of the English broadcaster is so stiff upper-lipped, that sometimes I miss out on words,' was his reaction in defence. 'Why can't they speak English like us?' he would complain. 'When we speak their language, we stretch out the word, roll our 'r's, and put a lot of expression into the sentence—almost like singing a song. At least the emphasis carries the message.'

It must be said that the energy of the BBC war broadcaster was very different, very serious. After all it had become a radio of combat, giving an anti-Nazi energy, filling the soul with a nationalistic spirit, mobilizing the population, giving courage that their side was doing its best, especially diffusing the lectures of Churchill. It was meant to provoke tears while giving news from the battlefront day after day. Although the correspondents were on the battlefront, technical facilities were not advanced enough to enable them to broadcast personally. The radio became a political instrument, besides being an organ of information. It was a way to influence its citizens. The BBC reserved its public monopoly.

It was mostly men who came, but there was one woman who never failed to show up. Minutes before four each evening, she was seen arriving with her umbrella. The boys started calling her 'chhatriwali'—behind her back of course. Rain or sunshine, Sarani was not to be seen without her umbrella. At the end of the news when most people had left, she would tap Krishen on the right shoulder. Shaking it a little, she would very naively tell him, 'Krishen beta, ask the radio if my son will return home safe and sound from the war.' Sarani's son had been taken as a soldier from their village in India.

Krishen hid behind the radio. Changing his voice to what to him was radio speech—deep and haunting—he answered her query, 'Masi (Aunty) Sarani, your son Bindra is fine.' With innocent concern, she said, 'Beta Bindra, my son, you are so far away. If you are hurt in the war, make sure you eat grapes. They are good for your health. You will heal fast.' The children gagged their mouths to stop the laughter from bursting out. Poor Sarani. Her son Bindra never returned. He died in the war.

The need to control the flow of information during the war, together with the rapid increase of political consciousness among African elites—who had found avenues for expression of their grievances in Indian-owned papers—elicited the government's wrath against the Indian press. Efforts were made by the colonial government to censor the media, which had gained prominence as an avenue for articulating views. They started a crackdown on newspapers with dissenting views; the axe fell on Vidyarthi, printer and publisher.

Born in 1907 in Mombasa, G.L. Vidyarthi arrived on the political scenario in Kenya without a formal education in journalism. His professional profile was both of a creator and a creation of the contemporary society of his time, constantly criticizing the colonial rule's racially discriminatory attitude. His *Colonial Times* and the Swahili paper *Habari za Dunia* brought him at loggerheads with the colonial authorities several times. Accused of sedition, or contravention of defence regulations, he was sentenced and fined.

Here was an example of an individual with an Arya Samaji background dabbling in political affairs through journalism. His training in a *gurukul* in India (residential school with strict methods of teaching based on Vedic traditions), and contact with a seminary of uncompromising followers of the Arya Samaj that had produced several leaders of the Indian freedom movement led him to develop an anti-colonial attitude. The political and economic struggle was long and bitter.

Life in the city could be dehumanizing. It tore people apart emotionally, as they functioned within the system of institutionalized racism. Between 1942 and 1947, the population would expand at the phenomenal rate of 17 per cent, while inflation would reach 400 per cent. Unemployment was rife and encouraged crime; the African working classes, with some help from Indian leaders like M.A. Desai and Makhan Singh, became increasingly politically aware.

'A self-proclaimed non-violent Marxist' is how Makhan Singh liked to be known. A radical young printer, Makhan Singh had been educated at the Government Indian High School in Nairobi. He built up the Labour Trade Union of East Africa among the increasing numbers of young African and Indian youth. From 1935 onwards, the multi-racial body tried to maintain the non-communal nature of the trade union movement; this in itself was a great achievement. Makhan Singh was interned during the duration of the war. Many years later, he would inspire 6,000 municipal workers in Nairobi to go on strike. Large crowds would witness the government's first use of teargas. Anti-strike laws would be passed. The government's nervousness would increase.

They performed dramas of all kinds—ironically enough—to collect money for war efforts. Alladitta Qureshi, Master Dunichand,

Alladitta Sadhuram were there, amongst others, to enact dramas from Hindu mythology—from the Mahabharata and the Ramayana. No woman was as yet ready to act on stage and face the consequent social stigma. The slim, young, dark Babu Chura donned false breasts under flowing Indian robes. A long *dupatta* was pinned up onto his short black hair. A red *bindi* was painted in the middle of his forehead. Suddenly the outcaste metamorphosed into the beautiful Radha, or into the upper caste Draupadi, consort to five princes. He played female roles in *Saide Hawas*, in *Yehudi ki Ladki*, in *Ram Rajya*, and many other plays, religious and social.

While Hindus and Muslims got together to enact plays in the Sanatan Dharam Hall, the Playhouse Theatre in the middle of town prepared to stage an event of a much less pacific nature. Krishen was about nineteen then, Muni could not have celebrated her tenth birthday—not that birthdays were ever marked. She would tell you today that she never had a cake with candles. April of 1942 was a month that left a deep mark on their adolescence.

The stage was well prepared, the dais was equipped with the necessary gadgets. Chairs, tables and loudspeakers were provided. A huge crowd had gathered. He arrived finally in a beautiful car. Walked up the steps leading to the podium, and stood for a few minutes to survey the crowd before addressing the public meeting. He explained why the workers' leave of passage to India was being cancelled. For a few minutes, they listened. But as he began to impress upon them the evacuation schemes, instead of avid listeners, he faced a mass of hostile demonstrators. He tried again; they booed him down once more. He started again. The howling grew louder. Potatoes, which were in short supply, were hurled at him. These were the men who had been denied permission to return to India. The demagogic rabble-rouser realized that this time his verbal virtuosity was not going to win them over. He walked off the platform and quietly sped off in his car.

Meet Isherdass, once upon a time a very radical and enthusiastic leader. Much admired, once the idol of youth. When he had first arrived from India in 1927 as private secretary to the businessman

Jeevanjee, he had come full of the nationalistic spirit against colonialism. Up until 1933, he had been advocating non-cooperation with the British government in colonial Kenya. In 1934, he joined the Legislative Council and established himself as a spokesman for the causes of Indians and Africans. He struck like lightening with his brash, cocky swagger and eagerness to rebuke convention. Riding on thrilling waves of rhetoric, his bombastic style soon swept him to higher echelons.

Eventually, he got appointed deputy director of manpower. Now they saw him as belonging to the 'other side', as seeking favours from the government, rather than airing their grievances. His speech was firm and sometimes became abusive. The Indian public began to threaten him. They insulted him. Isherdass remained unmoved. He made many enemies. Now that the war was on and the government had introduced legislation on issuing exit permits, the workers were prevented from going to India, for they had to perform services for the military and civil authorities.

The world war was not their war. Psychologically, Indians in Kenya never really identified with it, and they would soon forget it. Indian artisans of the time refused to cooperate with the war effort. As deputy director of manpower, Isherdass took upon himself the duty of devotion. He was as committed as he had been during his radical days when he used to advocate non-cooperation with the colonial government. He abused the men with hostile language and tough measures. Isherdass became the target of public anger and hatred. The men retaliated by sending him threatening letters.

In October 1942, Isherdass received a serious threat to his life, but he brushed it aside as of no consequence. They wouldn't dare, he laughed. It was a formula for disaster. On the morning of 6 November, two men, one by the name of Balwant Rai, a contractor, the other a Sikh electrician called Harbux Singh, walked into the office of Isherdass and shot him dead.

The murder, expectedly, caused a sensation. The government had tried to control the movement of Indian artisans and Isherdass had only been a pawn in the game. One who tried to do his duty as laid down by colonial laws. Six months later, the trial of the accused began. The interest of the Indian community in the hearing was intense. Opinions were divided. The assessors differed in their judgements. The judge finally gave his verdict and the prisoners were executed in a Nairobi prison at dawn on 12 February 1944. For once, the bodies were handed over to the respective Indian communities. In their death, contractor Balwant Rai and electrician Harbux Singh were accorded the highest honours normally reserved for saints. A huge crowd attended the funeral processions. Thousands shouted, 'Long live Rai', 'Long live Singh'.

15

In the classroom

When the disciple is ready, the guru comes.

— Indian wisdom

It was precisely 10.30 a.m. The bell for recess was ringing. The Arya Girls School paused for a break for half an hour. Classes broke up into groups or individuals. Some ran off to relieve themselves. Others rushed off into the playing fields to stretch their legs. Most of the teachers converged on the staff room for a cup of much deserved, much needed *chai*: hot, milky and syrupy. Many girls ran straight to the school gates. Two men were already waiting patiently for them. One carried an old wooden box with a small latch, strung from an old piece of cloth hanging tightly from his neck right upto his torso. That was Santo.

A few paces away, a basket full of *chevra* and *njugu*—roasted peanuts and beaten rice deep fried in oil—lay at Sethi's feet. He served it from a small cup into a piece of old newspaper that he carefully rolled into a cone. This way, there was less risk of the goodies falling to the ground. Both men had arrived just in time to catch the girls, as they did each morning. The girls knew that the peddlers were waiting. Rain or shine, they never missed out. After all, it was a livelihood—even if it was just peddling snacks to please little children. Very often even grown-ups were tempted.

Other peddlers had come and gone, but it seemed that Santo had always been there. He remained a favourite. Simplicity emanated from his being, drawing children naturally towards him. Eyes full of warmth stood out in a pale, undernourished face. He already looked elderly, although he couldn't have been more than forty—perhaps he was not even that. Already his back was showing signs of curvature. Doubtless, he was suffering from arthritis or a related non-inflammatory but degenerative bone or cartilege disease. He wouldn't have known that.

Although the X-ray had been invented many years ago, this poor man had not even heard of it, much less had his spinal column bombarded with electromagnetic radiation to get a picture of his bones. He could hardly afford the Ayurvedic treatment from Lajpat Rai's shop when his back gave him trouble at the end of the day. Many times, Lajpat Rai did not even charge him, but it embarrassed Santo to show up too often. He might have been poor, but he was certainly not a beggar.

Soon, a huge crowd of big and small girls in yellow uniforms surrounded Santo. Cackling, laughing, teasing and jumping. Gently, he removed another basket of goodies from his head. Dark green raw mangoes stood out among the small yellow guavas in Santo's wooden box. In his quiet, taciturn way, Santo started cutting them into quarters, carefully filling the layers with salt and red chilli powder. He did it with the air of an artist putting the final touches on canvas. Muni watched the whole process with glee; everyone one of them looked inviting. She took some time deciding. 'The yellow guava with its red inside . . . perhaps not. I think I will settle for the mango today.' As she brought out a big coin from her dress pocket, Santo's smile gave her the reassurance that she was going to enjoy it. The little hand reached out for the fruit, and she greedily bit into it, 'an acid green mango with chillies, which burns the tongue, shuts the eyes tight, and makes you jump'. She ran away happily to join her friends.

Sometimes Santo also brought *pakoras* wrapped up in pages torn out of old school textbooks. The *pakoras* were a little more expensive; each piece cost a whole ten cents. Muni was lucky, she got break money. Lajpat gave each of his children ten cents every morning. However, Santo was considerate. If the girls did not have the money, he accepted their old notebooks, or gave them credit.

When Master Arya Muni Verma joined the school, he put up fencing to bar these poor vendors from coming in, and the girls from going out. 'The girls must not eat such junk, they will fall sick', was his objection. But the girls were not to be denied their snack, nor the vendors their sales opportunity. A small hole in the corner of the fence behind a bush was the solution; the girls learnt to sneak out.

Another bell rang. They rushed towards the main building; recess was over and they better not be late. Lapses in studies or behaviour could be punished, but when it was Master Khushi Ram's period, they could not afford to make a mistake. His disciplining of students could be harsh and painful, very painful. Moreover, he carried a name that was an antithesis of his being—Khushi Ram, Happy Ram. He was anything but happy. No-one had ever seen him laugh. Or smile. It was as if he did not know what it was to be happy, or to give joy to others. Nothing seemed to give him pleasure. Stories of his idiosyncrasies were by now legendary. '*Khushki Ram, Khushki Ram*. He burns with the fever of prickly heat,' they were screaming away. 'Perhaps the constant rebukes and scoldings relieve him of his itchiness,' they added, hiding their giggles with palms cupped on their mouths, heads dipped into stooped shoulders. Indirectly, Khushi Ram did give them something to laugh and joke about.

One of the girls was keeping guard at the door. 'Shhhh,' she said, with a finger on her lips. 'Better not discuss it anymore. I can hear his footsteps at the end of the hallway approaching the classroom.' All whispering stopped immediately. There was dead silence. Master Khushi Ram walked into the classroom. The sound of the chairs shifting was all that could be heard. The girls stood straight, stiff to the bone. At attention. In the military style. In a united sing-song voice they said, '*Na-ma-ste-Mas-ter-ji*'— elongating each syllable. Master Khushi Ram did not return the greeting. The other schoolmasters and *penjis* always returned their greeting before giving them permission to take their seats, but not Khushi Ram. He went directly to the blackboard and began the lecture.

Suddenly, he turned around and darted a question at one of the girls. She was so shocked and frightened that she stood numb. She hadn't even heard the question properly. He neither repeated the question, nor did he wait for her to think. 'What, you don't know the answer?' She still didn't say a word. Master Khushi Ram pulled her hard by the ear and in the process his own wrist turned clockwise to the full. The poor girl was nearly on the floor. Red in the face and eyes full of tears, even her underpants had gone wet. But she did not scream, nor did she protest.

Khushi Ram often resorted to beating the girls—slaps, kicks with boots, his cane, or a stick. Any small provocation was enough to charge him—a sloppy answer, a late entry in class, or even just a weak smile—not that the students ever felt like smiling in his class. Sometimes the girls pulled their own ears, or started doing sit-ups as soon as he approached them. 'Show your palm,' he would say, and out would come his famous long ruler, waiting to strike with force. At times, he even inserted a pencil beneath the fore and ring fingers, before hitting hard at the knuckles. One day a student fainted from such abuse. Khushi Ram got a stern warning from the principal. He never again meted out physical punishment to the girls.

'*Hamara jhanda uncha rahe*. They have raised their yellow flag! Here arrive the *mugdar* ladies.' The boys teased their sisters when they returned from school a few days later. 'You know when the flag opens into the air, it releases flower petals of all colours; what a beautiful sight to behold!' said Muni, going on the defensive. Fingers clasped her chin in full admiration and wonder, 'Aaah . . .' she said looking up, as if she could still see them falling from the heavens above. The boys had more to laugh about.

The Arya Samaj movement that had laid its foundation in Nairobi way back in 1903 became an event for their annual *jalsa*, an anniversary celebration lasting several days in the Arya Girls

School. Mothers, wives, grandmothers, parents and teachers got together to exchange, to communicate, to play, and to have a large feast, or to watch films together. Contests and competitions were held and prizes given. Various fields of the school's activities were highlighted—dance, music, painting, needlework, cookery and sports. Girls put up displays of their expertise in sports with *mugdar* (dumb bells) and pyramid-making.

Muni was especially talented in cookery; she often won prizes. By the age of twelve, she was already known in school for her expertise. Her lentils and aubergine curry were appreciated, but it was the saffron rice pudding that won her the prize—that too recommended by master Arya Muni Verma, another hard taskmaster. The sweet smell of cardamom wafted far into the distance. The golden rice with fine strips of silver, *zarda*, was not easy to cook, for too much sugar, or too high a temperature was sure to burn it. Therefore, it was often a subject for examination.

Racial segregation, since long an established fact, continued in the same vein in the educational sphere. Separate schools for Europeans, Asians and Africans. Hosts of MAs, BTs, BLLBs and other qualified persons were denied teaching posts in Indian schools. With the pretext that they did not possess a personality or were unsuitable on this count or that, Indian teachers with British degrees were refused. Often, Indian schools remained short of qualified teaching staff. Funds for Indian education were often converted into European votes. Material meant for Indian schools was transferred to other sections.

All these years, members of the school committee and the advisory council sat comfortably in their chairs without lodging a strong protest with the government. Some journalists wrote that the policies advocated for Indian education were abhorrent and denied their children high literacy achievements or merit even in fields like agriculture, or mechanical and technical training. However, the likes of Sanjiwan Raj were few and far between, and the subject was quickly closed.

At the age of twenty-eight, Master Arya Muni Verma arrived in Nairobi from Jalandhar with degrees in Hindu scriptures and Vedic culture, Sanskrit and philosophy. Educated at Gurukul Kangri in Haridwar and at Amritsar, he had an impressive curriculum vitae. For a long time, he continued to be the headmaster and to teach at the private Arya Girls School. Finally, he was accepted as a teacher at the Government Indian Boys School. By this time the school had already been relocated from Whitehouse Road near the railway station to its present site in Ngara.

Master Arya Muni was a man with a mission; he became their new arts teacher. The Art Room was situated on the upper floor, right at the end of the corner; it was called the Drawing Room. Arya Muni soon became very popular with the boys. He filled them with enthusiasm. He encouraged and inspired them to feel proud of their cultural heritage. They learnt to sketch and paint. Arya Muni decided that some of the A4-size crayon sketches—mainly portraits of Rabindranath Tagore, Mohandas Karamchand Gandhi and Jawaharlal Nehru—were good enough to be displayed in the school gallery.

When he saw the display, the European principal of the school was furious. His face, which was usually red, turned scarlet, ruddy in appearance. In his heavily accented Hindustani, he shouted at the art master in contemptuous terms to remove the sketch of Jawaharlal Nehru. 'Don't you know that he is our prisoner in India?' Of course, Arya Muni Verma knew. This was precisely why the drawings were encouraged—to create a consciousness among the youth. The fact that Nehru and Gandhi had been in and out of prison so often and had openly criticized the British Raj had made a strong impression on the young man. 'They are only sketches, of no political significance,' Arya Muni tried to reason, but Soman was not satisfied and carried on his tantrum.

Arya Muni was uneasy at being accosted by so unpleasant a man in the morning hours of his class. The young and politically conscious art master refused to take down the portraits. 'Tear them down if you so wish,' Arya Muni dared the principal. Soman put out his right hand and with one stroke snatched them from the drawing board. Torn to pieces in full view of the teacher and the students, the once revered portraits fell as shreds on the floor. The class fell silent. They all looked at him in bewilderment. Within minutes, Soman became more unpopular than ever. The bell rang; the period was over. The boys rushed out. Master Arya Muni had resigned. He left school that very day. This was in September 1942.

The news spread like wildfire. The story did the rounds of the whole school. In no time every boy was in the picture. They were charged with anger. Some of the senior boys, including Manzoor Alam, Mohammed Amin and Bhogal, quickly became ringleaders. They did the rounds of all the twenty classrooms announcing an urgent meeting at City Park. 'Our leaders have been insulted,' they shouted.

The boys of Government Indian High School were getting increasingly politically conscious during agitations for independence in India. 'Don't you remember how they insulted some of our leaders in the past?' As president of the Indian National Congress in 1924, Sarojini Naidu had been offended while boarding a ship from Kisumu. The captain of the *Clement Hill* had instructed African sailors to hold her up on the gangway to show her ticket, while the rest of the European passengers passed her by, taking great pleasure at her discomfiture.

Speeches were given. Patriotism infused into the stream of consciousness, the entire school was brought in touch with its feelings. The sentiment reached a crescendo. They quickly called for the 500-odd boys—seniors and juniors included, to organize a strike. 'Soman must resign as our headmaster.' Ideological conflicts raged during the meeting. Some simply stood by idly, observing the show, listening to all the arguments, making desultory comments. Others gesticulated and shouted.

Photographs of King George were removed from classrooms and torn apart; those of Gandhi were hung on walls instead. The boys refused to attend classes. They threw stones and broke windows. Walls were covered with graffiti in huge letters. 'Soman is a fool' was scribbled everywhere. 'Death to Soman!' '*Hartal*!' 'Strike!' they shouted as they marched in a defiant mood. These boys had energy, but no clear political objective. At night, they made a small incision in the flagpole. The next morning, they said, 'We shall celebrate the Empire Day . . .' While the flag was being raised, it came down, broken.

They demonstrated on the streets. They did the rounds of Government Road and of River Road with banners. The flag-waving jingoism carried on for a whole week. The school closed down. The authorities would not give in. Some members of the Indian Congress who had initially supported their demonstrations, however, soon began to discourage the boys. 'Go back to school,' they warned. 'The rumours are that the school will be turned into barracks for the military.' The boys returned, reluctantly. Three were immediately expelled. Leaders of the movement were given a choice between being expelled or being caned in public. Many chose the former.

Those who returned to school came flaunting symbols of Indian nationalism. Some came in Gandhi caps. Others had pictures of Nehru pinned on their shirts. Cries of '*Jai Hind*' could be heard. Soman got most agitated. His withdrawal orders were fervently disobeyed. The boys defied him, 'How many of us can he stop?' Accusations and counter-accusations more or less subsided. The revolution as such did not come, but Soman decided to resign from the school.

Initially, all Indian schools had to have English headmasters, called by the pompous word 'principal'. The Government Indian Boys School at last managed to get an Indian headmaster—who, however, could never expect to rise higher in scale to become a chief inspector of schools, as could the likes of a Soman. Three months were to pass before the school returned to normalcy.

Krishen's younger brother had chosen to be expelled. But he dreaded the thought of going home to tell his family. He knew the scene that would follow. His father would get angry. His mother would be sad. And at the moment he he was in no mood to face the drama. He walked about, brooding and mulling it over until it got dark. I better face up to it now, he thought. He had felt so elated in the momentum of the decision, and now he felt bad under his skin. He was absolutely not in any mood to talk to his parents about it.

Yashoda was naturally very upset. When she asked him why he had done it, all he said was, 'I don't know.' Perhaps he didn't want to tell his mother that he was momentarily inspired. That he had been energized by the slogans, or that he was truly in agreement with the cause. Whatever it was, he was not going to discuss it with his mother. He sat quietly at the table with his head bowed. Not in defiance, but not in shame either. He stared at his feet, but was looking nowhere in particular. While her own mother Bebe Hardei had been anything but a fatalist, the daughter passed the litmus test. Yashoda was not really a pessimist, but she seemed to accept the status quo without fighting back.

Like other emotions, her grief and anger were expressed with great restraint. Deep in her heart, however, she had had high hopes for her son. That one day he would be a barrister at law, or a doctor, or even an engineer. But he had opted to be expelled. He had chosen to destroy his future. Where will it all lead him, she wondered. She gave a deep sigh. What was the use of thinking about it now; it was too late. People will forget the causes tomorrow. Who will remember that my son too had been among those who had fought a small anti-colonial battle . . . nobody! His future would have been destroyed.

'Zidd' and 'jawani' were two words used almost synonymously. Stubbornness and youth, both words were correlated with adolescence. The family decided that the cause of the problem lay with his teenage years. That he would have acted otherwise had he been slightly younger or older. Who was to know? But the period was certainly not easy. When one says that adolescence is a difficult period, one rarely specifies for whom. Obviously it was difficult both for the parent and the youngster.

Times were changing. Youth were demanding more freedom to decide their futures. It was hard for both Yashoda and Lajpat Rai to accept that the son was paving a path, his own way. That he had some right to do things which were not allowed before. That the death of childhood was necessary before stepping into adolescence and adulthood. Something had to die before he could be reborn as an adult. It was almost a paradox. It was like a necessary rite of passage to take him to the other side. The silent suffering of the mother lasted until the boy decided to look for employment. Yashoda started feeling better. It had been a period of transition. Her son had gained more freedom, but it had come at a price. The fact that he was to start work soon meant that he would be shouldering more responsibilities than before.

They were her source of joy, and in her own way, Yashoda indulged her children. So long as they had been babies, she had balanced them on the hip while walking around. They lay in her lap as she cooked. Or they snuggled at her breast. But even before their adolescence, the pampering and coddling had stopped. Responsibility was thrown upon the shoulders of the older boys. Henceforth, they would be called 'Papaji' by their younger siblings. Krishen became 'Wade Papaji' and Baldev, 'Chhote Papaji', the elder papa and the younger papa. Muni and her sisters were constantly reminded to be more sensible, sacrificing and tolerant. With the result that in some ways Muni grew up more quickly— older than her years.

Although no more a child, her small frame belied her age. The affection that her father had showered upon her over the years was reciprocated. Muni became as fond of her father as he was of her. The attachment of the adolescent was viewed as atypical, even though they had much in common. Muni looked forward to spending time with her father. He was so gentle. They talked about all sorts of things. However, it was quite clear that Yashoda did not approve. Whenever Muni rushed to her father, she immediately noted the signals sent by her mother: a stern look or a shake of the head. Her frown could spell wrath. Her silence could inhibit.

Her smile could be a plea, a look an offering. Obviously, her knotted eyebrows this time showed disapproval. On rare occasions—it was only once or twice—Muni actually heard her mother's low voice. 'Keep a proper distance. Come here! Don't sit too close to your father!' Yashoda never raised her voice.

'Go inside!' Wade Papaji's short and sharp voice impatiently rang out aloud, warning the sisters to take cover. Their friends had arrived. The older boys were soon able to exercise some control over their younger siblings, especially over their sisters. 'And, no need to bring in the tea. We will take care of that by ourselves.' Sometimes Bebe Gurdei also shouted at the girls, 'What are you doing here? Go away. Go inside. Girls must not stand at the door.' And the girls dared not interrogate her. If they asked why, Bebe would pretend to flare up. 'Why? What do you mean by asking why?' she would retort. The question was taboo. 'Never ask why. "Why" is a very bad question', she would say, 'It always leads to quarrels.' So, Muni stopped asking her endless whys and slowly learnt to respect the norm, the given, the sacred. 'Rituals and traditions have been tested and tried over generations by elders; their existence marks a mysterious purpose and blind faith is essential,' Bebe told her repeatedly. Meanings were rarely revealed, sometimes jealously guarded—if one knew them!

It was raining heavily. Playing outside was out of the question. Yashoda went to the *jiko* and added more coal. At least this will heat up the room, she said under a very tired breath. The coal fire never died in the house. When they were not cooking the main meals on the round frame, then the metal pot was put on for tea. They all drank tea here. Tea was served to adults; it was also given to children. Tea for *wageni*—endless guests who came any time of the day or night. Of course, they were invited to stay. 'The guest is our *atithi*—we are not goldsmiths to extend an invitation just for the meal. Lunch, tea, dinner—the guest must be encouraged to stay, and even feel free to spend the night if he so wishes,' Bebe Gurdei said forcefully when Muni had once made a face. Literally boundless hospitality was extended towards the guest—neighbours, friends, cousins, and other relatives. All had to be served savouries and tea.

Bebe Gurdei was a late connoisseur; her tea drinking habit did not develop until very late. Even then, she preferred a glass of hot milk in her favourite brass *bilori*. She could not remember drinking tea in her youth. Tea in those days used to be associated with 'high class' people. Coffee, why coffee was not even heard of in the Bhera of her youth! Even now, they had never drunk coffee: Muni had yet to taste it. She swore that her first cup came after marriage, when her husband had treated her to a cup of frothing coffee at a restaurant called the Rendezvous. She had enjoyed it, but she thought it made her heart race a bit.

She would make tea for everybody, Yashoda decided, and shuddered with cold when a small shower of raindrops fell on her arms. The family gathered around the *jiko* in a squatting position. Their hands immediately stretched towards the flaming embers; the warmth felt good. Yashoda passed around maize cobs. These they roasted with potatoes and *ngwachi* (sweet potatoes), which they actually preferred. And they listened to stories. Lajpat tried to dredge up memories of his own childhood days in Bhera, or those of his arrival in Africa, but the children were more interested in Wade Papaji's fancy stories—those of princes and princesses and many *hoor-paris*, the fairy angels.

Krishen's imagination was unrestrained. His eyes sparkled as he eagerly wove a tale of wizards and princes, having them in fits of laughter. Shivering with fear soon after. 'Wade Papaji, tell us the one about *Baingan Badshahzadi*', they insisted. Enthusiastically, he wove another tale of Princess Aubergine. And of Hira-Mani, the cobra with a ruby head who turns into a handsome prince. In his stories, he prided himself on being clever and extravagant, thinking up quick-witted ruses and escapes from tight predicaments. Being the eldest son, Wade Papaji assumed a paternalistic attitude in his dealings with his younger siblings. He pampered them and lavished them with his anecdotes.

Sisters were '*penji*' to the younger siblings. An elder, whether it was a parent or a relative, or not even that, could not be called by his personal name. Elder brothers and sisters, husbands, in-laws, uncles or aunts, each had specific designations and titles. Yet, peers and juniors were invariably stamped with a name peculiar to their personality. Fond of inventing names, Muni became *pindi-tori*, okra-marrow. Custard apple, aubergine, tomato, *Masi Mulo*, these were common too. 'Do you know why Bhiranwali, Chunilal's wife, was so called?' Muni asked, wanting to showing off her knowledge, 'because her parents were not getting any sons. So they named her "the one who has brothers", hoping that fate would be fooled into giving her male siblings. And, who can remember Jailwali's real name? No-one, I bet. She became Jailwali simply because her husband had a shop in the jail!'

The showers finally gave way to bright sunshine. The children rushed out to play. Yashoda had much work to finish before the day was done. The pulses and rice had already been sifted for tiny stones. The grinding remained. She pleated her sari neatly and tucked it in as if it was a part of her skin; her clothes were always ironed, whether she was going out or not. Sitting with legs apart on the floor at her hand mill, she started splitting her own lentils and making her own spices. Yashoda ground endless sacks of grain of all kinds. One hand constantly poured lentils in the hole, while the other moved the wooden handle to get the two pieces of stone moving. Yashoda sat quietly outside the kitchen in the little *veda* immersed in the laborious task, never once looking up; the *chakki* had to be handled with a certain kind of skill.

One rarely saw her let go—to cry, to laugh, to scream, to pray, to sing in total abandon, or to give vent to her emotions, whether in public or even when she was all by herself. Amma, however, lived a world of her own, day-dreaming. Were these the clues to her hidden self, one could not be quite sure, but for sure her day-dreams and the night ones had a synthesis of sorts. As if they were bonded somewhere, the images began to blend. As if the ones that she could expand at will, ended up in a sweet world, while the ones at night led to crazy worlds, parallel worlds where the impossible always became possible. The images had slowly taken root. She let them develop. And in fact, she looked forward to these sessions of a voluntary solitude. Then she let her sub-conscious brain take over. It travelled and she let it travel. The dreams of her day provoked the dreams of her nights. They were the illusions of her hidden happiness, and they comforted her.

One did not see her light the *diya* or do a *puja*, although she had of late started reading the Bhagavad Gita each morning after her bath. She opened the book at the celebrated section of the Mahabharata. This was at the battlefield of the Kurukshetra—just before the dramatic battle begins. She read and re-read the poem, silently at first. The reported conversation between the great warrior Arjuna and his charioteer Krishna, the incarnation of the supreme, uplifted somewhat her spiritual and physical being: Arjuna's conscience revolts at the thought of war and the large scale massacre that it is about to lead to. On the opposing side, he sees friends and relatives—the war is between the two branches of the same royal family. Yashoda read out aloud the text, 'I desire not victory, nor kingship. My limbs fail, my body quivers, my mouth is parched. I do not wish to kill teachers, fathers, sons, grandfathers, maternal uncles, fathers-in-law, grandsons, brothers-in-law and other relatives—even if they wish to kill me.' She closed the book; tears had welled up in her eyes. Yashoda did not read Krishna's response. That would be for tomorrow.

Yashoda had no friends of her own. She had never had any. She did not frequent the temple, nor did she participate in communal festivities. She kept to herself and to her work. She never learnt the art of sitting down and gossiping, giving vent to her feelings or discussing the lives of others, least of all those of her own. She was a very private person. She did not speak much to anyone. Except perhaps to her husband, and that too only when they went for their long walks. Her conversation never handled poignant, sentimental, heart-rendering, stirring issues, or the deeply philosophical introspective ones. These were laid aside for her own private space.

Yashoda's 'private garden' was full of fantasies. Here she could dream of a utopic world, of an ideal situation. Which was her true world—the one she was living in physically, or the other intangible one? It was hard to know. Perhaps it was all just *maya*. Perhaps neither was real. All was just illusion. Was she was afraid of plunging into close human relationships and social contacts? Or was she afraid of being hurt? Making another mistake? Was she insecure? Perhaps, it was just her way. They never knew. Not even her children understood where their mother hid her real self, but they were content in her assured smile and quiet security.

The world of her absent-minded reverie was rudely and suddenly broken by sounds of the quotidian, commonplace, routine material world. She looked up from her *chakki* and heard the call. '*Malli Malli, Malli Malli*'. Unenthusiastically, she got up to open the back door leading to the small alley reserved mainly for hawkers, vendors and toilet cleaners. The man laid down the huge bedsheet swinging from his right shoulder onto the floor and displayed his wares. Brass utensils of all kinds—of late even stainless steel ones—shone in the noonday sun. But Yashoda had neither the time nor the inclination to discuss and bargain. Moreover, she had not even sorted through the old clothes that she could exchange for the pots and pans, so she shook her head, saying '*Hakuna kitu*' (There is nothing), and shut the door behind her.

16

Alchemy

Sham-e-gham ki kasam
Aaj ghamgheen hain hum
Aa bhi jha aa bhi jaa
O mere sanam . . .

(I swear by this dismal evening
That I am in the depths of loneliness,
Please come, please come,
My beloved . . .)

— Hindi film song

Rugged, earthy and vigorous—these were perhaps the most appropriate words to describe Bebe Gurdei. The more she loved someone, the harsher were the words: *khasmakhaneya, marjaneya*. When Bebe Gurdei swung into a whirl of activity, you knew that her excitement was mounting. Today, her agitation could be attributed to the arrival of another grandson, Prem. Labi's son. 'Found's son is here', Muni announced from a distance. 'It's not nice, the way you put it.' Bebe Gurdei knitted her eyebrows and showed her displeasure. 'But that's what Labi Buaji is called. 'Found'. It's a strange name, Bebe. Why did you decide to call your daughter Labi?' Here was Muni with another 'why'.

This time Bebe Gurdei tolerated her incessant questioning. 'Her full name is Ramlubayi, which as you know means beloved of Rama. When I had her, I didn't expect that she would live, she had been born in such precarious conditions. To avert the evil eye, I decided that I would just say that she was found. So Ramlubayi came to be called Labi,' Bebe Gurdei explained. And precisely because Bebe Gurdei kept a special niche in her heart for the boy, the rest of the children teased him.

Dragging him towards the kitchen, Bebe quickly stuffed a big handful of almonds into his small mouth, forcing them in with her thumb. '*Jaldi kha, jaldi kha*,' coaxing him to finish. At the same time, she got into a frenzy preparing butter *paronthas* and heating a glass of milk, choosing carefully the creamiest layers. The cajoling carried on: he must finish before the rest of the family arrived.

She called him all kinds of names, but never used his real one, Prem—even though Prem means love. Bebe did not have even a nodding acquaintance with sweet talk; she used swear words instead, *khasmakhaneya* (husband-eater) being the preferred term. This was her way of showering love, especially for warding off the evil eye. No cuddling or caressing—instead, she treated children to luxuries, especially those she had been denied in her youth. Almonds were definitely a favoured offering. 'They are expensive, and come all the way from Kashmir,' she would tell Prem.

Undoubtedly, almonds were revered as food for the brain, and strength for the body; a must for the new mother, a tonic for the weak. When her son was not around, Bebe Gurdei actually pinched almonds from the big jar in the duka, quickly hiding them in the pocket of her *kameez*, thinking no one had seen her. But Lajpat always knew. 'These are for sale,' he grumbled. She denied vehemently pocketing them, sulked for a few days, and then carried on in the same way. Running to her numerous River Road friends, she would display her treasures to them. 'These are for you,' she would say. The pleasure was always hers, especially with all the risks it involved. Her appeal lay in a childlike wonderment—puckish one moment, provocative the next.

Bebe Gurdei was not the only almond-thief in the family. Of late, her grandson—Lajpat's younger son—had also learnt the game. His father would never even have known had it not been for a strange turn of events: Surinder stood first in class. Now this may not sound extraordinary, but the fact was that the boy was not up to the mark—or marks. It was impossible. Lajpat knew his son very well—as did the rest of the children. '*Susti, posti, vehemi—dulhe da pra*' (lazy, intoxicated, superstitious—an idle brother of the bridegroom). This was their way of poking fun at him, with some truth in the ragging. The boy lacked purpose, and seriously hated studies. On top of being incredibly mischevious, he had a passion for sleep. It follows that no amount of cajoling would induce the boy to pick up a book. 'Show me your hands,' Masterji at school would insist, and Surinder would plead, 'Masterji, please spare me the rod!' Even as he said this, he would be thinking up fresh mischief. Teasing younger siblings was his idea of fun—pulling his sisters' plaited hair, putting a grasshopper in their dresses.

Often, Amma ran after him with his *qaida*, but to no avail. He would find an excuse to get away. It was easy for him to deal with his mother, but his father was another story. Surinder was a little afraid of Bauji and could not look him directly in the eye, especially as he was in the wrong so often. The day he got the highest marks and was top of his class, Lajpat was not happy. Oh no. He did not go round the neighbourhood distributing sweets on his son's success. He became angry. There was foul play for sure.

'What is the meaning of this?' he accused his son, pointing at the piece of paper in his hand. The boy looked down at his feet, not daring to look at the fateful piece of paper. He had just assumed that Bauji would be pleased. But once again, he seemed to have done the wrong thing. He racked his brains but couldn't come up with a satisfactory answer. Shamefaced, he muttered inaudibly. For once, Lajpat did not restrain himself and gave his son a tight slap.

Lajpat put on his coat and immediately set off for school. It was vacation time, but teachers were required to report for duty daily for a few hours. He confronted Surinder's class teacher in a single breath. 'My son cannot even write *alif* correctly. How could he . . . what is the meaning of this?' he shouted, the almost crumpled report trembling in his hand. The teacher stood his ground, insisting on the boy's excellent participation and class record. Lajpat retreated, unconvinced. Ultimately, he extracted the truth from his son: Surinder had offered his teacher more almonds than usual . . . one whole kilo! Lajpat stared at his son almost in disbelief. He did not know what to say. It was disastrous whichever way he looked at it.

Without another word, he put on his coat again and was halfway to the school, when he hesitated. Removing his coat, he sat down on a wayside bench, replaying the whole incident—and visualizing where it was leading to: the principal's office. Perhaps here lay his discomfort. And he realized it was so when the face of the man flashed before his eyes. He took a quick decision. No, he would not report the young teacher to the principal. Not only would it ruin his career—for he was sure to be sacked—but also unleash on a fellow Indian a torrent of humiliation from a white man. For him to be the instigator of such an occasion was unbearable. 'My son, however, must not get away so lightly,' he concluded loudly. For sure, Surinder would get a sound beating that night. As Lajpat Rai slowly made his way home, he expelled a long sigh. He was glad that he had not barged into the principal's office. His frustration shifted focus.

Ask Surinder to read, and his mind would already be wandering. It was a punishment both for him and for the listener. But get him to mimic any character from one of the numerous films, and he was sure to come out with flying colours. Body language or dialogue, he knew them all.

The fascination with films was universal. First came silent English films. Then the long, melodramatic Indian motion pictures with eight to ten songs. The age of cinema had arrived. The children were mesmerized, most of all Surinder. Lajpat too was seduced. He ordered a projector from India, along with some films.

At first they were happy just watching slides of the Taj Mahal or the Lal Qila (Red Fort). Or even a bear dancing to the tunes of his master. A hooded cobra or a naked fakir—stereotypical images of India. But when Lajpat screened the first Indian film *Raja*

Harishchandra, the slides were immediately forgotton. Now, they were being treated to the tale of the truth-obsessed king, a film that had been released in Bombay just before the first world war, a time when they were not even born, when Lajpat had not yet met Yashoda, when he had not even arrived in this part of the world. Yet, even now, so many years later, they were mesmerized by the silent film *Raja Harishchandra,* with characters who communicated with each other through dialogue cards. By the time they had the pleasure of seeing the first Indian talkie *Alam Ara,* which was released in 1931, the film was already history in India. For them, however, the talking-singing-dancing was still a novelty.

All lights in the room were switched off as Lajpat Rai started the projector. It made a whirring noise. A ray of light bisected the darkened room. The white bedsheet pinned on the wall as a screen flickered alive. Their necks were already strained waiting for the show. Many children sat on the floor in half-lotus positions—those from other families had been charged ten cents on the quiet by the boys; Lajpat never got to hear of it. They clapped enthusiastically as the first images came up. For the next half-hour (before reel change), they watched in silence until the lights came on again. Then they cheered in joy. The vicarious thrills of the fantasy world had engulfed them.

Then came the era of K.L. Saigal. He became a celebrity as he acted and sang. What a poignant voice he had! His nasal singing haunted them. His nomadic persona only added to his attraction, from the dark eroticism of his brooding looks to the vagrant locks of hair. Saigal was bald and always wore a wig. Conventionally, he could not have been called handsome. But whatever his looks, Kundan Lal Saigal was a star. Even before the end of his era, he had become a legend. They all took to looking like Devdas in his career-defining role based on Saratchandra Chattopadhyaya's desperate character. They identified with the singing superstar with his sonorous sweep. His immortal songs *'Diya jalao'* and *'So ja rajkumari'* remained with them for a lifetime. Surinder saw Saigal's films not once or twice, but eight or ten times, and took to articulating the dialogue of the drunk mourning his lost love in a perpetual abyss of despair.

For the two hours or so that they could live in this idea of homelessness, it released them from limitations, filled them with a spirit of adventure. It was a world totally remote from the conventions and norms of societal rules. Here at least they could dream of another kind of life. Suspense thrillers, melodramas, musicals and love triangles; the cellophane-wrapped world of commercial cinema enamoured them. Noorjehan, Suraiya, Madhubala—the lives of stars and divas became theirs for a time.

When Liberty Cinema opened in the Pangani area a few years later, their Sunday evenings were reserved, and Lajpat's seats were booked in advance. Dressed in their best, Amma, Muni and her sisters looked forward to an evening of the latest films from India. Amma would become so hooked that she took to attending even the mid-week afternoon special ladies' show. The spectators were Hindu women in colourful saris, burqa-clad Somali and Punjabi Muslim women. Men were strictly prohibited in the séance. The women's long black veils would come off; they would shout in joy and excitement. They screamed at the moving images. They clapped at the good guys, they yelled their own dialogues at the bad characters, they sang with the singers. They even threw small coins towards the screen to express their happiness, especially during dance scenes. Sometimes, fights broke out. It could happen that in the dark hall a lady slowly opened the bag of her neighbour in the hope of pilfering her money!

Right next to Liberty Cinema was the clinic of a very popular doctor. The small waiting room was always crammed with patients. But that never deterred him from taking ample breaks to enjoy a few scenes of the film being screened, before returning to the waiting and the ailing. In fact, very often his first question to his patients was whether they had seen the last successful film—and whether they enjoyed it. He would even recite dialogues, criticize the actors and heroines or confirm the lyrics of a particular song—and give the same antidote to all in little packets wrapped in newspaper! Alas, many such old cinema halls would become future churches due to intense Christian missionary zeal.

Half a decade reeled under the impact of the serendipitous forties. Movies and stars ruled their minds. There was the beautiful Anglo-Indian actress Ruby Myers and her handsome Parsi paramour—acting partner D. Billimoria. Then, Sohrab Modi's *Sikander*, immortalized by the presence of the great actor Prithviraj Kapoor. Alexander, the Macedonian king, became their new mythical hero as the movie showed them horse battles, court scenes, and of course his romance with the beautiful Persian Ruksana. There was also *Jhansi ki Rani*—one of the first Indian films in technicolour—leading her army against British forces in 1857.

All the children were clearly inspired. They cut swords out of cardboard biscuit boxes, silver lining intact, and led their one-man armies against each other. They internalized the bold and dramatic dialogues; their language became more and more colourful. Surinder even managed to copy all the onomatopoeic sounds that went with the dialogues—the ooohs, aahs, dishyums.

However, once Nadia made her appearance on celluloid, their restless spirits found the perfect channel. With her, the stereotype of a passive, compliant, meek, obedient, quiet and unassuming heroine was quickly buried as she fenced with villains atop moving trains. She swung from chandeliers and whipped the bad guy. The Greek-born, Australia-bred Nadia did wondrous acrobatics without ever resorting to a stuntsman. Caged with a lion, jumping from dizzy heights, her role as *Hunterwali* earned her the title 'fearless Nadia'. Fortunately, Surinder didn't—rather, couldn't—try any of these tactics! He neither possessed Nadia's energy, nor her guts. Clearly though, the chimera of films was consuming his youth. As poetry was seizing Baldev's. And dramatized story recitation Krishen's. If cinematic possibilities had existed in the colonial Kenya of the time, Surinder would have found his vocation.

Later in life, Surinder became—what else—a dukawallah in his father's shop. Soon after Kenya's independence, he migrated to Britain and ran a grocery shop. But only after trying to work in a London office: a job he quit the first evening because he was asked to sweep the floor. After years of hard work and long hours, Surinder would die in his London shop aged sixty.

'*Qaid mein hai bulbul, sayaad muskuraye, kaha bhi na jaye, chup raha bhi na jaye*' (the bulbul is in the cage, the trapper smiles ... but look at my plight ... I can neither protest, nor remain a mute spectator). Tausif Hassan had burst into song. This was his way of respiring. One could almost visualize him exhale and inhale his lexicon in melody and in rhythm, as if his breath was being liberated from the mundane tasks. He blotted out the clinic and Lajpat's medical store from his conscious self. Instead of having a cup of tea or taking a nap, *hakim sahib* took a break from work through song. He switched off the world of the body and its ailments and entered a different world altogether. The poetry came in flashes, full of rich imagery.

His 'other' world was a realm devoid of any limitations. It was even beyond time. It was contained in a capsule—a world within worlds. His world had seasons, and all the colours of the rainbow. The emotions were strong. The sensations brought goose-bumps. Here everything was feminine. Tausif Hassan captured imagined worlds in words. He gave them life. The words that manifested gave him and his listeners complete exaltation.

It was a period of dreaming. '*Wah wah*!' listeners standing around praised the poet, demanding encores of their favourite lines. The power of the poetic word, the magic of Urdu *shairi* was in evidence. The mood of the listeners heightened Tausif Hassan's mood. He talked in verse most of the time. In Urdu verse—even while describing the body and its problems. 'Your *nadi* is unsteady. The gait is serpentine. Increase in wind, too much *vat* ...' Any occasion inspired him to come up with beautiful *shairi*—philosophical, romantic and spiritual. By the end of the short break, he was fully revived. When he wasn't singing or looking into the mouths of his patients, he smoked his *hookah*. Or he made kites for the children.

Right then he wasn't doing any of these. He picked up his walking stick and walked over to the group of young boys. He wore a white *chust* pajama, a black *sherwani*, and a red fez hat with a pompom—all these gave him a dandy look. Tausif Hassan Naqvi, Luckhnowi *shair* and *hakim*. Tall and handsome, belonging to a family of physicians and one in his own right. He was suffused with the Urdu poetic tradition, and was especially impressed by the verses of Mir Taqi Mir, Momin and Iqbal. '*Jeetey raho badshaho . . . kya haal hai . . .* may you live long, O king . . . how are you?' Krishen and Baldev greeted him in open admiration, as if he were their peer.

These were the heydays of poetry, of Urdu *shairi* in particular. And Tausif Hassan had already become a mentor of sorts. The guidance they couldn't get from school, Tausif Hassan provided. His command of Urdu and Persian influenced many a young boy. Wade and Chhote Papaji had been seduced long ago, when he first started coming to their father's shop. Even when they were at school, either during the recess, or if the teacher happened to be late or absent, they teased masterji in verse. Flaunting and honing their poetic eloquence at the same time.

With his elbow leaning on a friend's shoulder, *salaam*ing before showing off his *shairi*, how much pleasure Chhote Papaji would take in impressing his friends! And when they told him, 'O *praji*, you are an elevated man already. You have been hiding this talent from your *yaar*s (friends) for so long,' the young man would beam with pride. Those were some of the big moments. He would treasure them for a long time to come. Even Krishen was so inspired by Indian films and Urdu *shairi*, a la Tausif Hassan Naqvi, that he started spending more time rehearsing dialogues, or with the maestro himself, sitting at the father's *duka*, rather than attending school. All sense of time would be lost when they got together. The result was obvious; he failed his exams yet a third time. And so, much to Krishen's joy, Lajpat took him out of school and inducted him in his *duka*. Here, as was to be expected, he did very well, and the shop benefited.

They were called 'unqualified medical practitioners' as they did not possess valid certificates from recognized institutions. Letters of rejection had been sent to the various Indian dukas selling herbal medicines under the aegis of knowledgeable medicine-men. The government introduced legislation to prevent *vaids* and *hakims* from practising. But the dukawallahs were not to be outdone. It was simple: the refusal letter from the authorities was framed and hung on the wall. It acted as the 'approval certificate'. Who would have known the difference? What with English being spoken by so few, much less read, it would probably have made little difference even if they had known. Lajpat had his letter of 'approval' hanging right behind the counter, clearly visible to customers—who came happily, with full confidence. This was the medicine they had always known and were used to. It made them well.

The reputation of Popular Medicine & Industrial Stores grew, its clientele and their faith in herbs expanded. By now, Krishen's interest in herbs had become phenomenal. Lajpat often took both of his boys into the fields in search of all kinds of plants. Very early in the morning they set out towards the higher altitudes. Here, he pointed out the medicinal uses of various plants and herbs. 'Keep your eyes open,' he whispered softly, as if not to disturb the waking beauty of nature. 'A keen, concentrated vision is absolutely essential, for some of the tiny herbs lie hidden beneath other shrubs.' Bending down to collect a herb, Lajpat looked at it carefully before showing it to them, '*Brahmi booti* is bitter and cool; it stimulates circulation, revitalizes the nerves and brain; strengthens memory and intelligence,' he said, before putting it carefully in a cloth bag.

They walked for a long time, checking the texture of leaves or the firmness of roots. 'Learn to respect nature, and it will reveal itself to you,' he would say. They talked of the kinds of leaves best for poultices and the wonders of pure ghee. 'It isn't merely a matter of swallowing potions and pills, but a state of affluence of the whole body in conjunction with the universe,' Lajpat continued, disclosing secrets of nature. 'How herbs are grown and collected affects their efficacy. Branches are best taken during the rains, when they have sap; roots, in summer or winter, when they have shed their leaves'.

Lajpat Rai had also started growing his own little medicine garden—especially marigold, so necessary in the preparation of ear ointment—in *debes* on the toilet roof. The famous four-gallon aluminium *debes* were still much in use. Square-shaped with a round opening at the top, their utilization was almost limitless: carrying water, measuring rice, storing wheat, heating water for a bath, roofing houses—any and every purpose, almost. Gurdei grew herbs in them, on the toilet roof at the end of the *veda*. Here on high, they were well protected and received the most sunlight.

She grew parsley and mint, claiming that chutney of the two helped treat gastritis. Aloe vera formed a notable nutritional supplement in Bebe's diet. Sun-dried, pickled with *ajwain* (caraway seeds) and salt, and stored between two chapatis. All ready for the following day's lunch. Holy basil was of the utmost importance. 'The fragrance of *tulsi* purifies the air. It is good for the stomach. It evacuates bile, destroys worms, aids urine retention, calms asthma, treats bronchitis,' she used to say. Almost a magic cure. Her list went on as she tried to insist that it form a part of the diet of the children as well. For Gurdei, *tulsi* was the embodiment of goddess Laxmi. The modest aromatic shrub had its place of honour in the centre of the *veda*.

Even Bebe Hardei's oil and water pickles were famous. During the hot dry weather, she made preserves of carrots, turnips, beetroot and radish immersed in water, with red pepper, green ginger, mustard seed and garlic. 'Purifies the blood,' she said.

It was decoction-making day. All types of pots had been laid out in the verandah. A few copper—and one or two brass—pots shone in the light. The rest were clay. Lajpat was soon busy heating iron for pounding into powder. Sometimes he just prepared the required remedy in an iron vessel, allowing the metal to be directly absorbed into the decoction. 'This way, those suffering from anaemia or digestive weaknesses can benefit,' he explained to his boys. Gold was left buried in a bottle in the open soil for several months before being used 'because gold is hot. It improves intelligence and strengthens the nerves. Even wearing gold is beneficial—perhaps that is why we shower our women with gold,' he added with a laugh.

Like alchemists, they extracted the *ark* from the metals—its essence. 'If any of you girls are in cloth, keep away from the *ark*,' Bebe Gurdei shouted a warning before beginning the process. It was a time of purification, and menstruating women were not allowed anywhere in the vicinity, for even their shadows were polluting. The girls obeyed without arguing, but she saw them knot their eyebrows. 'You will not be able to concentrate on this important function,' she said as if pacifying them. How Bebe Gurdei loved feeling important!

The decoction process was finally over for the day, to recommence at dawn. They were all exhausted. Soon after dinner, Lajpat came with a spoonful of *gulkand*, for every member of his family. 'What is it Bauji?' the younger children screamed in horror. 'It's your favourite . . . *gulkand*. Here, open your mouth. You know that it's good for your digestion,' said Lajpat forcing the jelly-like mixture down the little girl's throat. *Gulkand* was Lajpat's own concoction of fresh rose petals and raw sugar syrup taken at bedtime as a laxative, especially during hot days. 'Cleanse the system,' was his constant advice. 'Clear the intestines, keep the stomach light. Bad digestion is the root of most problems.'

At least once a week he gave some such laxative or tonic to the family in addition to one medium-sized onion added to a tablespoon of honey before breakfast. Bowel movement was a key indicator to health. Constipation was regarded as a proper disease. If any member of the family failed to defecate even one day, this was taken as seriously as fever. In fact, they spent long hours discussing digestion and digestive processes. *Isabgol* (psyllium husk) was soaked in water for diarrhoea, in milk for constipation. *Churan* to cure flatulence, gastritis and indigestion; neem for fever or liver problems. *Karela* was also a stimulant for sluggish livers, or to help dissolve kidney stones resulting from dehydration. *Mulathi da sat*, liquorice root mixed with purgatives, for colds and cough. Garlic burnt in oil for earache.

'Amma, my stomach aches again,' Muni came running a little later. 'Again!' Yashoda scolded. 'What have you been upto this time?' But she already knew what was wrong. 'It must be her *dharan*,' she said under her breath. This is an ailment for which there is no Occidental equivalent—a condition in which the navel is displaced from the centre of the body line. It brings pain, a feeling of being bloated or distended. It usually leads to days of acute constipation, or diarrhoea. Bringing it back to its proper place requires manipulation of the navel while rubbing the sides of the body.

By then even Yashoda was well-versed in cures. She took a long piece of cloth and twisted it into a small knot. Muni too was used to the procedure and was already lying flat on her stomach on the ground. Carefully, Yashoda placed the knotted cloth under Muni's stomach, in such a way that her navel pressed against the knot. And then she pressed the girl's back with her foot. Muni protested softly, 'Slowly, Amma!' Yashoda continued, a little less forcefully. Then she put a few dry pieces of chapati mixed with sugar in Muni's mouth before turning her over carefully. Relief came in no time.

Not that its medicinal role had declined or become secondary, but Lajpat decided that his store, better known as 'Kiche *di* dukan', would diversify into soap, nail varnish, dry fruit, *papadum*, and even *murabba* and *achar*. Lajpat himself had become quite an expert at some of these. Gurdei, Yashoda lent a hand at times. They processed fruit and made preserves. Their chutneys and pickles were already becoming popular.

Also in stock was material for traditional ceremonies, such as colourful, fancy *rakhis*. At a certain juncture in the month of August, every Hindu family came in search of these sacred threads, whether simple, colourful, fancy or plain. This was for the Rakhi festival, where sisters tie a sacred thread on their brothers' wrists to symbolize their bond of love and affection, extract a promise of protection, and bless the wearer. Each year, days before the festival, Bebe Gurdei was sure to relate to the children the origins of the tradition.

'In the Mahabharata, Lord Krishna once cut his finger. Immediately, Draupadi, common wife to the five Pandava brothers, tore off a piece off her sari and tied it round Krishna's finger. Krishna smiled at her instant concern, and asked her what she wanted for this favour. "Just your holy presence in my life at all times," Draupadi replied.' As she tied the *rakhi* on her brothers' wrists, Muni thought of herself as Draupadi.

Besides making *rakhis*, the girls and women of the *biradari* spent long hours rolling long black strands of thread between the toes of their feet and thumbs of their hands. Muni was still learning the art of making *parande*. Today she had managed to get the threads entangled. Bebe Gurdei screamed at her. Amma Yashoda quietly got up from her sitting position. Gently and very patiently, she started undoing the knots. She showed Muni once again how the *parande* were to be made. 'Here, take these three strands, roll them very carefully. Like this. Now tie them together. We will add colourful tassels at the bottom,' she said.

In the film world, the *paranda* had become a tool in the art of seduction: tassels held in the right hand would be swung in rhythm to endless songs. Even in the real world, the simple and inexpensive *paranda* was special. Any festive occasion called for new offerings of *parande*. Whether it was for Karva Chauth or for Diwali, fathers, brothers, husbands (few women went to shop) turned up at Lajpat's duka to take back *parande* for wives and sisters. Muni had not yet started wearing one—in fact, she would wear her first at her wedding many years later, a long black one with red and gold tassels at the end. That day, the women would lovingly massage her black hair with coconut oil before entwining the beautiful *paranda* into her tresses tenderly.

In the hot months of January to March, Gurdei began making endless *wadiyan*. They were mostly for sale in the shop, but some were for their own consumption. How they loved them—Bebe Gurdei, Amma Yashoda and even Lajpat. Bebe also managed to keep quite a number of them aside for her numerous River Road friends: Basant, Chachi Bhagwanti and some of the other Perewaliyan. How these women relished Bebe's Amritsari *wadiyan*! In fact, Bebe's recipe was not from Amritsar at all. The secret formula was a Bhera speciality.

Every woman of Bhera could make these shapeless, muddy brown, stone-hard but weightless blobs. They were salty, spicy additions to an otherwise insipid dish like rice or potatoes. Surrounded by all kinds of masalas, lentils, marrow, chillies, Bebe Gurdei was in for another long day. She did not go out visiting that day. Instead, her friends came over to help. She even made *papadum*s out of *khichri*, spreading the paste out to dry on a *gunia* (gunny sack). The day Bebe chose to do her laborious tasks was important: the sun had to be at its fiercest. Papadums dried in a day, but *wadiyan* took time. They needed to be turned over now and then.

Running the shop was a collective effort: they all felt part of it. Bebe Gurdei, Amma Yashoda, Muni, her brothers and even the younger members of the family contributed to this endeavour. The whole family became involved. The duka became a place of work, worship and socializing and, of course, much gossip. The children helped whenever they could, which was often, for school meant little or no homework. The duka and its wares taught them a lot, and they thoroughly enjoyed themselves.

They collected maize cobs, and ate boxfuls of *jamun* fruit to obtain the berries for medicinal use. Beneath the flesh of the deep violet, almost black, *jamun* berry lies a pit which is crushed into flour for treating diabetes. The juice itself is known as a liver stimulant, while decoctions from the bark cured mouth ulcers. The *jamun* had a reputation larger than itself: formal Hindu rituals like marriage commence with an invocation to it. 'In the continent of Jambu *dvipa*, where the land of India lies . . .'

* * *

It was the slow part of the afternoon. Few customers were about. Bauji was not around. After a short nap, Lajpat was either busy making medicines, or looking for new avenues to develop the business. So Krishen put his favourite record on. As usual, it burst forth at full volume. The old Kikuyu record started with a small giggle. Then came the chuckles—once, a second time, then repeatedly; several times over. Eventually, it broke into continuous loud laughter. At the end there was sobbing. By now a huge crowd, mostly Africans, had gathered round the shop They too burst into laughter, some holding their bellies and rolling on the floor. Krishen was satisfied. At least it attracted customers! It worked every time he put the record on.

River Road was usually a busy street. Business carried on till dark; sometimes beyond 7 p.m. Many *fundi*s and dukawallas went home for supper, only to return soon after. Since his home was at the back of the shop, Lajpat Rai was encouraged and tempted to work long hours. 'From 8 a.m. to 6 p.m.—just like the *gora* shops', he added, amused that he had found something in common with the Europeans. But following British norms was not his objective. He just wanted the evening walk with his wife. Not infrequently, however late at night, clients requiring emergency medicines knocked on the back door of the house. Lajpat Rai would always serve them.

One night, there was frantic banging. The whole household woke up in fear. Lights were switched on everywhere. It was 4 a.m. Hesitantly, Lajpat asked, 'Who is it?' The man on the other side of the door pleaded for help. 'My father . . . his eyes hurt . . . please . . . he needs medicine urgently.' Reluctantly, Krishen had to get up. Preparing a drug at dawn was not very amusing, the fact that no profit accrued made it even less so. The cost to the man was five cents for the packet. The man was back in the morning to express gratitude, as the cure worked.

Many vegetable vendors came to the duka in the mornings with their produce. This morning too one had just stepped in. The man put down his heavy load of *kikapus* and *gunias* and smiled at Lajpat. '*Habari Mzee*,' he wished Lajpat. Lajpat was not yet an old man, but the term signified respect. '*Mzuri sana* . . . very well,' replied

Lajpat. '*Unalete nine leo* . . . what have you brought?' Lajpat asked the ageing African. '*Viazi na vitunguru bwana* . . . potatoes and onions, sir,' the old man replied. Lajpat did not buy a mere pound or two, but took the whole *gunia* of whatever the man had to sell. Often friends brought in *gunias* of wheat, potatoes and onions to the duka. On the festival of Id, the milkman was sure to stop by with milk cans. Like the other dukas of the bazaar and River Road, Lajpat's store was a hub of sorts. It was situated across the Indian Bazaar, right at the beginning of River Road, and so got custom from both areas. Most clients were Punjabi-speaking, both Hindu and Muslim. Rarer were Gujaratis, Goans and Parsis. Even amongst the Punjabis who visited the shop, many were 'non-buying' callers, and quickly came to be known as such. These precursors of window shoppers went from shop to shop—to Assanands, to Shankardass, to the *paan* shop—and moved on. Just to chat, gossip, exchange rumours, socialize. Simple people with little pretensions, they did not have to search for topics of conversation. They read little. Most of them did not even own a radio. They rarely bought newspapers. Their topics of conversation usually meandered around day-to-day lives. What was common, however, to all these visitors at the duka, was that they were men.

There were also those who could be categorized as *muftikhor*—freebie-seekers. On the far end of the long glass sideboard at the entrance, behind which stood either Lajpat or Krishen—sometimes both—lay a silver tin of *paan-supari*. Betel leaf and nut were essential to welcome customers. Serious buyers rarely partook of these; they were in too much of a hurry. The *muftikhor* never came from the front, always from the side. His hand automatically and inevitably went towards the green leaf and chopped brown nuts. These he stuffed at the back of the mouth, before indulging in a conversation of no value—the red liquid oozing out from the *paan* in his mouth.

Somewhere in the middle of his long monologue, his hand gravitated towards the *gunias* of other goodies in front of him—fennel seeds or dates. Digressing into some other topic, the *muftikhor* would ask to try out specific products; the intention was never one of purchase—just a 'trial'. Bebe Gurdei had many *muftikhor* friends to whom she offered *wadiyan* and *papad*, pickles and spices. 'Useless and idle persons,' Krishen shouted behind their backs, although Lajpat took them on as a matter of fact. They didn't seem to bother him—even if they did, he rarely commented.

There was a freeloader who often came to the shop with complaints about various products, and true to his nature, was always back to 'test' another—free of charge, of course. Eventually, Krishen decided that a lesson was called for. When this client next reproached them with, 'Your *surma* is *khara*, it is not strong enough to clean my eyes,' Krishen had the right mixture ready. 'Open your eyes and I will apply it for you. This time I doubt you will complain.' No sooner did the black antimony of sulphuret touch the corner of his eyes, than the man burst out screaming and jumping, 'Oh! Oh! You have burnt me, you have destroyed my eyes!'

Eventually the poor guy calmed down a little. He squatted by the door of the duka, and held the sides of his head, shaking it to and fro. When he returned a few days later, Krishen did not have the time to conceal himself, so he just smiled weakly. But the man was beaming with contentment!

17

The matriarchs

A man lives again
Through his children,
Through the trees that he has planted,
Through the words that he has uttered ...
                                    —African wisdom

Lajpat's Chachi arrived from Nyeri with her family. She didn't have to give advance notice—they knew she always stayed awhile. The boys vacated their room and slept on mattresses on the shop floor, amongst sacks of grain, rats and all kinds of odours. Guest rooms, sitting rooms, salons or a formal dining room were luxuries they never had, nor missed. All the rooms were flexibly used—according to occasion and time of day.

The boys were happy, as they got a few days of freedom from adults—freedom to indulge in more mischief. Yashoda came every night carrying glasses of hot milk. The older boys waited until the younger ones had fallen asleep. Then they took the cream atop their glasses and smeared it on the toes and fingers of their brothers. The little ones would awake in the middle of the night with itchy bites on their toes where rats had gnawed them!

If it wasn't rats in the duka, it was mosquitoes in the *veda*. That was when more than one family came to visit from Nyeri, Nanyuki, Meru or Londiani. Charpoys with mattresses and blankets had to be put out into the uncovered space of the *veda*.

Visiting *bebes, chachis, lalajis* and *baujis* developed red bulges on the skin, dark circles under the eyes—the visitors took it all with a laugh.

In fact, there was no major partition even between shop and home in the duka-houses. The *veda* was cemented, often rectangular in shape, and used flexibly. The compound created the varying moods for the ambience of the home. Here, they cleaned their lentils, and put out other cereals in the sun to rid them small black bugs. Bebe Gurdei, Amma Yashoda and the other ladies worked here making *mathian, sevian*, and all kinds of savouries—fried stuff with lots of red pepper, green chillies, topped with tangy spices. How the children loved them! Yashoda actually had to put these under lock and key in huge *debe*s, safe from her growing children. 'Then, at meal times, you will have no hunger,' she would say gently but firmly.

When the weather was fine, Bebe Gurdei cooked just outside the tiny kitchen, and served the family there. Children played there, studied there, sitting on small wooden stools. Most mornings, Yashoda brought out her little Singer sewing machine. Sari blouses and petticoats for herself, *salwars* for Bebe, school uniforms for the children. Until lower primary, the girls wore yellow frocks to school. Bright yellow *kameez* and white *salwar* for upper primary, yellow sari at high school—'the colour of *laddus*', the boys teased their sisters. It was actually the saffron of the Arya Samaj. They wore the colour for so many years, Muni refused to include a single yellow item in her wedding trousseau—not even a ribbon.

Yashoda had learnt stitching, knitting and crochet by imitation. Apart from getting Lajpat's trousers tailored by the Gujarati *darzi*, she sewed everything herself, including grey shorts and white shirts for the school-going boys. Only a wedding in the family warranted a *darzi* coming home for a few days with his machine. For Diwali, Yashoda managed new clothes for the entire family. Sitting in the *veda*, stitching, cutting, hemming—the entire activity without a single word, sometimes. And, when new fabric was required, Lajpat would say, 'Muni will come with me'. Muni was always ready, 'Wait

Bauji, I'll get my *chunni*.' At Sethi Silk Store, or Fulchand's, Lajpat allowed Muni to choose the material.

At bedtime, Muni climbed up to the top berth of the bunk bed, taking care not to knock over one of Bebe's precious little gods lying on the small table beneath. Bebe Gurdei's little *mandir* took up a large part of space in the little room. It had such a profusion of paraphernalia that it appeared to be colourfully chaotic. But the truth is that she knew exactly which object served what purpose in her endless ceremonies so full of symbolism. Pictures of so many different gods and goddesses—Sheranwali (Durga) astride her lion, different weapons in each of the four hands, *Lachmi* (that's how Bebe pronounced it) on a huge pink lotus. And, of course the colourful and ever-smiling picture of Krishna, with a mischievous look in his eyes, flute in hand, his cow in tow. Krishna's *murti* was found in most Hindu homes. Like a miniature temple, Bebe's small shrine radiated blessings constantly. It was her private sanctuary. Her *puja* was a simple affair: she rang the bells, rotated the flame. She lit the small lamp and offered flowers at the feet of the pictures. A brief chant, love and reverence in her heart, or a fight with her god.

One day, when Muni blew out the *diya* before leaving the room, Bebe was terribly upset. 'If necessary, the wick must be snuffed out with the thumb and forefinger,' she exclaimed sharply. Hands on hip; you could see that she was furious. 'Why do you want to do that anyway?' Extinguishing lights was not a good omen. Asking for the blessing of the gods, Bebe bowed her head as she lit the flame. She even covered her head with the *dupatta*, and said '*Jai!* Let there be light in every home!' when switching on the electric light first time in the evening!

Bebe had a habit of locking the door before embarking on her famous social calls. One such afternoon, smoke seemed to emanate from her room. '*Bwana, Mzee, Mzee!*' Meru, the young houseboy had shouted frantically, '*Moshi, moshi*! Smoke, smoke!' Eyes popping with fear, body poised to flee, Meru let out a loud scream, rooted to the spot. Immediately, panic prevailed. Lajpat left the shop unguarded, and rushed to the back. The door to Bebe's room was broken open as huge yellow flames descended upon them. Apparently, the *diya* from Bebe's *puja thali* had overturned—perhaps with the wind—and Bebe's mattress was entirely burnt!

The Indian Bazaar glittered with lights. Every shop had been cleared of furniture. Instead, carpets, *dhurries* and cushions had been laid on the floor. The walls were covered with cloth. In the centre stood a priest chanting mantras, blessing new account books, while hundreds of oil lamps lit the way for the goddess of fortune to find her way in. Diwali was an especially important time for the duka; there was more work than usual, and the entire family got involved. Many nights before, one could hear the pounding of charcoal, the preparation of fireworks and *phuljhari* (sparklers). The children collected wild pink roses to make *gulkand*, or put them in a *hamam* to manufacture *attar* by distillation. They also made rose water and sherbet. Lajpat could be found cutting up melon after melon, and stirring the sugar syrup at the same time. *Petha* was a speciality of Bhera, and Lajpat Rai was an expert at making them.

Many friends showed up. It was a time of much laughter and hard work. Lajpat's friend Sevaram had arrived, insisting that he wanted to help. The older boys—in their usual playful manner—made him crush coal! Someone burst a cracker, it landed in the potassium, and the whole place nearly caught fire. A huge figure in *salwar-kameez* was seen approaching the duka. Even in the distance, they could recognize it as that of Bebe Basant. Before she could identify the children with her astigmatic vision, Krishen had already dashed into the house to put on a record. 'Ai Basant re—here comes spring', Suraiya's voice was soon heard.

Basant wasn't going to let him get away with it. She breezed into the room where Krishen was hiding behind the door. Catching him by the ear, she marched him outside. 'Bebe, *vekh tere dotre diyan kartootan* . . . Bebe, look at the deeds of your grandchild,' her diatribe broke the harmony of Suraiya's sweet voice. Gurdei's friend Basant stood there like a general of the army. The rest of the *paltan* of children peeping from behind the door couldn't control their paroxysms of giggling. *Basant* means spring, but this lady was its very antithesis: fat, loud, aggressive and hard. Bereft of the lightness of romance and fun, Basant was tough and rough, always looking for a reason to assert her authority over the children, especially the girls.

Basant felt it very much her business to mentor her friend's grandchildren. 'Lower your head, *sirmunniye*.' 'Cover your head with your *chunni*, *sirmunniye*.' 'Go get me some tea, *sirmunniye*.' Muni hated the term, which was derogatory. 'I don't have short hair, why does Bebe Basant keep on calling me *sirmunniye*?' she complained to Gurdei. But Gurdei had not felt it necessary to explain. Muni's younger sister by a year was still very young, but she was already conscious of her looks. '*Aa gai wain tikkiyan kadke* ... so you think it fit to do *thumak-thumak* with your hair waved like that,' Basant would scold the poor adolescent, 'and dare I see you with lipstick on your lower lip!'

Now Krishen was into another round of mischief. He put the record player on again at full volume. Passionate dialogues between Prince Salim and the beautiful dancer Anarkali were heard all over the *veda*. Basant was scandalized. '*Oy mushtandeyo*. O hooligans—leave us alone,' she shouted from the *veda*.

Basant nudged Gurdei when she saw Hardei approaching them from a distance. '*Pind Pera te Miani, hath lagani te jani* ... touch the towns of Bhera and Miani to assess their strengths,' she said. 'Shhh ... quiet. What a thing to say! What if she hears you?' Bebe Gurdei retaliated. Gurdei was never very comfortable when Hardei was around; her emotions were easily stirred. It was quite possible that Gurdei was even a little afraid of her. But Basant was enjoying herself tremendously. Before Hardei came within earshot, she continued, '*Kudi ayi Pere di, gut pute gi vede di*. Be careful of the woman of Bhera; she will pull the plaits of all the girls in the courtyard'. By now, they could all sense Bebe Gudei's discomfort.

Both Gurdei and Hardei were strong women. Their facial expressions and body language were quite impressive. But it was clear who was more lethal. While Gurdei could easily be manipulated to melt, or to break into a smile—even a nervous one, with Hardei one always had to be careful. The two Bebes were stamped, marked out to play the roles demanded of them by their ancestral towns. They had become caricatures; miniaturized models of the strengths and weaknesses of Bhera and Miani. Gurdei was always proud to be known as 'Perewali', a Bharochi. Her chest swelled perceptibly. But in front of Hardei, the Miani-ite, her status seemed as if immediately washed out, even though Bhera was the more powerful town.

Somewhere in a corner of her heart, Hardei had not forgiven her daughter Yashoda—not even after so many years—for marrying this woman's son. Nor had she learnt to liberate her own soul from the torment amidst the many grandchildren that Yashoda had given her. On the contrary, Hardei's anger had only deepened. Yashoda's insistence on marrying Lajpat Rai was still a thorn that pricked. The hostility came out in strange ways. Betrayed a second time, Hardei found it hard to be in total control. It was plain for all to see that Yashoda had become the poor relation in the matriarch's eyes.

Yashoda's last born, not yet ten, had already started asking questions. More than once she had retaliated when Hardei pulled apart her beautiful two plaits, braiding them into one—a tight one at that—enough to give the poor young girl a headache. 'Girls from poor families have no right to be fashionable. The way you walk, flouncing around with two plaits—as if you were rich,' she would rebuke her. Certain words are so harsh that they can never be forgotton; these made a deep impression on the girl. Lajpat held the excited child and tried to calm her. 'Remove that anger from your heart. A fiery temperament weakens your immunity; a cool head enhances longevity.' The little girl smiled at her father as if she understoood.

When Hardei felt that she had gone a little too far with her sarcasm, she tried to make up to Yashoda in the only way she knew: she offered her services. She brought little gifts. She got physically involved in helping around, especially during festivals.

Diwali was only a few days away: the children were already counting. They knew they would be spoilt by everybody. By Bauji, who would come laden with all kinds of *mithai*. By Amma Yashoda, who had already started stitching lovely dresses. Even Bebe Gurdei would offer them something. She had already started springcleaning in earnest, '*Lachmi* will not come to a dirty house,' she would mutter under her breath. Stores, shelves and cupboards were cleared of clutter; old clothes given to the poor. Many dead rats were thrown out. The whole house was painted. Two days before the great day came Dhan Teras: old utensils were disposed of, new ones bought. Lajpat bought only a symbolic serving spoon, pot or *karhai*— anything made of iron. It pleased his mother.

In faraway India, it is the darkest night of the darkest period. On this side of the Indian Ocean, the days are warm and lazy, the nights fresh. The children were up early, impatient to get into their lovely frocks and suits. They would visit many households with Bebe Gurdei, with Bauji and Amma Yashoda, carrying plates laden with *mithai*—*laddus* and *jalebis*—as offerings.

Chanting was already being heard in shops and individual homes as prayers were offered. For the dukawallas especially, this was an important ritual. Left open the whole day on Diwali to enable the goddess to enter, the shop had to be beautiful to welcome Lakshmi. Her footprints were painted in front, leading towards the entrance, in a way requesting Lakshmi to enter. 'In ancient times, the festival celebrated prosperity in agricultural societies,' Kirparam had once told the children. However, Lala Kirparam never had Lakshmi *puja* in any of his shops.

Kneaded wheat, moulded into little lamps filled with oil and cotton wick, lit the way for Lakshmi. His shop remained open all day and he sold more than usual. Lajpat Rai was not a very religious person, but a traditional upbringing brought its convictions. It was believed that on this night Lakshmi in the company of Vidmata, goddess of fate would take a round. The ones lucky enough to have her visit would be bestowed with immense prosperity.

At the foot of the image of Rama and Sita, a lamp was lit and the coconut, symbolizing plenty, was cracked. The little flame burnt bravely dispelling, as it were, all darkness in the world. It was a light to still the mind. For a heart filled with divinity, with the eternal. Gurdei held the small prayer ceremony with much aplomb, at the end of which the little *diya* was passed around and *charan amrit*, foot nectar of the goddess—water with a few tulsi leaves—was sipped. Lajpat Rai offered money and small tokens to the children. The servants were given generous gifts.

The goddess of fortune was also honoured with gambling throughout the night. Indian society favoured games of chance over competition. Life itself was one vast lottery in which the circumstances of birth in a certain social niche predetermined the stakes, played out according to the inexorable laws of dharma.

Lajpat Rai's house did not honour the goddess with cards. The lights and colours of Diwali were more in his line of enjoyment. Red, yellow, green, saffron, white—sweets of all colours (except blue and black perhaps), sizes and shapes—round, elongated, flat, square and triangular—invited the eye.

The aromas of cardamom, caramel, and cinnamon pervaded the air, from Indian Bazaar, passing through River Road, up to Ngara. Then as the lights dimmed, fireworks were let off. The children rushed up to the rooftops to watch. As the rockets soared invisibly into the black darkness to explode into stars of dazzling green, white, ruby, red and saffron, 'Ooh, aah . . .' sounded all around. A giddy dazzle, it was a visual feast to look forward to for the rest of the year.

18

Another voyage

Mera joota hai Japani ye patloon Inglishstani
Ser pe laal topi rusi, phir bhi dil hai Hindustani . . .
(My shoes are from Japan, trousers from England,
A red hat from Russia, but my heart remains Indian . . .)

—Indian film song

He had landed on the soil of British East Africa at the height of the first world war and was returning to India at the height of the second. The only sea transport available to Indian passengers was the dhow. Bigger passenger ships were being used as naval bases for attack. Lajpat made up his mind. 'Ship or no ship, we will go. If it is to be by dhow, then dhow it will be.'

Like Kirparam, he planned his visit twenty years after arriving in Kenya in search of a new life. He had been back only once, briefly, to get his mother. The longing to return to his roots grew; he wanted to share it with Yashoda, and their four-year-old daughter Bitia— neither of whom had been to India. Little did Lajpat realize that this was to be a final *darshan* of his native land. Somehow, he would never return to Bhera again.

Despite her subtle ways, Yashoda's apprehensions were all too visible. The idea of discovering India was in itself not inspiring, the voyage even less so. She lacked her father's sense of adventure. Lajpat was insistent, 'You must know the land of our ancestors. Would you not like to see where your father and your mother came from, where I was born, and in what conditions I grew up?' Halfheartedly, bags were packed. Somehow, she consoled herself: their eldest son's wedding date was not far away, and she may as well shop for the trousseau. A suitable bride had been chosen in Nairobi.

Yashoda cried constantly on the dhow, but always when no-one was watching. Her hair was soon filled with lice, she felt sticky and dirty all over, no matter how many sponge washes she took. Yashoda lacked the toughness that was the forte of her mother, Bebe Hardei.

Going back to the terrritory of his boyhood meant a lot to Lajpat, however. He was suddenly filled with a childlike excitement. He wanted to do so many things at once. To trace the family heritage, to feel the familiar surroundings, to run into people he had known and grown up with. Yet, once he arrived, he went about it with some reluctance. Suddenly, it was as if he were negotiating a labyrinth. So much had changed; perhaps, somewhere, Africa had changed him. His style of dress had been influenced by the British. He walked with some haste, as if time was more valuable now, looking constantly at his watch. Even his language had different nuances: words in English and Swahili came unbidden amid the somewhat accented Punjabi. *Msambi* (orange) was now *mchungwa; jharu* (broom) became *fagia. Choori* (knife), he called *kisu.* Moreover, the Punjabi he spoke had regional influences: Amritsari, Lahori. The Indians who met Lajpat and Yashoda also sensed the difference. They had become foreigners.

They began their pilgrimage with a visit to Matan, near Kashmir. '*Kahan ke basi, kahan ke basi*', the shouts were heard all over the throngs of people who crowded the bus that came to a halt at Matan. Pilgrims were scrutinized, and the all-important question darted at them, 'What is your native place?' As soon as the *pandas* received their answers, the crowd around the pilgrim thinned.

When Lajpat Rai replied, 'Bhera's my birthplace. And Miani for my wife's family,' the *panda* connected with these towns of north-west Punjab came forward to continue probing them about their caste and immediate families. By a lightning process of elimination, he was determining whether any other members of their families had previously been his *yajmans*, religious clients. Leading them to a corner, he bade them sit on a stone slab, while he took out his relevant red cloth *bahi* to search for the specific villages and entries of their clan. Lajpat glanced at the ledger, and was overawed. 'They are complete with dates, names and signatures of other members of our families who have been to this place before', he whispered to Yashoda.

To anyone witnessing this entire procedure, it is unbelievable—this remarkable institution of the *pandas*, and the important records which they have accumulated over the past 300 years or more—at Hardwar, Banaras, Matan in Kashmir, Allahabad, Kurukshetra in Harayana and Kangra in Himachal Pradesh. These papers provide proof of hereditary ties between families. Here, Lajpat and Yashoda added their own records, together with names and details of their children, for the sake of posterity.

* * *

Muni and the rest of the children had been left in Gurdei's care. Gurdei never left Muni alone at home—wherever she went, Muni tagged along. Whether it was to the Sanatan Dharam temple, or to the gurudwara, Muni was not far behind. Gurdei did not frequent the Arya Samaj temple, nor did she participate in any of its ceremonies.

Not far in the distance, Chachi Bhagwanti was seen heading towards them—Bebe Gurdei's first, and till date, closest friend in Nairobi. The synergy between the two had been evident even when they had first met many many years ago. They still continued to conjure up all kinds of meetings and stories. 'Bebe,' she called out in her full-throated voice, 'Listen. Dhano's son has passed the tenth standard. We must all go and congratulate his mother.' Congratulating the son himself was less important.

Chachi Bhagwanti was feeling especially proud—why, wasn't she also the maternal grandmother to the lad? Here he was—the first in his *landhi* neighbourhood to have passed his matriculation, and with a special distinction in Urdu. The women, of course, did not bother about the details. It was more than enough that he had passed. '*Wadaiyan* Chachi ! *Tera pala howe!*' they showered blessings upon Chachi.

Bhagwanti beamed with satisfaction. 'Isn't Krishanlal your favourite grandson, Chachi?' Gurdei nudged her with her right hand. Chachi burst out in laughter. It was true. How often she would force *laddus* and *barfi* down Krishanlal's throat, coaxing him to eat. And then she would laugh, 'My Kichen has a sweet tooth. He has a special weakness for milk pastries, but it's quite normal. With a grandfather from Lahore, what else do you expect?'

'Dhano lives very far away, on the other side of the town beyond the *tation*,' (railway station), remarked another of Bebe Gurdei's numerous friends. This one was a Chakwalan, 'How will we make it?' The quarter was a few kilometers from the bazaar. Like all public works department staff, Dhano's husband had been given a small quarter in the *landhis*. Ultimately someone agreed to ask her husband for his lorry.

A few days later, sucking lemons, singing songs, the women were jammed together in the back of the lorry, many with babies in their laps. 'O *karmawaliye* (fortunate one)', they shouted from a distance even before they had descended upon her doorstep. Dhano ran out of her house. She was not expecting them. But then, who came with an appointment? She was pleased in any case, surrounded by women belting out '*Wadaiyan*! *Wadaiyan*! Congratulations!' She led them inside. The women never saw the boy. Neither did Muni. Yet fate was to bring her to him after marriage.

Muni was moping about the house this morning, waiting for familiar sounds: her mother's almost silent footsteps, or Bauji inviting her for the usual promenades . . . his loud laughter, how she missed it! She even longed to hear her youngest sister calling out for her 'Kina! Kina!' Yes, where was Bitia? How I miss the baby of the family wailing away! Muni thought. What she had otherwise taken almost for granted now seemed to reverberate with its absence. They had been gone not even a month, yet the house was not the same without Amma and Bauji. Habitual sounds and smells from their day-to-day activities were absent. Of Amma Yashoda grinding her endless *dals* and spices in the *veda,* their aromas emanating ad infinitum. Cinnamon, ginger, cloves, bay leaves, garlic, cumin, fennel seeds—freshly ground masalas which normally filled the air with their smells now left her nostalgic by their lack. Moreover, Muni was not especially fond of her grandmother's cooking. When it was astringent, it left a sharp, caustic feel in the mouth. *Karela* (bitter gourd), watery dals—all her so-called 'health conscious' food. Muni missed her mother's cuisine—sour, acidic, salty. She dreamed of trying her hand at making *alu-matar* the way amma Yashoda did, but Bebe would not let her potter around the kitchen.

'Muni, Muniiiiiii . . . ,' she heard Gurdei call out. 'Uff-oh, where is this *bacchi*? *Arre* Munniye, get ready, we must leave for the *mandir* in a few minutes.' The sulking forgotton, Muni smiled. All said and done, life with Bebe Gurdei was never boring. (Nobody of that generation used the word 'bore': their days were always crammed with small simple pleasures.) Bebe's whole existence was a fiesta . . . one of incessant activity, noise and laughter!

Once a year, the Ramlila procession did the rounds of the bazaar area. Bebe Gurdei and Muni arrived just in time for the pageant. The *jaloos* went from Ram Mandir in the Eastleigh *dhobi* temple right up to Azad Maidan in the centre of town. Vedic chants and Tulsidas' Ramcharitramanas *slokas* were sung. Conches were blown. Big *dhol*, hung with ropes around the necks of strong men, were beaten with two sticks. Auspicious sounds, divine worship, incense and fragrances; the ceremony had commenced well. Particular rites and *pujas* were performed. A coconut was cracked, *diyas* lit, petals thrown on performers. They would play being gods and devils.

There was colour and movement, and marvellous heroic figures. None of the participants belonged to a professional theatre group; such a company did not even exist. These were amateurs, but acted with great zeal and devotion. Demons wore large masks, Rama's army was well equipped with bows and arrows, Hanuman had a long tail appended, and boys in their early teens performed the role of girls. 'In the time even before mine', Bebe Gurdei had once told Muni, '*Kshatriyas* would polish their swords and other weapons during these nights'. They had the time, the patience and necessary faith to complete these tasks scrupulously.

Essentially a warrior celebration, Ramlila seems to have once been particularly appealing to the martial Punjabis. What started as a glorification of the nine nights of war between the good king Rama and the evil king Ravana was now also seen as a symbol of the victory of good over evil. Every night one part of the Ramayana was performed. Commencing with the first Navratra, different parts of the mythology were enacted over the next nine days.

They came, they participated in the performing ritual and in this way they worshipped the mother goddess. Gurdei's attendance record was meritorious. Never missing a single night, she was totally immersed in the spirit of the Ramlila. They dressed up eagerly as Rama, younger brother Lakshman, or the spiritual old rishi, their guide. Yellow paste adorned the faces of gurus; blue was reserved for divine characters, while red signified the bad. A crowd of young and old followed the big *jaloos* as they walked to the Sanatan Dharam temple on Duke Street.

From 9 p.m. to 11 p.m. for the next nine days, the temple became a theatre. Men acted female roles, a slim boy played Sita. Muni never understood why the other members of her family chose to miss out on the fun. Of course, all of them were familiar with these stories from the Ramayana, having heard them umpteen times, yet Muni swore that each year, the Ramlila came with renewed life.

'The dramatic moment when Ravana captures Sita, the wife of Rama, turned into an anti-climax in today's episode at the temple grounds,' she reported breathlessly at the breakfast table next morning. Apparently, the two pieces of padding supposed to be Sita's breasts kept on falling through 'her' *choli*. The poor fellow tried to hold on to his short blouse with the right hand while crying out, '*Ram! Ram!*' with the left hand stretched out. 'Everybody burst out in laughter instead of breaking into tears,' she added excitedly. 'And then came Rama in his glorious crown and white canvas Bata shoes calling out, "*Site! Site!*" Almost every member of the audience joined in as chorus. The hall resounded with *"Site! Site!"* The audience took cathartic pleasure in seeing Rama suffer. The tragic situation became a hilarious comedy.'

Men in the audience and children laughed unabashedly, while women watched seriously and respectfully, their heads covered with their sari *pallus*, hands folded in true devotion. When they could not control their laughter, they simply stuffed a corner of their sari *pallus* into their mouths, or covered it with their right hand to suppress the laughter. A member of the audience prompted, at times even directed the cast. 'O Ravana, now jump, speak louder,' and the characters followed suit. The crowd was at arm's length, the audience on the floor in a semicircle. As usual, big Gandu Halwai would play at being Ravana, king of Lanka, in the short war scene. Massive and imposing, Gandu looked every inch the stereotypical image of Ravana. 'Do you know what he did?' Muni went into uncontrollable fits of laughter again. 'He is doomed to making *laddus* forever! Even at war! You should have seen him shouting out to his soldiers, "Kill! Kill!" There was blood in his eyes, strength in his extended legs, but his arms were stretched out limply, the fists opening and closing alternatively—as if he was still making *laddus* in his pastry shop.'

For several years now, young Roshan had been playing the part of Rama. Fair and good-looking, tall, with sharp Aryan features, without a blemish on his body, Roshan came from a 'respected' family. The young man had everything to be proud of. The temple priest garlanded him and a small *puja* ceremony was held before the actual commencement of the *jaloos*. As usual, some women who saw him as the incarnation came forward to touch his feet. Soon after one such parade, Roshan became ill. The anxious mother got upset and passed a message, 'Please stop touching his feet. You are placing too heavy a responsibility on my young boy.'

When he heard about this incident later, Lajpat had said, 'Times have changed. In Bhera, when I was your age, the actors participating in the Ramlila stayed at the house of the director right from the time of rehearsals, upto Dussehra. Here, they underwent rigorous training. A big part of their instruction included spiritual exercises and meditation, besides the physical and technical preparations. The devotional aspect was of utmost importance. They fasted regularly, or ate only *satwik* foods—abstaining from meat, alcohol, garlic, foods cooked in oil.'

The tenth day finally arrived. Gurdei was up early, ready to go to the venue. This night, Gandu Halwai would not play at being Ravana. All efforts were made by Rama and party to ensure that when they fired shots at him, their arrows would bring him down on his back. 'Should he fall flat on his face, the year will bring ill-luck,' they were constantly warned. The attack at sunset was cheered by spectators as the effigy went up in a tremendous burst of flames. Rama's victorious army was then escorted away to make rounds of various temples and receive blessings from people.

The second world war was already into its 2,000th day, yet the nine days and nights war that presumably took place over thirty centuries ago was of far greater importance to many of the Hindus of Kenya. Emotionally and sentimentally, spiritually and culturally, they could identify with it. The ongoing war was not theirs; they never identified with it as they continued to do with the Ramlila. The Ramlila was their war. At its heart, Hinduism is a non-dual system and does not share the Christian concept of absolute evil. Forces of negativity and enemies of light do exist; they differ from gods in degree rather than in kind. Demons can win boons from gods by penance. They are allowed to repent. They can become great devotees, or even end up as benefactors of mankind.

Muni loved this time of the year. She so enjoyed the festival and all that went with it, never missing an opportunity to go visiting with her paternal grandmother. Her brothers were not interested. Ma Yashoda feared the crowds. Bauji did not participate either. Austere feelings on religion kept them both a little aloof from community participation. At times, Lajpat tried to impress his own thoughts on his children. 'How one truly prays is through action, my child—through good deeds.' These beliefs were enough for him. The symbology of the rest, according to Lajpat, was more or less superfluous.

Theirs was a quiet and reserved religion, a private, rather than a community affair. However, neither Bauji nor Amma ever refused Bebe Gurdei's *prasad* that she brought from the temple—not even when it was already stale. Sometimes, especially during the festival days, Bebe Gurdei would have visited many houses for *bhajan* sessions. *Potlis* of *prasad* collected on different days would finally emerge from her *kameez* pocket. *Halwa* dripping with ghee, the excess of which she massaged gently into her hands and immediately onto her hair. *Jalebis, pedas, mishri*, almonds, peanuts, dried coconut slices, even squashed baby bananas. Syrupy Indian sweets leaking from brown bags or even newspapers wrappers—these she offered to her children and grandchildren with much love.

Shaking her grandmother by the arm, Muni was putting in her plea, 'Bebe, Bebe this year can I keep the Navratri *vrat* with you?' 'As long as you are not in your unclean time of the month,' replied Bebe nonchalantly. Secretly, Gurdei was delighted, especially as the girl's mother never fasted—not even for the all-important Karva Chauth. Her Arya Samaj loyalties to the fore again!

Another nine-night Navratri was dedicated to Amba, the goddess of fertility. Barley was sown in a small pot in the house, and for nine days women fasted in worship of the goddess of the earth, partaking of only one meal a day. Neither wheat nor salt were permitted. Roots like potatoes, or sweet potatoes, milk and its derivatives like yoghurt and fruits were allowed. Gurdei prepared *laddus* of barley and *gur* (jaggery). She also cooked *khichri*, the all-time favourite *goulash* of broken rice, but without salt. On the morning of the first fast, they both cleaned their teeth with twigs of the neem, bathed, took water in the palm and sprinkled it in the four directions, all the while pronouncing the name of Amba— the deity for whom they were fasting.

'Yoghurt and boiled potatoes never tasted better, even without salt,' Muni whispered into the ear of her best friend at school. She couldn't risk being overheard by the rest of the class. Or reported to one of the teachers by those girls whom she did not trust, for these so-called superstitious beliefs were against the principles of the Arya Samaj. She knew that if she was caught fasting, she could get into trouble.

For that was exactly what happened to her friend Sharda. Poor girl, she had obviously showed off too much, and some traitorous friend reported her. Master Arya Muni was known as a *kattar samaji*—an Arya Samaji to the core of his being. He forced the young girl to drink water and break her fast. Sharda did not utter a word, even her brimming eyes dared not flow. One did not argue with teachers. So, even though after a few days Muni started feeling a little weak in the body, her mind gained strength, and she participated in the normal school routine guarding her secret.

On the last day, Gurdei called over all the young non-menstruating girls of the neighbourhood, Muni and her younger sisters included—at least seven of them. Sitting on *pidi*s facing each other, the boys washed the feet of all these sisters with water. The virgins were worshipped with *diya*s and sown barley. Today, they were the representatives of Sheranwali, the goddess who rides a lion. Their heads were covered with red *chunni*s, green bangles on their wrists, and money was offered in their laps. A feast of *puri*, black gram and *halwa* was offered in honour of these future mothers.

One Navratri after dinner, Gurdei and her granddaughters walked down to witness a Gujarati *garba-raas* folk dance. It was about nine at night, not far from their own house. It was a pleasant walk, and the girls were having fun. 'We ought to do this more often,' they felt. 'Life with Bebe is full of fun and surprises.' With Gurdei, there was always a feeling of being at a festival or—even better—part of it; she created the situations and they participated.

There was already a huge crowd when they arrived. Photos of various goddesses hung everywhere. Personifying the awesome power of good, Durga astride her tiger, in her unmarried avatar, was the object of worship. 'The one beyond reach', as her name suggested, she was a creation of fiery thought—forms of other gods to restore righteousness on earth. Kali, the black one, the most formidable aspect of Durga, the destroyer of time itself, was adorned with a necklace of skulls, her fiery red tongue protruding. All the seven divine mothers were present. Different aspects of Shakti— Kaumari on her peacock, Varahi standing on a man, Chamunda on a corpse. The *devis* had the power of compassion or forgiveness on the one hand, fury while destroying evil forces on the other.

A *puja thali* of coconut halves, mango leaves, incense, *kumkum* and rice had been placed in the centre. Coconuts placed on top of brass jugs were lined up on either side. Round and full, these were the lactating breasts of mother earth. She who feeds and sustains, and then takes the being back in her womb, the mysterious creativity of birth and death was worshipped in all its forms. Wasn't it Shakti who created the cosmos? They were to evoke that energy of female divinity which fills the space, which gave birth to her ancestors through her intellect—the energy whose *yoni* (womb) is an ocean of creativity.

Women in brightly coloured *ghaghra*s and flowers in their hair danced around the *thali* singing hymns. Drums and cymbals gave the accompaniment; it was a merry occasion. Suddenly, a man got up and began to dance fervently, reciting prayers at the same time. The others stopped their dance, and encircled him. He drew power from this chemistry. His dancing grew more and more vigorous. Then he began to tremble. He started shaking violently. His steady gaze did not waver. It seemed as if he was growing and growing. By now he was perspiring profusely. Strange sounds emerged from his throat.

The trance continued for what seemed to the girls a long while. Muni and her sister held their fascinated breath. For a moment, the man became still—like a Gandhara sculpture. His piercing eyes froze. Then he fell to the ground and began writhing and hissing. He had invoked the blessings of the mother. '*Mata aa gai!*' they whispered to each other. The man had become possessed by Jagadamba, by Durga, Kali and Shakti. It was obviously a cathartic experience. Gurdei folded her hands in obeisance.

The devotees saw their own devotion mirrored in him. When he calmed down, the women put the sacred red *tilak* on his forehead, touched his feet, asked him questions, and demanded predictions. He blessed them and distributed holy ash and *prasad* to the rapt audience. And then he spoke. His voice was haunting, as if someone else was speaking through his body. The medium of Shakti was revered. The medium could be anybody, man, woman, even child. Tonight, Shakti had honoured the man by manifesting herself in him.

The crowd drew closer. There was much pushing. It was suffocating. Muni and her sister were scared. They were to witness this spectacle many times afterwards, each Navratri. But this first time, refusing the holy *prasad*, they began to run, faster and faster, as quick as their legs could carry them. Gurdei ran behind them, shouting, 'Stop, wait for me!' But the girls didn't let up until they reached home. Gurdei shook her head, and said to herself, 'Girls today have no respect for traditions.'

Abstention, purifying, cleansing—the word *vrat* had so many connotations. There were those who saw it as sacrifice—as renouncing, or giving up food for religious observance. But for Gurdei, all fasts had only one meaning: they were a celebration. A celebration of life, or a celebration of being—she was just happy to be alive and to celebrate it through fasting—whether they were lunar fasts or solar ones, those marking the end of a season, or the beginning of a new one. Whether they were celebrating *punya*, the presence of the full moon, or coming of the new moon—even the eleventh lunar day held significance. In Kartik on the fourth lunar day, Karva Chauth fasting was voluntary and supererogatory, the duration and manner of abstention differing. Gurdei celebrated all the different fasts, keeping in mind the name of the god or goddess whose benevolence she wished to gain thereby.

On the night of the full moon, Bebe fasted as usual. She cleaned up her temple in the little store thoroughly. No one could intrude during this process. 'Have to do it myself, otherwise it will not be *succha* to prepare the *prasad*,' she declared when the girls offered to help. They smiled, nodding their heads, though they did not share her purity fetish.

Sacrifice was one way of communicating with a deity, or becoming possessed by it. This day, Gurdei's one meal consisted of milk and *parontha*. Salt was usually taboo during this type of fast, so Bebe caramelized her deep fried *chapati*s with sugar. Washing her hands carefully before plucking flowers, she took care not to smell them, for then they could not be offered to her gods. She grew the little wild roses herself, as she did marigold, in tin *debe*s. Left hand in the elbow of the right arm, Bebe waved the *diya* around the icons, singing and swaying with the melody to her own song before distributing the *charan amrit*. Placed at the feet of the gods, the water with a *tulsi* leaf in it had been blessed and was drunk for spiritual merit and benefit.

19

New beginnings

The dead are not under the earth
They are in the tree that rustles
They are in the woods that groan
They are in the water that runs
They are in the water that sleeps
They are in the hut, they are in the crowd
The dead are not dead.
Those who are dead are never gone
They are in the breast of a woman
They are in the child that is wailing and in the fire that flames
The dead are not under the earth
They are in the fire that is dying
They are in the grass that is weeping
They are in the whimpering rocks
They are in the forest, they are in the house.
They are not dead.

— Francis Nnaggenda, Ugandan sculptor and poet

He aged suddenly. The Bangalore topee still clung to his head, but the spirit lost its essence. News soon spread that he was bed-ridden. The family took turns to visit, quietly accepting the end that was to come.

Kirparam never recovered from the accident in which he drove his lorry into a tree. He only limped at first. Dr D'Souza diagnosed it as a stroke and insisted on hospitalization. Lalaji vehemently refused. Instead, he went to live in Nyeri with his youngest son Kundanlal, the one he was very fond of. 'I want to die near you, close to you,' he told him. For many days, he lay there, convalescing. But bit by bit, his condition started deteriorating. He lost weight, and grew weaker by the day. At first his limbs became dysfunctional, then his speech slurred. Finally, he could just move his eyelids. After all the dangers he had overcome, how could his life have drained away slowly in six months in bed? The willpower that helped him adjust determinedly to all the changes that came his way was all but sapped.

His children gathered around him. He knew his time had come: his life's thread was only that long. A film of tears on his much wrinkled face, he struggled to say something, but no words came. Only the eyelids blinked. Once. The end was at hand. Lala Kirparam Ramchand Wason died that night. It was 15 August 1944.

An ocean lost a breath. Finished with happiness, unhappiness, and the duality of these. Perhaps here, in the heart of Africa, he had found his arcadia. Independent of mind and spirit, in matters spiritual and mundane, Kirparam had been a pioneer in his own right.

When a man draws his last few breaths, he is laid on the floor, in the lap of mother earth. He touches the *diya bati*, a lamp immersed in a water vessel to light up his own path of darkness. That night, no such ceremony illumined his way. The last rites of *anteyeshti samskar* were simple. That is perhaps how he may have wanted it. No sacrifices were offered to any Brahmin. *Aaliyan*, such as may have been sung in his native town, were not conferred upon the mourners. He had rejected Hinduism, yet in the end he was cremated according to Hindu rites. Throughout the simple cremation ceremony, Hardei remained dry-eyed.

His ashes were immersed in the Tana river, which flowed to the Indian Ocean. As flowed the Jhelum, which had baptized his birth. The road that ran behind Jamia mosque and McMillan library, right opposite Jeevanjee market, came to be called Kirparam

Road. Amongst the two lines of *mabati duka*s on this road, Kirparam too had his metal sheet structure with a wooden floor. But after independence, the street no longer bore his name.

Neither an edifice nor a memorial would be erected to tell the story of those who died on construction lines, or those who survived. There is not even a small plaque to commemorate the hundreds of coolies working on the rail lines. No names. No backgrounds, no identities of their own. Just a mass of poor labourers; loaders, bricklayers, workers, they would become statistics, reduced to numbers: 3,000 of them, forgotton as soon as their work was accomplished.

After paying her condolences to the Wason family, soon after Kirparam's death, Gurdei washed her face and feet before entering her own house, whereupon she immediately had a bath and changed clothes. The assumption that a dead body was dirty was part of the culture that Bebe grew up with. While alive, the body is your temple, but no sooner than the soul flees, a certain taboo is associated with the corpse. Sprinkling of water, a ritual bath, drinking water—the temporary pollution was overcome by ritual purification. Never did she say that 'Lalaji has died'. The word 'death' was taboo too. Once she said, 'Lalaji has become beloved to God'. Dreaded diseases too were nameless. Neither disclosed nor whispered—cancer, tuberculosis, heart attack—such fatal illnesses were best left anonymous, unexposed. One would have thought that even uttering the name was enough to make it infectious, that it could somehow spread. Dare her grandsons voice the name of a disease to Gurdei, the dissemination of the plague had already commenced. Hands on both ears, as if to stop the words entering her inner being, she would burst out, pleading with them in panic. '*Bas!* Stop!' And the debate would end, cut short before it had begun. Death would not be discussed in the house.

A hand lifted Hardei's left thumb, applied printer's ink to it and pressed it on the paper. The will left behind by Lala Kirparam was formalized. Kirparam's property and estate was divided amongst his sons and eldest grandson. As for Hardei, she got enough for maintenance for life. She chose to live independently in her house in Ngara, with the five tenants.

The war ended soon after. Indian defiance of the European colonizers subsided—with the exception of a few notables like Ambu Patel and his courageous wife. It looked as if the so-called Indian leaders were more willing to accept colonial rule and the injustices that went with it. Was it because they possessed a lesser degree of the fighting spirit of their forefathers—despite a higher level of education and perhaps more skills? Or was it because, as distributors of consumer goods, some had profited from war-time shortages? One could also see it as a period of accommodation—both with the white rulers as also with the emerging nationally conscious Africans, who had the force of numbers.

Lala Kirparam's son Chunilal's prosperity escalated by leaps and bounds. In closer touch with western ways, he was socially more comfortable with the white regime and psychologically better adjusted. He became a member of the Legislative Council. He rubbed shoulders with men who had 'real' power. He had contact with government officials. He was closely associated with the highly formal bureaucratic set. All this improved his business prospects. Soon he was accepted in the prestigious position of an alderman in the colony, next in status to the mayor.

After the raspy boom of the war was over, even the likes of Prakash correctly assessed the mood of the times. Within the narrow parameters of their limited choices and psychological maladjustment, it was easy to exploit certain situations. Gurdei referred to him as '*patija*', not because Prakash was her nephew, but simply because he was from her beloved Bhera, her ancestral village. Such relationships were fabricated quite easily, and had social sanction.

Alliances were sometimes even contrived on the spot, just to handle an embarrassing situation. 'Do you remember Shantaram?' Bebe Gurdei herself had brought up the subject one day in the course of a discussion with her friend Bhagwanti. How she had chuckled then! 'He was a good man, God bless him! Schoolmaster. . . a bachelor even in his late thirties, looking for a good match. By chance, he was introduced to Rampyari. This girl had no interest in the man, so to stop any dialogue or embarrassment she went and tied a *rakhi* on his right wrist. Any ambiguity was promptly handled,' recalled Gurdei. A simple knot of the sacred thread turned a potential lover to a brother—without the war of words, or painful moments that went with it; the tradition of *raksha bandan* could certainly be useful.

Prakash was what you could call an *aflatoon*—an imposter posing as a respectable citizen. A con-man, in short. Like most of them, he could be sheer charm. To him, Gurdei was another pawn in the network that he had very artfully established—an acquisition web. Each social contact was a necessary part of his survival tactics, as Prakash had no other means of subsistence. He was not employed, nor was he a businessman, *fundi*, or a dukawalla. He just used his charms to worm his way into hearts, especially of older women. He had the right mannerisms to make them feel wanted and cared for. Prakash lavished attention on his chosen ones. 'Bebe, how are you feeling today . . . how is the pain in your back?' Or, he would indulge in spicy gossip, 'Do you know that Guddi ran away with Pali? Hai Ram, *toba toba*', and he would touch his mouth, then both his ears with his hands—three times precisely.

One day, Prakash turned up with a bunch of red roses for Gurdei—the very ones that grew in her tin garden. Plucking them without any shame, he offered them to her. 'She won't know the difference,' he sang confidently to himself. And he was right. Bebe took the bunch and kept it in the room. In her reckoning, flowers were only offered to the gods, not used for mere decoration of a house. Nevertheless, it made her feel good. He held her hand. The touch was sufficient to increase the probability of making her agree to one of his demands. He had perfected the art of seduction.

The preparatory act was always the same. His understanding of the science of human psychology was innate. 'Your delicious *parontha*s are the talk of the neighbourhood, your *achar*s are out of this world, no-one makes them as well as you do,' he would sweet-talk her. Muni and some of her siblings would be listening at the kitchen door, gagging their laughter. But Wade Papaji and the other boys were less amused. Were it not for the respect that elders were automatically given, Prakash would have been thrashed and chased away a long time ago. When he had had his fill of Bebe's famous *paronthas,* Prakash promptly asked her for a bottle of her lovely *achar*, mango pickle, and the lemon chutney that she had spent hours preparing. This would be his offering at the next house for his next meal.

Food and captivation went together; it was a question of chemistry. He transformed himself into a consummate, spontaneous poet, with the perfect words for the right situation. With a voice full of emotion and passion, stories full of colour, of perfume, of music and dance would be invented on the spot. There was something of the dandy about him. One could almost visualize him with a straw hat, white suit, leather shoes, a slim cane in hand. Prakash was quite good-looking, actually. Immaculate in dress: a three-piece suit with a beautiful white or matching blue shirt. Of course, he lived on borrowed shirts. He thought he had the 'Majnu look', on the lookout for his beautiful Laila.

Sometimes, he tried his luck with young girls. One day, he found himself on the same bus as Muni and her friends. He was wondering whether to sit on the upper or lower deck, when he met their eyes. Lower, for sure. He saw that they had noticed him. Adjusting his jacket—imitating what was done with such flair in films—he ran a comb through his hair, Dev Anand style. His painstakingly primed puff was now in place. They were still looking at him, giggling away, which to him was a sign of surrender to his charms. That is how they show it in films, he thought again to himself, smiling quite confidently at them. I will make them dance on my fingers, he seemed to say as he passed by them, trying to brush against their bodies. It was a formula for disaster.

The bus conductor approached him for his fare. Proudly, Prakash took out a shiny black wallet and showed off a five shilling note. 'Cut the tickets of the girls as well', he told the bus conductor in his chivalrous manner, 'and give the change to the girls,' he added. The ageing conductor gave him a suspicious look. The girls were horrified; Prakash had made the mistake of acting too swiftly. His monkey tricks had seduced neither Muni nor her friend. When the girls refused his money, he shouted at the top of his voice, insisting that the conductor keep it. But the conductor rejected his money. Prakash's mask of seduction suddenly dropped; he lost his composure. He petulantly threw the money out of the window. 'Who knows where he got the money from . . . where he lives . . .' the conductor said under his breath. They had not expected him to get so worked up.

When the bus halted a few minutes later, the girls got off, even though it was not their stop. Muni decided not to say anything about Prakash at home. An unspoken taboo existed on serious or open conversation between boys and girls. If their brothers got to hear of it, the boy concerned could end up getting a beating. Alternatively, they themselves might be reprimanded for straying too close to him. As it is, the brothers kept a stern watch on their sisters, especially when their friends came visiting.

In fact, if Muni even stepped out of the house immediately after washing her hair, Bebe screamed at her, 'Standing outside with your hair let loose—very bad! Like a *dayan*—a witch,' Munni would cover her head with a *chunni* and run inside. The girls dared not look at a man directly in the face—they stared at their own feet instead. Looking out of a window was strictly prohibited. Their father and even brothers enforced the rules strictly. Only their mother was quiet.

20

The 'other'

'. . . the average Englishman . . . tolerates a blackman who
admits his inferiority, and even those who show a good fight
and give in; but he cannot tolerate dark colour combined
with an intelligence in any way equal to his own.'

—Sir Charles Eliot, Commissioner, E.A. Protectorate,
From *The Lunatic Express* by Charles Miller

Lajpat and Yashoda's promenades, hand-in-hand, continued
for a long while—even many children later. Yashoda still
reddened in the face and quickly released her husband's hand,
but Lajpat insisted on firmly regrasping his wife's fingers. This
he did almost in defiance of society. At first he even had a mind to
lift their gripped hands so that he could kiss her soft fingers. Only
modesty on her part prevented him from doing so. The gesture
would have been too much for her to handle.

However, as the children got older, Lajpat's pace changed; he
seemed to walk faster, ahead of his wife. Or perhaps Yashoda had
slowed down. The route was still the same—from River Road up
to Hardei's house on Fort Hall Road. But something was missing.
Maybe the passion was on the wane. Perhaps Yashoda was tired
after numerous pregnancies.

Now, whenever Lajpat Rai went for his promenade, he either
went alone or with one of his children. Invariably, it was Muni.
She had come closer to her father, despite her mother's fears and

disapproval. A particular intimacy developed between them; they understood each other well. When with Muni, Lajpat was adventurous, as if a weight had fallen off his shoulders suddenly. A renewed youthfulness would descend upon his soul. Full of vigour in the spirit, and light in the body, it was almost as if he was reliving his adolescence through his daughter. He wanted to show her this, or experience that, all at the same time. They never followed the same path twice in a row; each time, Lajpat would guide his daughter through a different part of town.

One day, Lajpat led his daughter into the restricted 'whites-only' area of Muthaiga. It was an eye-opener for Muni. 'It is so beautiful, Bauji!' Muni had 'ooohed' and 'aahed' so many times as her eyes darted about. Huge bungalows—so white and clean—with all kinds of flowers, many she had not seen before. Giant fencing wires layered with green creepers surrounded the villas. Red, white, orange and purple bougainvillea. Huge hibiscus bushes. Pink *datura*. Giant jacarandas in bloom. Rose shrubs of all colours. 'Truly a magic place,' said Muni. Her eyes shone with wonder. But it was so quiet, very unlike their street. Not a person in sight, not a sound to be heard. 'Why, we can even hear the sounds of our own footsteps,' she whispered to her father. She dared not speak aloud, and suddenly, a chill ran down her spine, 'Perhaps this is a ghost town,' she declared, and held onto her father's hand tightly.

He looked at his daughter and gave her a reassuring smile. Truly though, it did feel as if this part of Nairobi was cooler. And fresher. Perhaps because there were so many more trees here. There was more breeze, in any case. Sure enough, his sinuses were soon blocked up, the air cavities restricted, and he had a little difficulty breathing. Lajpat blew his nose with his hand to release the mucus. And, there, as if by the turn of a sorcerer's stick, stood a white policeman. Shouting from where he was, he called out, 'Hey, you! Come here. Do you understand?'

The voice sent a cliched cold sweat down his flanks; Lajpat's knees gave away and he staggered.

'What are you gibbering away in your *babu* English?' The policeman repeated himself in Kiswahili, '*Kuja hapa*!'

Lajpat stood rooted. Muni nearly peed in her salwar. The *mzungu* walked over briskly in their direction and pointed his finger insultingly at Bauji, 'You have no right to blow your nose here, understand?' His finger was still shaking violently. Repeating himself, he went on severely scolding Lajpat Rai, in front of the terrified girl, 'Blowing the nose in public places is against the law.'

The white man turned as if to go, and then checked himself, 'What are you doing here anyway? Don't you know that this is a whites-only area? Indians are not allowed.'

Agitated at heart, Lajpat folded his hands and bowed, but the police officer was in no mood to accept a mere apology. Taking out a paper and pencil, he scribbled something on it. Lajpat Rai had to pay a fine of a few shillings before he was allowed to go.

Their spirits had faltered but the steps quickened. Neither of them spoke a word on their way home, but for sure they were determined not to walk to Muthaiga again! That night, Muni's eyes were full of tears, 'Bauji has been made to feel so small and so ashamed,' she kept repeating until she had cried herself to sleep. When her brothers heard the story, they were naturally angry. Confronted by a white police officer . . . *chitta chua*—white rat, they called him. '*Gore gun de bore* . . . white on the outside but full of rubbish inside', they carried on, swearing racist remarks at the absent white colonial—as if these would alter his behaviour!

Thankfully, their walks were not terminated. Only temporarily suspended, just a few days at the most. Sometimes Lajpat and Muni went to Government Road to window-shop. All sorts of people had begun to crowd and gasp in awe at these upcoming bastions of hedonism. They peeped into the interiors almost in reverence. It attracted; it seduced. They could not afford to buy anything, but the feast for the eyes was pleasure enough for the young lady. Lajpat could not deny her that little. Muni was always a little shy and self-conscious when she came to this part of town, for it was all sophistication. Luxurious buildings, window displays, beautiful cars, and white-laced robes! The clothes of the *angrez* were beyond description. Antagonism from the white people surfaced every now and then, but Muni still looked at them with wonder in her eyes.

Lajpat had taken to walking with a stick by this time. On one such promenade on Government Road, a dog came at Lajpat's leg, almost biting it off, it seemed. The dog yapped and growled aggressively.

'Shoo, shoo, go away,' Lajpat pushed it away defensively with his walking stick.

Hardly had he done that, than he felt someone grab him from behind by the collar of his coat. 'You bloody Indian! You dare touch my dog! I swear I will take you to the law courts for that.' A crowd surrounded them. The white man felt that much stronger.

His language became more dramatic and colourful. 'I am sorry sir,' Lajpat had to apologize, for he knew that was the only way to be released. Tears of shame and rage welled up in the eyes, but what could he do in front of the sahib *log*? He felt utterly defenceless. He looked at his girl, she appeared so distressed. He knew that she wanted to cry out, but wouldn't. The tears stuck in her throat. The unreleased emotions gave her more pain. Why, why did it have to be this way?

'We looked at the *angrez,* the *wazungu*, the white-skinned people, in awe. We were forever being given the impression that they were above us . . . so polished . . . so beautiful! We would never have dared to dream of comparing ourselves to them. Sometimes, when we were children, with my sisters, we wore *gurgabian*. The high heels gave us airs. With our heads held high, we felt as if we were looking down at others. We were playing at being *mem* . . .'

The next time Muni saw them, memories of these incidents flooded her being. Why, why did it have to be this way? Why did these white people, whom she had secretly admired, have to provoke such sensations in her? They inculcated the cult of fear in her being, something she had never known before.

A few years after this incident, British India was partitioned. The rift created by the divide-and-rule policy—India for Hindus and Pakistan for Muslims—had clearly been transplanted in Kenya. As the relationship developed cracks, the boys at Government Indian School too lost the feeling of unity. The infection spread quickly in society. Hindus and Muslims now demanded separate seats on the Legislative Council. The Kenya Muslim League was born.

Night of 14 August 1947. An *azadi* procession was taken out on River Road. All houses were lit. The new Indian and Pakistani flags were raised. Hindus, in celebration of the new India, Muslims rejoicing in the birth of Pakistan. Arms raised high, eyes aflame, necks strained, veins sticking out, they held banners and flags. Some were dressed as Nehru. They shouted slogans. 'Hindustan *amar rahe*!' Muslims yelled, '*Inquilab*, Pakistan *zindabad*!' In between there were the sounds of hundreds of firecrackers.

While demonstrating at one point, their paths crossed. The slogans changed immediately. 'Pakistan *murdabad,* Death to Hindustan' was now heard. A fight broke out. Butchers took out *pangas* used for cutting meat. *Jembes* and *saroors* (metal bars) were used. Many closed their shops and went to the safety of rooftops to witness the hell let loose. Yashoda and Lajpat screamed out to the children, pleading with them to stay indoors. But the children were certainly not going to be denied this excitement and clambered to rooftops, joining many others already there. Finally, the police arrived to control the explosive situation. Fortunately, there had been no deaths, though many had suffered injuries.

A year later, he came. The new representative of an independent India to colonial Kenya. They went in large numbers, garlands in hand, to the Nairobi railway station to welcome him. Many *Wahindi* listened to him that day—even those with no political leanings: men, women and children. Muni sat on the floor in the large hall with other classmates from school. Some came from the neighbouring town of Machakos; others from Nyeri, Nanyuki, and Nakuru. Hands folded in their laps, they stared at him in reverence, an avatar in person. Not everybody listened; among those who did, few understood. There were women who gossiped, children who played about. And yet, they venerated him. They listened as if in a trance. They had had a *darshan* of this follower of Gandhi and close associate of Nehru. They had felt his energy and drunk of its well, felt his silences, been drawn into his fascinating magnetic field. Apa Pant's aura stayed with them for a long time.

Handsome, with a great command of the English language and a very open mind, the man who had taken an active part in the Indian struggle now took an active interest in the African movement for independence, angering the Kenyan colonial government. Apa Pant, also consul general for Belgian Congo, Rwanda and Burundi, looked at the colonies with eyes still aflame with the spirit of India's independence. Paradoxically, with India's independence, Kenyan Indians lost an ardent spokesman in Nehru. The new Indian government was more concerned with African interests than the problems of the local Indian community.

Apa Pant quickly became a spokesman of the Afro-Asian world and a leader in the non-aligned movement. Together with the new high commissioner of Pakistan, Nawab Sadiq Ali, also from an aristocratic family, they did help reduce the chasm between Hindus and Muslims in colonial Kenya. The two high commissioners opened their houses to both Hindus and Muslims, encouraging intercultural meetings and events which, fifty years ago, had never needed an outside hand.

21

New mansion

Mama mbetsi mbindi nzi khumitsa
Nzi nzi nzi nzikhumitsa . . .

(Mother give me chickpeas to plant
During drought we would starve to death otherwise . . .)

— Luhyia song

In 1948, a new urban 'multi-racial' plan was designed for Nairobi. Thornton White, a South African architect, was asked to lay down concepts of planning based on separate development of neighbourhoods, each with its own infrastructure—clubs, schools, shops, etc. South Africa was of course the role model. The aim was to 'protect' (i.e. isolate and separate) Europeans from other inhabitants.

The new Pangani, lower Parklands, Ngara and Eastleigh became Indian areas, and the first true suburbs of the city. Indian shops, places of worship and cinema halls came up. Very much divided by language, religion and social customs, Indians were never a cohesive group. By now, the majority were Gujarati-speaking Hindus: tailors, carpenters, goldsmiths, lower caste traders. Many were Shahs, mostly of the Jain faith. There were some Parsis. Punjabi Hindus and Sikhs had the strength of numbers. Muslims were Sunni, Shia or Ahmadiyya. Nothing had been done to integrate them in society. No mechanism had been created for people of one culture to communicate with another.

Indians had been restricted to the very small areas of Bazaar and River Road. Their persistent demands for more land were not met for a long time. Finally, to pacify them, the colonial government decided to demolish the area of Pangani to make way for Indian development. The suburb was zoned. The 'illegal' settlement of Pangani by Africans was regarded as squatting. Many of the coastal Swahili living there were moved out to places like Pumwani and Shauri Moyo.

Pangani had grown from a safari camp; it had quickly developed a Swahili ambience. With three mosques, it was a stronghold of Muslims. Along with tea shops and hotels, it had soon developed other amenities. Butchers, barbers and brothels with prostitutes of every race made it a place full of life, especially on Sunday afternoons. It had become the nerve-centre of African political discussions, a welter of communication—the lingua franca Swahili mixed with words from English, Kikuyu, Maasai and Hindi. A new urban language and lifestyle began to evolve.

Land was now being leased out to Asians. Vohras, Kapilas, Khoslas—many Punjabi families moved in. When Lajpat Rai began construction of the house for his family, this part of Pangani was still seen as a jungle. No huge enclosure surrounded their territory—but no hawkers shouted from the street either. The compound was open, with empty spaces that we never had before.

For the first time, the family had a 'real' garden of their own. Violet agapanthas and golden showers were growing in the wild even before they settled in. Lajpat left the flowers as they were and decided to plan the house around them. It was a good idea, especially as the golden showers quickly covered the red roof. From a distance, it gave the house a fire-like appearance; it was easily recognisable. With her fast weakening eyesight, this would be a good marker for Bebe Gurdei—to begin with, at any rate.

The house in Pangani was a single-storey building with a modest front on a branch road. Its roof had curved trimmings in pseudo-Arabian fashion—like two crowns on either side of a long head. This was actually an imitation of South African Cape-Dutch architecture. The main door opened into a *deorhi*, a transitional space between the door and the courtyard. The *baithak*, generally reserved as the men's drawing room facing the street, was accessible from the *deorhi*. The open courtyard would still be the dynamic centre of their home, the lungs. The Brahma *sthanam* was the energy field, left open to the sky so as to have contact with outer space. The part of the house that received the most sunlight became the dining area. For the first time, a large table with seating capacity for twelve became part of their furniture; the dining hall became the hub of the establishment. This was where friends and relatives—those who dropped in at all hours—naturally gravitated.

A few nights before the shift, Gurdei rebelled and ran away. She couldn't see herself torn away from the duka-house that had become home. She refused to give up the bazaar, with its smell of ghee and spices, and constant peddlers' calls. 'What right do you have to isolate me from all that I am familiar with?' Bebe tried to reason with her son. 'No one lends me an ear, nobody cares, such is my destiny,' she complained. It was a very unhappy moment for her. The world outside, in the midst of those not her own, had no real meaning for Gurdei.

Wiping her tears with her *chunni*, Gurdei insisted, 'You forced me to leave Bhera, and now you want to uproot me again?' The modest duka-house in the vicinity of the bazaar was not very different from Bebe's life in the *mohallahs* of Bhera. True, it was becoming small for the growing family, but such issues were of no importance; space may be an individual need, but in the minds of the likes of Gurdei, contact with the community was the real issue: the compactness of a tightly-knit village-like existence, in close proximity to the neighbour, where everything was within walking distance. More importantly, it was security against the unknown openness of African spaces. At least she could call on any of her friends when she wanted. To live alone, without the protection of an adjoining house, was too much to ask of her. Bebe burst into tears again, stopping for a while to yell for her tobacco. 'Meru, *lete tambaku yangu*,' she shouted through her tears. Their young

Kikuyu servant brought Bebe her usual snuff. Noisily she snorted, pinching it up each nostril; it made her feel a little better.

Running away from home was in fact a habit with Gurdei: the family was quite used to it. Each time her son scolded her, especially when she had offended Yashoda, Bebe Gurdei sought refuge with her friends. This time, it was a little more serious. Bebe was older, and she was afraid. It was as if she was being wrenched away from the niche that she had been able to slowly carve out for herself. Lajpat tramped all over the bazaar. He searched her usual hangouts. Eventually, when he did locate her at an unlikely friend's place, Bebe refused to come. She stayed there several nights before Lajpat was able to persuade his mother to relent.

Malan had already delivered the usual orange marigold flowers. Mango leaves strung in *mauli* were tied above all the doors. Blossoms were strewn on the floor. The sacred red thread was also tied around the wrists of family members and friends. Water from the earthen pot that had been placed in a corner the night before was now sprayed everywhere and returned to its place with a lighted oil *diya* on top. This was to be the holy image of the protective mother. A pandit lit the holy fire and began the *havan*. Their songs in unison appealed to vibrational forces to protect the new house from the evil eye.

Festivities continued for three days and nights. Lavish feasts were prepared. By this time, Bebe Gurdei was resigned to the situation. She would fall apart under the slightest stress, and regain her original joyful form in equal measure. Her friends made arrangements to come over. An uncovered truck was hired. Sitting on the floor in the back of the truck, their colourful *dupattas* waving in the wind, they sang and danced to the rhythm of the *dholki*, the vehicle tugged along under their heavy weights. Laughter and merriment were again in the air.

Lajpat Rai had much to be proud of. The new mansion was an abode beyond his dreams. He had been lucky. Perhaps, the gods had been favourable. He walked around the garden thinking about where he would grow mulberry and *luqat* trees, *jamun* and mango. Yashoda remained her usual quiet self. Displaying neither excitement nor emotion, she went about the process of furnishing the new house in what would seem an indifferent manner. Or perhaps this was just her style, for Yashoda did take an interest in stitching new bedcovers and bedsheets. She and her girls embroidered pillow cases in red and blue with the words 'Goodnight' on the upper right-hand corner. Bedsheets flaunted decorative borders, some with tassels.

Right across their new house in Pangani lay a Muslim butchery. Huge chunks of animal parts, raw, red and bloody, dangled from metal hooks near the entrance. Odours of animal grease emanated from within. It was, after all, what a butchery was supposed to be—a place where meat was cut, stored and sold. Most Hindus of the time did not eat meat. But if they did, they generally went to Kasai or Diwan butchery. Pehelwan Thuman Singh's butchery near the Sikh colony was also frequented. But meat had never been bought, brought, cooked or served in this house before. Not until the day Baldev got it into his head to show off to his cousins in typical adolescent style—'*Yaaro*, come over for *kukkar-shukar* session tomorrow'. The sisters, listening from behind the curtains had stood aside aghast, 'Chicken-shiken! As if he has been eating it all his life!' When Amma Yashoda saw the boys arriving with the packet of meat in their hands the next day, she was so upset that for once she threw a tantrum. 'Meat will not be cooked in my pots . . . not in my kitchen!' she screamed. A drama ensued. Baldev broke dishes. Amma protested until she was hoarse, close to tears. This was the only time the children could remember their mother raising her voice. A compromise was finally reached— separate utensils for meat, on a day reserved in advance.

Very early in life, Yashoda had adopted the abstemiousness of the Arya Samaj: meat and alcohol were severely abhorred. To pre-empt any more hysteria, the boys took to warning their mother a night or two before the desired 'meat' day. Up very early the next morning, she would make herself some *khichri* and store it in her bedroom. Split lentils of *moong dal* and rice is considered light food—cooked when one has an upset stomach, is recovering from illness or is fasting. For Yashoda, this became a day of penance to atone for the sins of her sons.

They cooked meat in the verandah. Once a month at the most, but an important event when all the male cousins let themselves go. Gurdei forbade the girls from eating meat. 'You will become a *habshan* in your next life,' she told them. There were some Hindu Punjabi families where the girls ate meat, but it was always done in hiding, away from the eyes of any onlooker—the dish lying concealed under the *pidi*. Consumption of flesh was correlated with attributes like aggression and crude behaviour, even acts of violence. Toxic essences were supposedly passed on from the psycho-physiological system of an animal violently done to death.

It was an unspoken rule. They had always known it. Right from childhood, they were conscious of the difference between them and the Muslims. Despite cordial relations, Hindu families generally did not partake of a meal in a Muslim home. Muslims ate meat—beef, to be precise. To the Hindus, even the thought was abhorrent. 'Your mother fed you with the milk from her breasts, but you didn't eat her. Now that the cow supplies you with milk from her breasts, how can you think of consuming her?' The justification was as simple as that.

Sharing fruits and sweets, even biscuits and tea with Muslims, had of late become more or less acceptable, although Gurdei did not like even that. She would make a face and just walk off. Sometimes, Bauji would bring Tausif Hassan for a meal. Bebe had separate plates reserved for him. And even if she liked him well enough, she did not serve him. The task of handing out food was left to Yashoda that day. The rules were so well understood that nobody took offence. Tausif Hassan happily shared their vegetarian meal. But he never ate meat with the boys: it was non-halal.

'Bebe, why do you make so much fuss about eating meat? Early Aryans were meat-eaters. A guest in ancient India was called *goghan*—one for whom a cow is killed. Yes, the holy cow. When and why did the change come about? Since when did it become "bad" to eat meat . . . surely, it must be those Brahmins!' What a wonderful scuffle of words they had! But Bebe was not at all impressed with their new-found knowledge. Her own religious beliefs were firmly planted in her system. What they said would not lead to an iota of change.

One day Gurdei fell very ill. 'Pneumonia,' the doctor said, and directed her to have brandy and chicken soup—he did not prescribe any other medication. Lajpat knew that there was no way that his mother would agree to these, not even as medicine. So, he just packed them up nicely in medicine bottles and fed her. Gurdei got well. Later when she was told what cured her, she wailed, 'You have destroyed my dharma, my religion.' Lajpat, however, knew his mother's nature well enough. He was sure that she was more thankful to be on the path to recovery than hurt by the blasphemous cure.

Bebe's naughty grandsons, however, one day took advantage of her. Secretly, they mixed a few spoonfuls of the mincemeat that they had prepared for themselves into her puree of aubergine and tomatoes. They watched her carefully from a distance. When they were sure that not a morsel was left on her plate, they all spoke in unison: 'Was it good?' 'Of course,' she affirmed, '*baingan ka bharta* is one of my favourite dishes.' 'Do you know what ingredients were added?' they teased her. And then they burst out in loud laughter, revealing to her the 'additional' component. Bebe was not amused, and chased them with loud curses. Neither Lajpat, nor the boys, however, would have dared to play such tricks on Yashoda; she would have taken it badly, perhaps fallen very ill, suffering silently within herself. It would have torn her apart.

Lajpat's small herbal duka remained where it was, on the edge of River Road and the bazaar. The medicine and industrial business continued from there. But the break between shop and home became distinct—as it had never been before. Now Lajpat drove to his duka. Previously, he just had to step out. This small change in itself brought about other changes in their lifestyle. Yashoda had never been seen around the shop much anyway, but now even Gurdei was hardly ever there. Bebe could not so easily steal almonds and other goods for her friends. For another, Lajpat made it a point to have more strict timings for himself and the family. Clients were no longer able to call upon him for medicines in the middle of the night.

The old house behind the duka was let out, room by room. More often than not, Lajpat was inclined to give it gratis. Clients, friends, visitors from his ancestral town, newcomers, they all came with the same cry, 'Bauji, we don't have money, but need a place to sleep.' Some were genuinely in need, while others took advantage of his generosity. One such tenant, legitimately needy, was Hasharam. The poor man saved every cent of the little that he earned to send to his married daughter in India. When Hasharam arrived at what he felt was a princely sum, ten thousand shillings, that he could proudly gift his daughter, he left for India. Little knowing that it was soon going to be presented to them, one night the daughter, with the help of her husband, stole the father's money. Hasharam was so heart-broken that he never returned to Africa; he took *sanyas* in the Himalayas.

On Sundays, the shop would be closed. Lajpat went to the market instead. It became a sacred ritual, like going to the temple. Lajpat looked forward to foraging for vegetables and fruits, revelling in the sight of those fresh legumes with their crisp textures. Touching a ladyfinger to check that it was not too ripe, before filling his basket, he beamed with satisfaction. Customers who broke a vegetable in two to examine their consistency infuriated him: 'No respect for the trader or for the vegetable.' Throwing up his hands in the air, he added resignedly, 'Alas, it remains a common habit.' Father and daughter, Lajpat and Muni—each Sunday without exception, they went together. For many years, this rite continued to give them much pleasure.

They passed by the Colonial Dairy of Suleiman *doodhwalla*. Huge aluminium milk cans remained piled up outside after the day's supply. On Diwali and Id, he made sure he sent extra milk to some of his favourite clients, Lajpat included. The City Market lay in the centre of town, towards the beginning of the bazaar; it was a big outlet. Baskets full of apples, pears and oranges lay open, enticing customers. Each small-scale farmer or trader—and there seemed to be quite a few of them—had a little stall for his produce. A soft palm leaf *kikapu* shaped like a fish kip in one hand, Lajpat stopped every few paces to chat with traders.

Most of the fruit sellers were Hindu Punjabis; Lajpat seemed to know them all. Lala Bhagwandass came on a bicycle to buy fruit. He stopped when he saw Lajpat Rai and shook both of his hands before moving on. Master Lahori Ram was also around. They called him Mehta because he did the bookkeeping and accounts for some clients. There were Gurbux, and Mahajan and Arora. Atmaram, Sitaram and Mayaram—all the 'Rams' seemed to be there selling fruits. 'Namaste *beta*,' they wished Muni. One offered her a plum, another, a banana. These visits were fascinating, for here she learnt about so many new vegetables that only the 'white people' ate—broccoli, asparagus, fennel or avocado—though somehow her father never bought these, so she never got to taste them.

22

Towards independence

Sangchhadadvam sangdadvam Samvomanansi jaanataam
Samaanamastu to manoh yathaavah suhaasati

(Let us all go together, speak together
Let us understand with similar minds
Let us live together with equanimity of mind happily . . .)

—Sama Veda

Andi a thii ino itakena ni imue menyaga wege ali
Turi andi amme bururi witte ni wa ngai umme . . .

(The blood of all people of this earth is the same
I know that we are one people)

—Gikuyu song

The main streets were hung with flags and bunting. Many were lit up, with flowers decorating nooks and corners. Portraits of King George adorned shops. Even the horse-driven rickshaw laundry was in full colour regalia. There was a carnival in town that afternoon, with pretty little fairies in the float. Every shop offered its customers something—sweets, chocolates, free gifts. On Government Road, each retail store—boutique, bakery, shoe-shop—vied with others for the most spectacular window display: a prize was to be given for the best. Muni and her brothers had spent much of the night helping their father decorate their little medical store. Already seventeen, Muni still felt like Alice in

Wonderland as she walked with her father down the street. She did look young for her age and was often mistaken as the younger of the two sisters.

On 13 March 1950, Nairobi celebrated in style its rise to the status of a city when the Duke of Gloucester presented on behalf of King George VI a royal charter to the people of Nairobi. Much of the city, especially the European-frequented areas, looked like a fairyland. Ngare Naerobi that had been baptized as 'Nairobi' in 1899 was this day converted from a town to a city. 'Kenya' as the name of the country did not come into existence until the late 1890s, until when it was only a province of the British East Africa protectorate. In 1920, the protectorate became Kenya colony. Almost half a century after its inception, the land the Maasai used for grazing their cows, their place for cool waters, became the authorized hub of British colonialism, with privileges and amenities that accrued to a city.

The police force feared assassination attempts, and security was tight. Many African leaders boycotted the ceremony even as, with great aplomb, the Duke of Gloucester handed the charter to Alderman Woodley. In this period of prosperity and expansion in the city's history, most Africans and many Asians only saw blocked aspirations and frustration of legitimate demands within the system. 'Whether Nairobi is called town or city, there is no change for the better. The lifestyles of the people show no improvement as long as the policies of the government remain as they are,' declared Makhan Singh, general secretary of the East African trade union movement.

Nairobi would become a city under siege for the next five years. Resentment against European domination and inequitable distribution of arable land gave way to African nationalism in various forms. Behind the officially organized groups and varied public meetings, clandestine meetings were held in Kikuyu country. An underground movement, the Mau Mau, formed to recover the land that was rightly theirs, quickly spread in the 'reserves', among those working in towns and hundreds of squatters on European farms.

The British response was classic and forceful. The Royal Air Force bombarded villages, surrounded regions and displaced populations. Houses were searched, thousands arrested. On 20 October 1952, a state of emergency was declared. Many Africans would die; others would be detained in special camps. More than 10,000 dead amongst the rebels, over 80,000 arrested, several thousand African loyalists killed by the Mau Mau. Thirty-two Europeans out of 40,000 would be killed over the years. The year 1956 would mark the end of the revolt, but curfew would continue to be imposed on Nairobi until 1960.

Meru was only fourteen when he had come to work for Lajpat and Yashoda. That was many moons ago. By now he was an old man, very much a part of the household. One evening, the police came looking for him. It was his day off, and Meru was not in. The surprise was Lajpat's, for he never suspected Meru's political leanings. Involved in his domestic duties in a mechanical, nonchalant way, Meru had never seemed anything but a simple person. One would assume that he was content with life.

When Lajpat asked him, Meru did not reply immediately: he continued ironing gently. He folded the last shirt carefully. At last he spoke, '*Ndiyo bwana*. Being a Kikuyu, it became my duty to support the Mau Mau movement. All we are asking for are our land, our rights, our commitments.' Lajpat nodded his head in sympathy. 'Why did I not think of it before?' he asked himself. 'Nationalist feelings are only natural. Not so long ago, did we not also see such a turn of events in my native country?' Their conversation ended there. And naively, Lajpat thought, so had the whole episode.

Nationalist Indian films like *Jhansi ki Rani* were banned, as were journals like the *Blitz* and M.R. Anand's *History of India*. India regarded the Mau Mau movement as an 'orthodox nationalist struggle on the lines of ours' and sympathized with its aims. Apa Pant, the first Indian high commissioner to Kenya, freely and openly supported the Mau Mau movement. The colonial authorities in Kenya wanted to deport him for his incitement to rebellion.

Some Indian lawyers would defend Jomo Kenyatta at the Kapenguria trial, despite strong objections of the government. Others ran an underground press for the movement. Ambubai Patel and his wife started a paper, the *Mau Mau High Command*. Once again, the Indian community was caught in cross-fire. If it sympathised with native aspirations, it was regarded as politically dangerous. If it kept aloof, it was said to be doing nothing for the local people. Many chose to live in fear of the whole situation. Their position during the emergency was ambiguous. On the whole, though, they were sympathetic to African nationalistic demands.

The Home Guards took to passing by the house every now and then. They surveyed the area and watched every move. Entry and exit of every person was monitored. Each evening, Lajpat would hide Meru in the loft. As life turned to normality, Meru returned to sleeping in his own quarters at the back of the house. It was when they had been totally forgotten that they came again. Around midnight, they surrounded the house. Many torches shone from the garden in the dark. Every member of the house got up. '*Mwizi! Chor!* Thieves!'—that was the first thought that occurred to everyone, and they huddled together in fear. There was a knock on the door, 'It's the police. Open up.' They forced themselves in. Everyone was pushed aside. 'We won't harm you. We just want to check.'

The big chief barged in. He kicked open the door to Meru's room. Meru lay with a high fever in bed; he was sweating profusely. The chief pulled him out of bed and kicked him. The children started crying. Gurdei screamed at the top of her voice, '*Apana piga, wacha mtoto yangu*—leave my child!', but the beating continued. She rushed to get him a cup of tea, the officer threw it away. Meru was subjected to intensive interrogation.

He did not resist. The home guards dragged him outside and whisked him into the police van—to nobody knew where. No one slept that night.

His strength was drained away, his manhood shattered to pieces. Sometimes he felt empty, till memories of the beatings flooded his brain. His soul cried out in anger. He was full of rage and bitterness. For the moment there was nothing he could do. But he swore to himself, 'One day the *wazungu* must go, and then our people and our land will be free.'

Years later, Meru passed by the shop. He looked thinner, his face scarred with age. Lajpat was glad to see him alive. He had suffered in jail, he said. 'But I was released on oath that I would not join the movement again.' They had put him to work in a mission hospital.

23

Soulmates

Kikli kaleer di, paag mere veer di,
Dupatta mere sai da, phite muun jawai da.

(Round and round we go, honour for my brother, my body is for my husband
And, damn that nasty son-in-law.)

—Punjabi ditty

H e was dark, like the dark half of the lunar month, the
Krishna *paksh*. It was the colour of the rain clouds. So he
was named after Krishna, the black God. Kishan, Krishana, Krishen,
Krishanlal, the variations were many. It was a very common name
those days. His white bosses called him Chris. In inter-office
memos, the name was reduced to plain initials: K.K. To his parents,
he was Krishanlal. And to his younger siblings, Papaji. As a poet,
he signed as Kamal, the lotus. His grandmother Bhagwanti called
him Kichen. In the generation after, hardly anyone would use the
name, but then, almost every Punjabi family had at least one
member called Krishan, or a variation.

'He looked pale, haggard and woebegone as he loitered about
in the lonely wilds of love. Pierced by the arrows of love, but
disenchanted, and disillusioned; his frustrated desire lay empty.
The insurgent youth felt martyred. Hounded by a hostile society,
his thwarted passion led nowhere. He longed to break away from
the metaphorical pot of societal constraints. But he couldn't . . .'
the rich voice paused. There was a sigh before he continued.

The radio play that was just being transmitted on the air was
an extract from Krishanlal's latest Hindustani play *Achhoot Kanya*.

He read it out himself. Structured around the inevitable man-woman encounters in life, the tastefully conceived play had the fillip of strong tensions, evoking moods which probably complemented the author's, for obviously a great deal of feeling had gone into it. Repeating a romance—told and retold in all cultures umpteen times—a tale that never became stale, because love and hate are such human emotions. Articulate, detailed, voluble, the sensibilities of the 'Untouchable Virgin' were all too clear, the topical issue held up to scorn by means of ridicule and irony.

The era of Hindustani films had arrived, and it was no wonder that Krishanlal was inspired by the legendary Devika Rani playing the role of the Harijan girl in a film of a similar name. Released in Bombay in 1936, the bold theme of lovers who could not cross the chasm of caste differences remained revolutionary, but naively so. Krishanlal's satire too was based on forbidden love between a high caste Kshatriya boy and a Shudra girl from a lower caste. 'You cannot marry the girl,' the boy's family laid restrictions. '*Nichi jat* . . . low caste,' the mother said. 'She is a Sood,' the grandmother added. Although they were above the outcastes (who did not even form a part of the hierarchy), the Soods belonged to the lowest rung of the caste-based society.

Caste rules were so strongly ingrained that even those on the lower rungs did not dare defy them. In Krishanlal's play, the girl's parents reject the match. 'Love marriage': those two indecent-sounding words were considered bad taste. To look for a 'suitable boy', the family whisked their daughter off to India. Fretting under the strain of societal and parental taboos, the lovers could not boldly respond to each other. Under these conditions, their love could hardly end happily. The story in all likelihood referred to an ideal— a mystical love, desirable, yet unattainable. Written in the style of a *masnavi* (a long, romantic narrative poem with rhyming couplets), the piece described in some detail romantic attachments and the attendant complex of contradictory emotions.

Krishanlal's play was a bold attempt in a contemporary social scene steeped in myopia. It had an ability to appeal to both head and heart. 'This is the vernacular service of the Kenya broadcasting service. You were listening to a play written and directed by Krishanlal Kapur.' Allowing herself a deep sigh, Muni switched off her father's huge radio.

Pregnant silences accentuated the tension; Krishanlal's sonorous voice had its own impact. The dominant motif of the hero as the '*anukula nayak*': a faithful, obliging lover, who has only one beloved—was not watered down. Portrayal of personalities was an incisive rationalization of the pernicious caste system. Uppermost was a desire to be liberated of caste pretentiousness. Selection of marriage partners on caste lines was not confined to Hindus alone but was even observed (though less overtly) by Christians and Muslims alike. Catholic Goans had their 'Lobo' Brahmins; the tailor caste were the D'Souzas, D'Costas and Braganzas. The Muslims' restrictions included caste and could also be territorial. *Halwais, nais, kasais, dhobis, chools* (confectioners, barbers, butchers, washermen, cooks) some were not even allowed to sit on the same charpoys, others were not allowed near the *chulhas* (clay ovens).

As in his play, his own love had been taken away from him. Far away, beyond his immediate reach. And there was nothing he could do about it. He epitomized his misery in his own composition. '... There was this girl in my life. The experience was the inspiration behind my story,' he would later share with his new wife on their first night together.

Krishanlal spent hours steeped in melancholy behind the closed doors of his room. Plagued with ennui and growing listlessness and unable to contain himself any longer, he composed. The pen was his ready weapon of defence, driven by a rich imagination. Untiringly, he tracked the trajectory of his thoughts and moods. Krishanlal had always written short stories, poetry and essays. His artistic sensibilities could be traced to his father Hiralal, who was known to have acted in Shakespearean plays in Hindustani at Capitol theatre: *Khoon ka Khoon, Zindagi ki Kamai, Hamlet* and *The Merchant of Venice*, among others. But perhaps this was

Road show of the play *Khoon ka Khoon* (*Hamlet* in Hindustani)
in the late 1920s

Krishanlal's most creative and philosophical work to date. With that his pent-up sentimentality found an outlet.

His inspiration worked in flashes. Very often it was difficult to sustain it for long at the high-voltage level that it demanded. Moreover, his own love situation was for real. The play had only been a reflection. His depression was aggravated by his decision to resign from an employment he did not enjoy. Selling spare parts for motor cars was neither the most creative nor exciting job, although it gave him some financial consistency. Of course he wrote, and he acted, but these did not bring any monetary returns. They only added to his expenses, even though they gave him satisfaction. Whoever heard of artists being paid?

They called it *junoon*, obsession; an idler's vocation. It may be good as food for the mind and soul, but not for the body. His passion appeared excessive. Thoughts of suicide crossed Krishanlal's mind; he tried to suppress them. He did not talk very much to anyone, even less to Bauji. One never argued—much less discussed—such affairs with one's father. At twenty-one, he longed for love and understanding, but at this moment felt ridden over roughshod by his unsympathetic environment. It was hostile and repressive, he thought.

He went into a sort of emotional self-exile and an overflow of self-pity. With spirits down to rock bottom, he was overcome by a melancholic languor. He lay in bed dreamy-eyed, but weary in body; his long silences interspersed with deep breaths were oppressive. For a long while, he could not collect his thoughts. He brooded and moped for days, cloistering himself in a corner of the little house. Health problems pursued him much of his life, but at this time, lack of love was the most painful sorrow.

Initially, Hiralal would smile as he watched his eldest son heave and sigh every now and then, languish and moan. 'The gloomy look on his face will disappear with time,' he said to himself. 'The young man will soon understand the ways of society. Grief will lead to wisdom and maturity.' However, Krishanlal got worse. His lack of appetite, the self-professed malady, became a cause of anxiety for the family. The epileptic attacks returned.

The matter was not to be taken lightly, the *biradari* called a conference. 'The boy must be married off,' they concluded. Krishanlal was consulted. The trend of having a say in the choice of one's own partner had not exactly set in, but this was no ordinary situation. When it came to marriage—that ultimate litmus test—one would rather see one's son or daughter married within the familiar confines of caste, region and religion. However, the custom of the couple not being permitted to see one another beforehand had gradually begun to be relaxed. Romantic movies, plays, novels portraying modern sensibilities had to some extent influenced society.

It was not his wont to speak up before his elders, but after a little thought, Krishanlal softened, and confided that the only other girl he was prepared to wed was Krishna, daughter of Lajpat Rai, granddaughter of Lala Kirparam Ramchand. Chachi Bhagwanti was watching her grandson carefully. His face had relaxed, his restlessness eased to some extent. As the tension melted, Chachi's spirits lifted. She was fond of her daughter's son 'Kichen' as she called him. How she enjoyed spoiling him with *peda* and *jalebi*, *rasgulla* and *gulab jamun*—all kinds of sweets that the typical Lahori Punjabi in him loved.

She jumped in excitement. She blurted out, 'My friend Gurdei! Why, the young girl is her granddaughter.' That should be easy, she thought to herself: Gurdei will never refuse me. Before anybody had a clear idea of what she was talking about, or where she was headed, Bhagwanti was off. With deft fingers, she arranged the thick white cotton *dupatta* on her head and vanished.

Chachi's brain could be impervious to reason when it wanted, and just then she decided to keep it that way. Holding the edges of her starched *dupatta*, Chachi boarded a bus and soon announced herself at Lajpat Rai's new residence in Pangani. 'I have come to take something', she called out from afar. Her high-pitched voice could be heard everywhere. It pierced into the room, through the courtyard, and out into the street. Lajpat looked at her short but confident self—not that he was much taller himself—and smiled generously. Chachi Bhagwanti was tough and fit even after fourteen children. Loud in a typically Punjabi fashion, respected of course, a close friend of his mother—moreover, she hailed from their own town of Bhera.

'Ask what you will,' Lajpat acceded without the slightest hesitation. A 'no' to her request would have been in bad form; nobody refused her usually. She is not usually unreasonable— Lajpat thought he knew. 'Your daughter—Muni . . .' Chachi said, her hands holding the edges of her *chunni* in front of her, as if in readiness to accept the gift. Chachi's screechy voice continued, '. . . for my grandson Krishanlal.' The room fell silent. For a moment, nobody dared say a word.

Yashoda sat aghast, dumbfounded. She leaned forward as if in protest, but felt completely tongue-tied. Her throat was parched. She was flushed with emotion, wanting to object for the sake of her daughter. 'Too young . . . she is still in school. Muni should be asked if that will make her happy.' Yashoda yearned to speak up for once. But her voice aborted. She felt so helpless that she could not utter a word. Her timidity let her down; it denied her the right to speak in front of people. No words came from her. She was reduced to a silent bystander in her daughter's future. In the quiet of her own space later, Amma Yashoda withdrew into a shell, reliving the moment when her own father had given her the privilege of making her own decision, despite his wife's rejection. Strange, how she felt at this minute the very antithesis of her mother.

Lajpat raised his eyebrows, he too was taken aback. He looked at Chachi, and then momentarily fell silent, as if searching within himself, 'I have already given my consent in front of the family,' he thought, 'and I can't go back on my word, it would be against our dharma.' 'What's the matter?' Bhagwanti was either naively oblivious of the effect she had created, or was being very clever. Lajpat smiled weakly. The smile exuded nervousness, not confidence. 'Are you changing your mind?' Chachi wanted to know.

Her laughter reverberated through the room. With the exception of Yashoda, they all laughed, and the tension in the atmosphere melted. Chachi Bhagwanti took this as a sign of reassurance and continued quickly before anybody put in a protest. 'Then pass the sugar around.' They obliged. Her impish face lit up as she folded her hands in front of her chest in thanks.

Some people gossiped afterward that Bhagwanti had been in a hurry to see her favourite grandson married off and had defied social conventions—the rule that ancestors of prospective brides and grooms must come from different villages. Both the grandmothers of the prospective couple—Bhagwanti and Gurdei—hailed from Bhera, and in this matter of marriage, village exogamy should have been observed.

An unofficial engagement of the couple took place. Neither Krishanlal, nor Krishna Kumari, alias Muni, were present during this ritual confirmation. There was little idea of individual interest; marriage was a social duty towards the family, the community. The news of her engagement came as a shock to Muni. Before she had had time to swallow the news—let alone digest it, almonds and dry dates arrived from the boy's side. She did not even know the boy's name. Nonplussed, Muni begged to be allowed to sit for the approaching exams. 'What for?' retorted her grandmother. 'Muni is wise enough. She can read and write a letter, thread a needle, cook a dish. What more is there to know for a woman? Moreover, "youth" has come upon her.' When the initial shock died down, Yashoda complained bitterly, but no one heeded her words; it was too late. She sulked for days to come. She tried to reason it out with her husband, 'Muni has just a few more months before she finishes her Form Four.' 'We have eaten the sweet,' concluded Lajpat with a note of finality.

There was a special tug at Muni's heart-strings whenever someone mentioned his name. Krishanlal. The name had already gained a special niche in her heart. His soulfully romantic image had worked its wonders on Muni. She felt like Radha drawn to Krishna by the melody of his flute. No power on the earth could restrain her. She wasn't even put off when Wade Pabji, her elder sister-in-law, made the remark. 'Don't you know that he used to like another girl? How can he want our Muni now?' she had said in anger. That was how Muni had learnt that she had been betrothed. The incensed words rang loud in her ears; disturbing her equanimity. For a while, her sensitivities were hurt by such insinuations. She looked up, almost in disbelief. But when she realized who it was, all fears disappeared. She wanted to ask more, all the details, 'How did it happen, who came with the proposal?'

Suddenly, she was shy. Pretending not to show much interest, for a moment she carried on with her embroidery. The needle pricked her finger, and little drops of blood stained the white material. When she couldn't control the emotions any more, blushing, she ran inside. Into another world, a realm filled with dreams. A whole galaxy of images opened up before her. Krishanlal . . . author . . . poet . . . dramatist. He was a very prominent person in the community. All the girls yearned for him. She had seen him so often but had never spoken to him. The boy she had watched umpteen times on stage, at the temple, and had secretly admired for a long time. A thrill of familiarity whenever she chanced upon him made the small brown hairs on her arms stand up.

The midnight curtains of the shrine had been drawn aside by the temple priest to reveal the infant god Krishna in a cradle. There was joyous chanting and ringing of temple bells. All thronged to cradle the image of baby Krishna. They caressed him, cradled him, cajoled him. One devotee took the pose of Krishna playing the flute. Another male devotee donned a *dupatta* on his head and adopted a feminine posture to recreate Radha's responses. *Bhakti* was eminently feminine in orientation. The love for Krishna was envisioned from a female point of view.

The love between Krishna and Radha, Radha and Krishna— how it was feted! The story is one of the world's greatest mystico-erotic poems. Lord Krishna gave sexuality the status of the sacred. Radha had not even been Krishna's wife. She was married to another. No one knew his name. But it did not matter. As soon as his flute was heard, did Radha not leave everything to go to him? It was so easy to forget that Krishna was a god. Krishna characteristically upset all predictable limits. Breaking rules of social propriety with his amorous exploits, he mischievously encouraged spontaneity in life.

The images of Radha and Krishna penetrated deep into the consciousness and effected a transformation. A dazzling richness of perceptual possibilities was evoked, especially as Krishanlal had been fasting the whole day. At last at midnight, *panjiri* was distributed as *prasad*. Krishanlal took the mixture of brown sugar, spices, gum arabica and almonds—usually given as a tonic to the new mother—in his cupped hands. Before putting it in his mouth, he saluted the priest with folded hands and then burst into song. Dark-skinned Krishna had been reborn in the heart of his devotees in faraway Africa in the small new city called Nairobi. '*Jai Krishnahare Sri Krishna Hare, Dukhiyon ke dukh dur kare, jai jai jai jai Krishna Hare . . .*' Krishanlal prayed to the god after whom he had been named.

A store in their house had been converted to a *puja* room with small terracotta idols, coloured calendar cut-outs of Radha and Krishna, oil lamps, incense and hand bells. Here, he inhabited his own solitude, perceiving in the reflection a continuous vision of himself. Fixed on the idol, all objects lost reality. Except for the ego. He easily entered sacred time. An eternal, timeless motion leading to a transcendental state of bliss. He opened his eyes at last as the song crescendoed. They glowed with a sublime state of *ananda*, bliss.

He always began the evening on an auspicious note at *bhajans* and *satsangs*. Muni could still picture him singing. 'What a deeply spiritual voice he has,' she used to think then. She had never spoken to him, but each Friday, no matter where the devotional session was held—at peoples' houses or at the temple—Krishanlal was always present. To the beat of cymbals and the *dholki*, the crowd enthusiastically taking up the song. Krishanlal tirelessly repeated in crescendo, '*Jai* Siya Ram *jai jai* Siya Ram. Praise be to Ram-Sita-

Ram.' At the ecstatic end of each cycle, another singer carried the crowd with him in this display of devotion, which continued upto 9, sometimes even 10 at night.

Those were the days when she accompanied Gurdei. Whether it was at Dussehra festivities in Ramlila grounds, or celebrations at the Sanatan Dharam temple, Krishanlal played a part. And Muni watched. Year after year, just before Diwali, had she not sat glued to every move he made? Each word he spoke in the Ramayana had been etched in her memory; she could even recite some of the dialogues. 'And, when he recites *shairi* in Urdu, his voice is most romantic, mystical.' Muni could not contain her admiration.

They came with huge brass plates piled high with dried dates, *laddus*, fresh fruit and coconuts. The ladies of the Kapur *biradari* brought clothes and took charge of dressing Muni within the assembly of other women, separating the onlookers with white bedsheets. Muni was now officially accepted by the new *biradari*. Adorned and clothed by them. A gold coin with King George V's face engraved on it was placed in Krishanlal's lap: *shagun* was offered. Relatives from both sides formalized the bond with a drink of almond, pistachio, saffron and cardamom cooked in milky syrup. The Kapur *biradari*'s priest from the orthodox Sanatan Dharam temple was asked to decide on an auspicious date for the marriage ceremony. The official engagement ceremony would last for six months, it was decided.

He was called Laxminarayan. The name was a derivative of two Hindu deities—Laxmi, the goddess of fortune and Narayan, another name of Vishnu, the preserver. Such conjunctive names were based on the Hindu concept of the *ardhanariswara*, the deity as female and male. The son of Pandit Jagan Nath Shastri from Dera Ghazi Khan district (not far from Bhera and Miani), the title of '*Shastri*' was conferred upon Laxminarayan by the University of Punjab, whereby he had been declared a scholar of sacred Hindu texts. In addition to these, Laxminarayan decided to learn Urdu in a *madrassa*. His reputation as a scholar was already established when the Sanatan Dharam temple in Kenya sent him an invitation to be their temple priest. Laxminarayan accepted and arrived in 1935. Krishanlal was about six years old then.

Since both his parents were Sanatanis, he began frequenting the temple where Laxminarayan took up his post. Soon the priest became a frequent visitor to the Kapurs' home. When they wanted the Satyanarayan puja conducted, Laxminarayan was there with his books. For every religious ceremony, Laxminarayan was the preferred priest. Young Krishanlal would watch panditji's every move with keen interest. Whether he took the grains to place them on the floor, draw the swastika with turmeric, or sprinkle drops of water besides the lentils, Krishanlal's sharp eyes always bore witness. When the priest closed his eyes in intense devotion, Krishanlal took to doing the same. Whether he recited Sanskrit *slokas*, Vedic mantras or Hindustani *bhajans*, Krishanlal followed every word.

In Vedic thought, sound and form are inseparable. The universe is a continuous dance of vibrating energy forms. Man is not only formed of sound vibrations but lives and moves in them. This knowledge, this science of drawing the yantras with colours and grains on the floor, this chanting of mantras was passed on from generation to generation. Laxminarayan was now passing it on to Krishanlal. His eyes and ears fervently glued, his ardent gaze followed every move. Laxminarayan's poetic and devotional aspect made a great mark on the mind of the impressionable adolescent. It was then only natural that Laxminarayan be requested to conduct the engagement ceremony for Krishanlal.

Pandit Laxminarayan Shastri was also a noted scholar of Sanskrit, Urdu and Persian, palmist, astrologer. Above all, he was a poet of repute. The woman who stimulated his first poetic verse was seventy, at least. He laughed, 'Yes. I was only thirteen then. She was my first, what you would call today . . . girlfriend . . . an old woman . . . a poor woman. Bent with age, wrinkled. Just as Siddhartha had been motivated by the four noble truths, this old lady became my first *prerna*. She came in the form of spontaneous inspiration.'

After this initiation, there had been no looking back for Laxminarayan; poetry came easily to him. He could recite poetry on any subject, but would not tolerate any nonsense in or about it. No obscene poetry or mispronunciation was acceptable. An ex-student confirmed how one time he led her out of his Urdu class by her ear because he could not bear her insulting and inarticulate misuse of a great language. He was firm but not argumentative—never a hypocrite. Even Arya Samaji women came to him for astrological purposes and match-making charts of prospective marriage partners for their children—in total secrecy. He respected their privacy.

He ate with Hindus and Muslims alike, he mixed with the *chura*—the downtrodden, the outcaste, the cleaner. As he cherished the decisions of the others, they all respected him. He was not one to impose his views or his religion upon others, not even upon his own children. 'There is nothing in ringing bells or saying prayers. But fear the one god. And do not hurt others,' that was his main advice.

Sobriety in behaviour, humility in personality—it was the conduct of a great soul. A pandit by profession, a poet by temperament, he sang in front of Sikhs, and held *mushairas* with Muslims. He recited *sehras* (prothalamiums) at Muslim weddings. His *kavi sammelans* (poetry recitals) at the Arya Samaj were hugely appreciated—where even Muslims were invited to participate, to recite and to listen. He helped bridge the gap between the Arya Samaj and the Sanatan Dharam.

Many came to hear this great *shayar*, others to soak in his aura of profound humanism. Pandit Laxminarayan Shastri sat on the white sheet in the middle of the room and held forth. Extempore. In Urdu, in Persian, in Hindustani. The electricity that Panditji exuded simply lit up the hall as he sang. Each one seated there was touched at some visceral level. He could express profound truths in a few words, the best couplets being both secular and spiritual. His poetry was a chiselled expression of the Indian worldview. It was for this that he gained utmost respect and admiration. It is said that when he died in London many years later, thousands queued up to pay homage.

It was a time when Urdu *shairi* was at its height amongst the Punjabis in the city. Many years later, when he was packing up to leave, he found his poetry books stolen. For a moment he despaired, but did not complain to anyone. He knew the most probable culprit, but let it pass.

It was rumoured that the Sikhs who so valued and appreciated his *shairi* of love and of mysticism started him on alcohol. 'He is very advanced. Eats meat, drinks whisky,' it was said of him. He did not hide the fact either, but shared the good things of life in a congenial atmosphere of friends and fans alike. What had earlier been a shame started becoming a matter of modernity. He was not an alcoholic, but they say that if you wanted to hear his best, it was after he had had several tots of whisky. In the late hours of the night when much of the world had retired. When the junior poets had already regaled the audiences with their select compositions. When his glass of whisky had been filled and re-filled many times.

The Sanatan Dharam may have accepted his meat and alcohol consumption, but they did mind that he frequently visited the mostly Sikh *churas* at their Balmiki gurudwara near Kariakor. Why did he have to sit and eat with the lowest of the low? Their nagging did not make an iota of difference to Laxminarayan, who continued to be much in demand all over East Africa. Those in need of averting an unlucky star, a difficult problem, for an auspicious moment to begin an important ceremony—a job, a marriage, a business—all these people sought out Panditji.

'One morning, he left home to go down to the shops to buy butter for breakfast,' his wife shared with Panditji's devotees. 'The shops are just round the corner, as you all know, but this Panditji of yours,' here his wife broke out in laughter before continuing, 'why, he only returned twelve hours later . . . past midnight!' 'Did he bring the butter at least?' one of the fans asked. Of course, he hadn't. On his way, he had met a man whose daughter lay very ill

300 km away in Eldoret. The need seemed so urgent that Panditji agreed to drive all the way immediately, without thinking of informing his wife!

Even among the Maasais, he started gaining a reputation of sorts. Sometimes, when he went to Kajiado to look for herbs, they asked him to predict their futures, to help cure migraine or epilepsy. His cures included juices and powders, mantras and Koranic verses. A typical tooth cure might go like this: the patient would be made to stand under a green tree, three nails would be implanted therein. Verses would be recited. The patient would be asked to spit on the ground. And the cure would be immediate.

But it was mantras and verses for court cases that were the major need of the rich—Asians and Africans alike. Mantras that would make the opposing lawyer forget his case. A much sought after man, perhaps not always rewarded in equal measure.

This same Laxminarayan arrived at the Kapurs' residence in his usual black *sherwani* and white scarf. After conducting the rituals, Hiralal Kapur, as father of the prospective groom, handed him his *dakshina* in a brown envelope. Without looking at the contents, Laxminarayan put it in his pocket.

It was said that at times he did not even handle the payment. 'Deliver it at home', he would say. At other times, he would suggest that it be sent to so-and-so, who needed it more. In the event, he never had much. Laxminarayan did not charge a standard fee for his services, nor did he receive a fixed salary. If people did not pay him, he did not ask. Evidently, there were times when he and his family went without food. What about the offerings of food at the temple? 'I can't take that home. What will people say?' was his logic.

24

A poet marries

Ndereriruo nii baba
Ndaruta wira na kio niakaguranira . . .
(My father said if I work hard,
He will find a pretty girl for me to marry . . .)
— Gikuyu song

The whole school heard about Muni's betrothal. Only seventeen, and the first of their batch to be 'asked for', she acquired a new status. The girls would not leave her alone. They questioned her, taunted her, 'How is your *woh*?' Muni was too timid to open her mouth. To reply would perhaps have been immodest— not that they expected her to openly describe or discuss him! 'Is he handsome? Is he tall? Does he wear a moustache? Does he write couplets in your name? *Arre*, come tell us his name!' Muni refused to say a word. She became self-conscious, cast as she now was in another mould.

Gone were the carefree days of youth. Gone was the ease with which she had interacted with friends. Her head sank in shyness as she stood in a little corner against the wall. Being a mute listener made the discomfort worse. '*Ladiye ni tera sawan aaya . . .*' one sang, and ran away, then came another and teased her similarly; the whole chorus joined in, their bodies slumped with incessant laughter. Left hand covering the mouth, right hand holding on to the belly, tears streamed down their faces. They pulled her here and they pulled her there. They slapped each other on the back;

they tormented her until, red with embarrassment, she rushed home in tears. Unable to tolerate it any more, Muni refused to go back to school.

Soon the house was filled with all kinds of sounds. Someone was on the sewing machine, others ground cereal and lentils. As she started preparing her trousseau, Muni's thoughts often went to Krishanlal. Her face glowed with pride. Alternately, she flushed with embarrassment; she hid her face in the palms of her hands. Steel trunks were filled bit by bit with saris and matching blouses, petticoats, shoes and bangles—everything a girl needed to make herself desirable. Muni painted bedspreads, she drew flowers, outlined creepers. All that she had been taught at school came in useful. She embroidered bedsheets and pillowcases, flowers on the edges, 'Goodnight' in the middle. In all, she made six pairs of bedsheets and pillowcases, twenty-one pairs of clothes for herself, including *salwar kameezes* and saris and six pairs of underclothes.

Lajpat Rai did most of the shopping. Usually men went to buy jewellery, otherwise the jeweller was called in with his samples. He bought furniture for his daughter—a table and six chairs, a *balti* full of steel crockery. The bucket was filled with six of each kind—plates, bowls, glasses, pots and pans. Krishna's beloved Singer sewing machine was not forgotton, neither was a big portrait of Lord Krishna, Bauji's gift to her. Much of what she took with her was later passed on to her husband's sisters for their dowries. Thirty-five sets of clothes were offered to Hiralal's family. Her own old clothes were left behind according to tradition, for life must begin anew.

Red dupattas etched in gold adorned their heads. With a brass plate full of *laddus* in the left hand, *sada dena* was generally left to women of the family. They set off early in the morning, for they had many houses to visit—to personally invite close relatives and friends. It was a laborious word-of-mouth mission. Sweets were offered, some partaken. No way could you refuse, for the occasion was such. They 'sweetened and sweetened and sweetened their mouths' wherever they went. Cards were printed. The western system of sending out invitation cards written in English had arrived. Each card was stained red at the edges to give it that auspicious touch.

For many days, Muni was confined to the house in unattractive clothes. But she was never left alone, the women made sure of that. Gurdei reminded her, 'Remember your brother's wedding? He was not even allowed to have a bath with water from his own house. I had to go and fetch buckets from the neighbours!' They had all burst out laughing, easing the tension to some extent. Krishanlal too was never left alone until the wedding was over. Relatives came to rub oil and chickpea flour paste on his face.

All of Gurdei's noisy friends were there. Many Perewaliyan and Chakwalana, those from Miani, from Lahore, of course, and from other ancestral towns of north-west Punjab. Basant designated herself as the chief. The role suited her well. 'Lt-commander Basant', Muni's younger brother could be heard somewhere. 'Shhh,' someone else whispered, 'what if she hears you. Remember her last beating?' But Basant was in one of her best moods this evening. Dressed to kill in a blood red *dupatta*! The big gold *jhumkas* in her ears were clearly visible, despite the head covering. 'Why has your daughter not come?' Gurdei sat up and asked her. 'You know the youth of today. At least I am here to represent the family,' Basant said, a little embarrassed for once. Another old and ailing woman, dressed in white, walked in. She held on to her daughter-in-law for support. Everybody got up to touch her feet and to receive her blessings.

The night before the wedding was the night of henna, *mehndi ki raat*. Her hands and feet were massaged with the paste before she distributed the rest to seven virgins. A blob in the centre for the sun, and the palm was closed for the night; it felt cold. The soles of her feet were decorated in elaborate floral and fertility designs— mango leaves, peacock feathers, solar rays—with a paste made from the powdered leaves of the henna plant. 'How deeply red the colour of your henna has turned! Your mother-in-law is sure to love you!'

friends would giggle the next morning when Muni washed off the dried paste.

There was much clapping and playing of the *dholak*, during the day as well as late into the night. While one woman beat the drum, the other sitting opposite her beat time on it with a spoon. Songs were sung to honour the bride and describe her approaching trial by fire. Beauty was especially valued as it led to ready—even if temporary—acceptance by the bride's new relatives. Basant Kaur's satirical lyrics based on the groom's family, on reception of the *barat*, and especially her mocking of the future mother-in-law— stereotyped as a woman to be feared—brought joy and laughter.

It was when someone sang '*Doli chadhiyan*' that the whole room went silent. Amma's eyes filled up. Muni couldn't hold back her tears; every person present in the room could be heard sniffling, or seen wiping their eyes with their *dupattas*. Heer's departure as a bride from the parental home created a pathos that the composer Waris Shah had done wonders with. The eighteenth-century Punjabi poet deeply touched their souls. Gurdei took out a five-shilling note and waved it around the singer's head before offering it to the bride: 'Bless you, my child, may your turn come soon', she said to the singer, clicking her knuckles on the sides of her head. The gesture was meant to ward off ill luck.

Vast tents had been pitched; *dhurries* were laid on the floor for the religious ceremony. Long tables for meals had been set up further on. The big day dawned with the freshness of early September winds. Sitting on the floor all by herself for once, Muni clasped her raised knees tightly to her chin, as if wanting to hold on to the last day in a home she had known for all her eighteen years. Someone called out, 'Muniye, they have come, hurry up,' and her nostalgic thoughts were cut short promptly. Before she could collect herself, Gurdei was already there, rushing to get her seated on the low wooden stool.

Ladies from the Kapur *biradari* came early. They stood before her, and she bent her head low, not daring to look at them. A red *paranda* with gold tassels at the end was braided into her long black hair. They adorned her shoulders with a white *dupatta,* while an elderly lady drew a swastika in saffron powder in the centre of the scarf. Muni was symbolically now no more a virgin. She was ready to receive the *suhag patari.* Kohl for the eyes, branches of the neem plant to cleanse her teeth, henna for the hands. Red powder for the *bindi* on her forehead, perfumed oil for the hair, looking glass, sandal paste . . . the list was long. Her future in-laws placed all kinds of cosmetics in her lap—not forgetting coconut and dried dates, indispensable symbols of fertility—before they left to prepare themselves for the main ceremony later in the day.

The rest of the family sat cross-legged on the *dhurrie.* The priest started the ceremony, and Yashoda's brother offered the *choora,* formally establishing a responsibility towards his sister's child— perhaps a remnant of an ancient matrilineal tradition. Red and white bangles were placed on Muni's wrists, and immediately covered with her *dupatta,* hidden from any lurking evil eye. Cousins and other girlfriends came to help cleanse the bride-to-be. How they enjoyed washing her with *kacchi lassi.* While one rubbed chickpea paste onto her face, another grabbed her by the arm, a third massaged it onto her legs. Finally, washing her with yoghurt and water, they all remarked at the glow it brought to her skin.

She became an incarnation of *Indrani-karma,* tillable land. The pre-wedding rituals prepared her for reproduction and the start of a new generation. 'You look weak, my child,' Gurdei remarked, perceiving Muni's pale face and her delicate emotional state. 'Here, have a glass of milk, but don't tell anyone,' she whispered in her ear. The three of them were fasting this day. For the parents of the bride, the ordeal was perhaps not as great as it was for Muni, sensed Gurdei, but the fasting was necessary so that none would have the energy to get over-excited.

Mango leaves adorned the bamboo dais. Banana trunks and leaves ceremoniously flanked the entrance to the marriage area. *Kela* was synonymous with plenitude. Its fruits, the bananas, were offered to the gods in gratitude for the fertility with which they had blessed the earth. As a reincarnation of the goddess of plenty, the leaves of the tree and parts of the trunk became an integral part of the marriage ceremony. They stood in a line amongst yellow and orange marigolds strewn around. A garland in his hand, the now plump and bespectacled Lajpat Rai in a western suit waited anxiously to welcome the bridal party. The rest of the family stood beside him. Each member of the welcoming party had already been instructed whom to garland and how much to give.

Dense smoke from the smouldering charcoal fire drifted from a corner, bringing with it the aroma of curries. Enormous heavy brass *karhai*s simmered on several huge *jikos*; the *halwai* was surrounded by them, shifting from one to the other, stirring halwa here, checking spices elsewhere. Drenched in sweat, he wiped his forehead with what must have once been a white towel, before quenching his thirst with endless cups of piping hot, spiced, sugary tea. From time to time, Lajpat checked on him. It was the first daughter's wedding in the family, and he wanted everything to go well. He stirred the *halwa*, poured a little onto his left palm, 'Make sure there is enough sugar and ghee,' he alerted the *halwai*.

They did not have long to wait. Car horns blared in the distance. Their robust approaching figures gave them a look of authority. An impressive sight, the Kapur *biradari*. They turned out in full strength—on the dot. As sub-foremen with the public works department, Hiralal and Pannalal's training under the colonial regime had assured that.

The Kapurs arrived majestically in saffron-coloured turbans. Putting on the pugree was a ceremonial act, an elegant ritual. Hiralal fiddled with his turban until the pinch in the knot was just right. He was a big man, the pugree only adding to his stature and sway. Even to the most modest-looking men in the group, it imparted that particular mark of dignity. These were probably the last days of the turban. The younger generation was increasingly put off by the pugree's formality and tended to turn to the English hat.

Lajpat's gold *kula* cap—Pathani style—inside his pink turban shone brilliantly in the light. He looked royal as the father of the bride. His nervousness was barely visible as he sprinkled rose water on his guests. Relatives had assembled from far and near, at least 500 of them. Women in their most beautiful saris embroidered in gold and silver threads came singing *sithanis* to welcome the party. Full of humour and satire, their songs made fun of the groom and his family. No one took it in bad faith; it was tradition. The groom did not come riding a white horse. Instead, a black car decorated with flowers brought them in, his best man sitting by his side. The groom was dressed in white trousers and jacket, and jasmine flowers hung down in strands from his pugree. His face was covered completely with the *sehra*.

In her georgette blood-red sari with a heavy *zari* border, Muni stood resplendent. Gold *jhumka*s for the ears, *tika* on the forehead—gifts from Hardei. These, Muni had chosen herself. They had gone together with Bauji to their family jeweller Roshanlal Kapoor of Bhera; he had even come home to display special items. Indian Bazaar and River Road, by now, prided themselves on the number of jewellers and gold shops, from Gujarat, from Lahore—catering to the cultural tastes of the different Indian communities. There was enough choice, but Lajpat Rai had felt a special affinity with this family from their hometown.

The gold protected her from any lurking demons. Three pots of water, with little *diyas* on top, energized her spiritual being. Muni sat alone in all her finery looking into the flame, meditating on mother goddess. The *purnaghat*, full pot, was a symbol of the mysterious life force revealed as creation and auspiciousness. The ritual of *Chhandaliyan* made her more beautiful, brought out the goddess within her. Jacaranda trees were in full bloom. When bursting forth, they shed their purple bell-shaped flowers on the earth. A carpet had fallen all night. Huge plaintains ceremoniously flanked the area. The bride and groom welcomed each other with sandalwood and marigold *jaimala*. Muni's *pallu* hid her face from view completely; Krishanlal's was covered with long strands of jasmine flowers and gold trimmings. She stretched her hands to garland him, but would not look up, her eyes cast downward.

Pandit Satyapal nicknamed 'Gongulu' marrying Krishanlal and Krishna

The priest, Pandit Satyapal Sidhantalankar of the Arya Samaj, was known for his revolutionary activities. At one time he had even served a five-year jail term in India for being involved in the freedom struggle. To escape trial and, perhaps, a death sentence, he had fled to Africa. Even here, his outbursts could be heard from time to time, '*Angrezon ko nichoro*!—Squeeze the British like oranges!' The authorities in Kenya viewed him with suspicion, but they had yet to catch him at fault. However, children from Arya Samaj families loved him; his passion excited their imagination.

They called him Pandit Gongulu, and he did resemble a mature turnip. He was short, fat, round all over and fair to the point of being milky white. He stood just under five feet in height and had a close crop of short white hair. Pandit Gongulu never wore any colour besides white—Muslin white. A fine plain-weave cotton fabric covered his entire body, the loose-fitting *kurta*-pajama giving him an additional sphere-like enveloping mass. He was a frequent visitor to Lajpat Rai's shop and home, asking for a sherbet here, or a cup of tea there. Until one day, when he saw a tray of eggs displayed in the shop: he stopped coming by for trifles.

Every community had its own priest. The Arya Samajis, the Sanatanis, the different Gujarati communities, the Sikhs. Orthodox priests, conservative priests, lay priests, revolutionary priests, rebels, eccentric priests . . . the list was endless. Some served short terms. Others were more fortunate and stayed on. There were many of them. In Nairobi, in Mombasa, in Kisumu. Catering to the endless religious functions in families and communities. Often with very little formal pay, more or less surviving on what devotees gave as *dakshina*, anything from food and clothes to money. Contracted from India generally on a three- or four-year term, their tenure actually depended on their popularity with devotees and—more importantly—with community elders.

Pandit Laxminarayan Shastri left Kenya for London after thirty-five years due to force of circumstances. Some of his older children stayed back in Nairobi—they knew no other home. Pandit Satyapal of the Arya Samaj stayed for fourteen years. When he chose to return to India, rumours circulated that he was involved in income tax problems and that this time the authorities had reason to get at him. However, it was just a rumour. He returned tranquilly, his popularity within the Arya Samaj undiminished.

Demurely, Muni waited, preparing to enter the sacred space. The eldest brother's wife passed her a small hand mirror, 'Look, my child,' she had said. It was a metamorphosis of a spectacular kind. Muni had shyly surveyed herself in the mirror, her eyes settling on her reflection for not more than a few seconds. For the first time in her life, she was wearing make-up. Kohl in the eyes, rouge on the cheeks, lipstick on the mouth, *bindi* on the forehead. Her sister-in-law and cousins had worked meticulously with what little they knew of the use of cosmetics. None of them had ever used these before, apart from the red dot on the forehead. Soon, a mysterious transition had unfolded Muni's being. She seemed to have blossomed from a bud into a flower, her hair and ears adorned with gold and *kundan* jewellery.

The Vedic hymns resounded with a strong quality of magic and mystery; the power of the word reverberated its potency. 'Asma iva sthira bhava'. The bride climbs the stone slab barefoot so that she may have firm contact with earth. She is expected to maintain unflinching love and faith for her husband. 'Take thou five steps for offspring, sixth for reason, seventh as a friend . . . may you have many sons . . . .' This sealed their marriage and it became a sacrament.

She was given to the family of the husband, not to the husband alone. 'Remain firm and steadfast in your path of devotion; shine like a constellation,' Panditji concluded the ceremony while pointing out the dhruv tara, the pole star, to the new couple. A sehra (prothalamium) had been composed and read out to the gathering, showering praises on the couple's family. The whole congregation tossed petals at the couple and into the sacred fire. It was the finale.

The bride and groom had the faces of adolescents, young and innocent. They were clear, immaculate, flawless and naïve-looking, unblemished by the politics of the world. The groom did not even have a moustache yet. And yet, they were on their way to a new maturity. A new dawn that was to begin their lives afresh. Together. That not even death could part.

They stayed put on their low stools. The rituals were over, but the bride's girlfriends would not leave the groom in peace. All through the night, they forced him to recite chhands and riddle songs. He had been well trained and started off, 'Chhand prage di jai prage kesar. Sas meri Parvati, saura mera parmeshwar' (my mother-in-law is the image of Parvati, father-in-law of Shiva) Not bad, but it was only a beginning. They cajoled him, they flattered him, but they would not set him free. 'How will you cope with an Arya Samaji woman?' taunted one. 'She does not know the ways of the Sanatam Dharam,' sneered another. They asked him tough and embarrassing questions, hid his shoes, played tricks upon him. Finally, in the early hours of the morning, Krishanlal got to have some sleep—not with his new wife, but with her brothers! Muni spent the night with her girlfriends.

From a red cloth bag, Lajpat Rai took out a handful of coins and flung them in the air over the heads of the newly weds the next morning. Street urchins scurried after them. The red silk sari felt alive on Muni's body. The play of the morning light made it vibrate in two different colours. At one moment, it seemed red. The next, it was greenish. Muni took measured steps towards the door, and the new tissue rustled rhythmically. It reverberated, gave off a tingling sound. Almost as if she had anklets on her feet.

She threw rice over her shoulders. Virgin friends behind her collected the fertility symbol. She bid farewell to her parents, sisters, brothers and friends in a flood of tears. As if in a flash, the past reeled in front of her now kohl-smudged eyes: the first day at school and carefree days of fun and play . . . *Gulli danda* with her brothers . . . *Guddi patola* with Amma . . . marbles with Wade Pabji . . . walks with Bauji. She was leaving behind all that had been her universe for eighteen years.

Lajpat and Yashoda kissed their daughter on the forehead. She sat in the black Buick decorated with roses and marigolds, and waved her family goodbye until they were out of view. Lajpat continued to stand transfixed, his hand held up in a parting wave. Teardrops had gathered at the corner of his eyes. Amma stood in the doorway. She looked shattered. Relatives began to leave one by one. An awful silence descended upon the household. A sense of emptiness overwhelmed them. Her going away was an anti-climax, as if they had been robbed of something. The parental house was left quiet. No one was in a mood to clean up.

The drama had shifted to the groom's residence. The welcoming party arrived, together with the newly-weds. Oil had already been poured at the lower bottom corners of the main door. When the couple finally arrived at what was to be Muni's future home, her mother-in-law waved a jug of water around her before welcoming her in. 'Let us see who will be more influential over the bride,' she said. The groom's younger sisters jumped and clapped, awaiting the result excitedly. Twice, Krishanlal tried to snatch the jug from his mother to have a sip of this water, the third time he let his mother drink it.

She had delicate cheeks reddened with rouge, skin rubbed with Pond's cream instead of sandal paste; and she had sparkling eyes. 'Doesn't she look radiant,' remarked one. 'With our dark Krishna, the pale light of her skin will go very well', added another. '*Hai ni, kala* Krishna *te gori* Radha,' they laughed. Every detail of her costume, ornaments, behaviour and the colour of her skin were loudly commented upon. The new bride was an object of prying and prodding curiosity.

Muni had not even recovered from the shock of being separated from her family when somebody placed a young child in her lap. Another woman fed her the first *khichri* in her new home, and with that her *gotra* changed. From a Behal, she became a Kapur. A change of lineage, a shift of family, Muni was being absorbed into the Kapur *biradari*. Sacred threads and protective iron bangles were temporarily removed and immersed into a huge brass plate of milk placed on the ground.

They were made to sit on a white sheet in front of assembled family and relatives and had to endure much teasing and loud, often vulgar humour. The whole family sat on the floor surrounding the couple, thrilled to watch the game. He observed her carefully; she did not look up even once. Muni was small, one could call her petite. 'She is shy,' Krishanlal thought to himself, 'she will not fight.' Everybody's eyes were upon them. They played about in the milky waters. Not once did his hand scratch hers, or pull it roughly.

An electric feeling went through them at the same time when his fingers slowly caressed her hand; Muni went red in the face. Their eyes met for a fleeting second, Krishanlal let his bride take possession of the bangles. The victory was hers. But the night was not yet theirs. Muni had to spend yet another night away from her new husband. This time it was in her mother-in-law's bed. Krishanlal slept with his father. The ceremonies had exhausted her, but sleep would not come. She looked up at the roof of her new 'home' and realized that she had not been permitted to talk to him even once!

25

The life cycle

A movement in the right eye means joy; that in the left, grief.
Tingling in the right palm means gain of money; that in the left, loss.
Unlucky to meet a Brahmin,
But good omen to meet a *chura* . . .
Especially if he carries either a broom or a basket!

—Punjabi proverb

Railway quarter no. 139 on Desai Road was built on the English pattern: a small stone maisonette with a red roof. The walls of the small living room were adorned by frayed sepia pictures. Photos of children in a childhood long gone, family members immortalized in large portraits, innumerable stories locked in those eager faces. Some photos stood out clearly. The blues and pinks of the skies were vividly striking. A picture taken in 1925 by Knowles & Brothers, photographers for British East Africa, showed a twenty-something Hiralal Kapur in khaki shorts and shirt, knee-length stockings, black shoes—a typical British colonial uniform of the public works department—probably before his marriage. An unsmiling face, a taut body, right hand placed firmly on thigh, left holding that of a petrified five-year old girl, their entire attention focussed on the camera.

Another picture showed Hiralal's brother, sola topee on head, khaki trousers and jacket with large pockets almost everywhere. He held a railway lantern in hand. The photos marked presence as much as absence: where were the women? Hiralal's mother was nowhere to be seen. Neither was the step-mother. Although, come to think of it, Hiralal's wife was visible here and there.

There were only two bedrooms in the house. The children—seven girls and three boys—had the bigger room. At night, the girls were separated from the boys by an old six-yard sari that served as curtain. Hiralal and his wife, their one-year-old last born with them, had until then occupied the smaller room. This would now be given to the newly-weds. Hiralal moved to the living room divan. Clothes were stuffed in the childrens' room; others were stored in huge black steel trunks. Saris were hung here and there, adding colour to the otherwise drab surroundings. His wife and the baby slept with the rest of the children. At night after dinner, his wife sometimes stayed back in the living room to 'massage her husband's feet'.

The ceremony of visits from well-wishers continued for many days. Submissive and confused, fearful and sleepy, Muni would come face to face with an almost total stranger. Finally alone, the newly-weds found themselves in what was once Krishanlal's parents' room. For some time, neither knew what to say. Muni sat on the edge of the bed, head bent downward. Kneeling at her feet, Krishanlal took her hands in his and looked at them. He could feel her trembling.

'This is the first time that she has been so close to a man, other than her brothers,' he realized. He too was nervous. After what seemed liked a long while, his hand reached up to caress her face. For a moment, he stared at her without words, lost in her beauty. She radiated an inner simplicity that completely engulfed him. It seemed to immediately free him from his anguish, it was so refreshing. She did not need to philosophize, or complicate life with pseudo intellectualizing. She just was. He suddenly felt blessed for the way things had turned out for him. Yes, the gods were right.

Dekhna har subah tujh rukhsaar ka,
Hai mutaala matlai-anwaar ka . . .

To see your face every morning,
Is to see the glorious flush of dawn

Your beauteous glimmer, O flaming face,
Has caused a blemish in the moon's face
To hear one word from your lips,
Is to pluck the mystery's heart

He broke the silent communication with verses from the great
Wali Mohammed Wali, of the seventeenth century. Her silent
laughter burst into loud peals; it was infectious, soft and gentle,
just like the rest of her. It penetrated all his thoughts, his entire
being. He was completely mesmerized by this petite delicate woman.
The soft looks, delicate limbs. Drops of perspiration lay on her
forehead like little pearls. Her enigmatic smile drew him.

He wouldn't call her Muni, a name reserved for small girls.
This woman sitting in front of him would be his Kina. In later
years, he would rarely take her name—neither Kina nor Muni. But
he would continue to address her as had been done over the
generations. *'Mein kya . . .* I say', although he had a special way of
saying it that made the impersonal 'I say' a term of ultimate intimacy.

He gravitated towards her; she sublimated with dignity. 'Kina,'
he said, 'I am so glad you are in my life.' She felt herself redden.
Her hands were sweating as she clutched the white handkerchief
that she herself had embroidered with so much care. She had
been waiting for this moment for a long time, without really
knowing what would come to pass. Now that it was here, she
suddenly felt nervousness seep into her. The grip of his hand in
hers tightened, the strength coming like the affirmation of an
assurance, of a common bond. She felt better. The whole night
they talked. Of many things, of themselves, his likes and dreams,
his past and the previous girl in his life. Many days later, the need
to be physically one manifested itself. And then, it seemed so
natural and beautiful. She gradually became acquainted with the
new man in her life.

'Arre . . . wake up Kina! We can't afford to linger any longer.
What will they all think? Still sleeping . . .' It was very early when
Krishanlal shook Muni from under the covers. She got up without
flinching. It had been a restless night. Her back was a little stiff.

The hardness of the floor had penetrated through the thin mattress and left her quite cold. She held onto the edge of the new bed and slowly got up. She felt stiff to the bone. Once more, she looked at the bed that occupied the major part of the room, and yet was unslept on. This night or the previous nights. This can't continue, she was thinking. It's silly. Here we have a very comfortable-looking bed in front of us, yet we are sleeping on the floor! There's hardly any space on the floor either! She shook her head and said almost aloud, 'Tonight, we must make an effort to sleep on the bed.' Krishanlal had already gone to the kitchen to announce that they were up.

The whole issue started with Krishanlal's first glimpse of the double bed that had come as part of her dowry. 'We can't sleep on that,' he had said, looking at it as if it was a scandal—for two people to sleep together on one bed. What was supposed to have been a surprise had come as a shock. His parents had always slept on different beds. As had his uncles and aunts. And all the other people he had known. He looked at it again. He had never seen a bed this size before. The more he looked at the king-size bed, the more it seemed to grow. Monstrously, it expanded, until he was almost floating above it, he thought.

The huge bed lay before him like a pariah. How much difficulty his sisters and brothers had experienced in doing up the room, squeezing the bed into a room of about the same size. But Krishanlal was adamant for a while. They would not sleep on it, he said gently, almost shyly. At first he even looked at it with some embarrassment. The feeling was passed on to Muni. Neither of them dared glance at it. But they couldn't continue to ignore its magnanimous presence—after all, it hogged a large part of the small space given them. The big bed lay like a lone symbol of an unhurried modernity they had yet to come to terms with. A revolution, rather than a mark of evolution! The comfort and closeness it offered were soon revealed, and they both happily reconciled to the gentle brute.

Another gift that brought embarrassment in its wake was a diluted version of the *Kamasutra*, given by Krishanlal's Tayaji,

Hiralal's older brother—something that he himself had not had the privilege of reading in his day. Contradictory ideas about sexuality, ranging from pure ascetisim to the ordinary sexual life of a householder to eroticized ecstasy opened a new world before him. When, a few days after his wedding, the young man still had the book lying open in the bedroom, Tayaji started teasing him, 'Now leave these books, you don't need them.' Krishanlal reddened and left the room. Yashoda, on the other hand, had never briefed Muni about virginity, or about childbirth. No woman of her family had ever explained to her the intricacies of marriage. Muni had been too naïve even to ask.

The day was drawing to a close; darkness was descending. Traffic on the roads had almost ceased. Her heart filled with despair. She scanned the path by which he was to come, as far as her eyes could reach. Sadly, she took a step inside the house thinking, even now, if only he could come. She looked at the clock on the wall. It struck five. Already she was becoming sentimental. She turned her neck and looked back again. How much longer? Already ten days since he was gone. She counted each one on her fingers. Yes, it was ten, including today.

He had written to Bauji that he would be back by the weekend. But he had not written to her. Even if he had dared to do so, she would not have understood the script in any case. Muni did not read Arabic. While Krishanlal's excellence in the Urdu language (a product of Indo-Persian intercourse, begun under Muslim rule, continuing right through the British period in India) with Arabic characters, had brought him distinction, Muni's entire education had been in the Devanagari script at the Arya Girls School.

She gave a deep sigh and turned to the photos on the mantelpiece. The salon was full of them. Some hung on the walls, others lay on the mantelpiece—wherever there was some space. Most of the photos were of Bauji, her father-in-law Hiralal. His name meant 'the cherished diamond', and he looked special; he was special, Muni thought. He had arrived from Lahore with his parents as a

Paternal grandfather Hiralal in 1925 in the typical dress of a
sub-foreman with the railways, with a colleague

child, sometime in early 1903. The plague had been ravaging the
new town of Nairobi then.

The photographs flattered him. His strengths came out in full
force; the weaknesses gently obscured by the camera lens. Some of
the most telling and feel-good images that would become nostalgia
unlimited; these defined the family that she had just stepped into.
It was obvious that he loved to be photographed. 'This is perhaps
more recent,' Muni said aloud to herself . . . . left hand in the pocket,
Borsalino hat on head, cigarette in right hand. 'Reminds me of
someone', Muni thought. 'Ah yes, one of the Italian prisoners at
Payaji's house in Nyeri looked very similar', she exclaimed in
excitement. Conscious of himself and his looks, Hiralal was very
particular about his appearance. Impeccable in his two- or three-
piece, a cravat and hat to top it all, or in shorts with a horizontal-
striped long-sleeved t-shirt, arms folded across the chest, surrounded

by the rest of the football team. A black-and-white jacket, tennis racquet in hand, representing a team in Nyeri, or in a swimsuit at Mombasa beach. A simple *kurta*-pajama at home, or in the full regalia of Freemasonry—apron, cravat, tails and all.

The first time she had heard about this sect was one Friday when there was total pandemonium in the house. As soon as he had returned from the office at four in the evening, orders were given and everyone was put to work. One ironed his shirt, another polished his special black shoes, a third heated water for his bath, a fourth had gone to Kushal Singh's laundry to get his costume, while Bauji himself was busy preparing his special bag. In it went his apron, strings, compass and all.

None of them had ever had a full view of its contents. But right from its inception in the mysterious days of King Arthur, such had been the orders of the Freemason high command: 'Keep total secrecy!' The slim black bag was an important item. In fact, members simply recognized each other by their bags—even before they had made that special three-pointed handshake. It was a grip that bound the men in more ways than one, and the whole drama that went with it. A Lodge meeting was a great moment, and Hiralal put in a lot of effort readying for it.

It was an all-male affair: women had no business meddling in this ultra-guarded, enigmatic cult. Even in the family, they spoke about the almost-nothing that they knew of it in hushed voices. From their expressions, Muni had understood that she had better not show too much curiosity. She had been well trained: Gurdei had never encouraged her inquisitiveness. Hadn't she always been told that asking too many questions was bad? To have queried Bauji Hiralal, no! She hardly exchanged more than five words with him on any given day. What went on within the walls of the building was never disclosed. They didn't even ask where the Masonic Lodge was located.

Hiralal remained an active member of the Lodge for many years, even if he was never appointed to the status of Master. Some said it was a way to brush shoulders with the sahibs. It gave that added feel of respectability, a sense of worth. Drink in hand, they could share a moment of equality with their white brethren. They swore allegiance to whichever government was ruling. Right now they swore loyalty to the crown. Some said it was a respectable way to have access to alcohol. Others said that it was a *bhoot khana*—a ghost house . . . that they were vampires, sucking blood and eating the brains of people. In the formal atmosphere of the Lodge in Nairobi, which was at least ninety years old, railway *babus* had been the first Asians to become Masons. While the Hindu Punjabis took to it without much ado, many Muslim families were suspicious of the Bible studies, and the drama of oath-taking—not forgetting the imbibing of alcohol.

The big clock on the wall in the living room struck four in the afternoon. Another Freemason Friday. The routine was familiar by now, but she'd better not linger any longer. She heard the slight cough of a man outside, and knew it as his signal. Covering her head with the *pallu* of her sari, she went to open the door. 'Namaste Bauji,' Muni wished him in a low tone without looking him in the face, and rushed back to the kitchen to heat up his lunch. Initially, she had tried to touch his feet each morning as per custom, but he had demurred. Hiralal smiled and blessed her. The communication was formal and limited, but Hiralal was fond of his daughter-in-law. She is a good woman, he thought to himself. He knew that his wife was often rough on the young girl, and so from time to time he would press a five-shilling note into his son's palm, covering it with his own hand, and whisper to Krishanlal, 'Take Krishna to the movies.'

Under Gurdei, Muni had internalized various Sanatani customs. Now, in her marital home, these came in useful: she could assimilate with less difficulty. Muni did all that was required of her at Karva Chauth. She bathed and beautified herself. She dyed her palms with henna and wore the double-shaded silk sari called *dhoop-chaaon*, sun-shade. This one gave off pinkish-blue reflections. All over the edges, it was embroidered in gold thread with the words 'Sada suhagwati' in Hindi: 'May you never become a widow. May you retain the happy state of marriage-hood. May your husband remain alive and continue to be by your side throughout your life.'

Kavada was asked by a pandit to fast the whole day until she sighted the moon so that her unfulfilled desires may be realized. It rained heavily that day. The seven brothers, on seeing their only sister await the moon, felt guilty while they themselves sat down to eat. They looked up at the dark skies, and shook their heads in sorrow. The moon would not be visible that night. Finally, it dawned upon them that if they were to light a fire, perhaps their sister could be persuaded to believe that it was moonlight. Sure enough, Kavada was convinced. She waved her *puja thali* around the light and broke her fast. Meanwhile, the boat that the husband was sailing in capsized. He was saved, but lost his memory. On returning home, the husband took the maid to be his wife. Kavada was forced to become the maid. Once again, she started fasting. This time, the gods rewarded her for proper behaviour. The husband's memory was restored, and things were back to normal.

Listening to the story was an act of devotion in itself. Effigies of the *devi* were made out of dough and offered to Kavada in remembrance; others were given to their mothers-in-law, or to some other elder.

Muni had much more to learn. Black lentils must not be cooked on a Tuesday, nor black grams on Saturday. Perhaps she had forgotten the day, but one Tuesday, as Muni set the pot of black lentils on the table, and the family sat down for the meal, the mother-in-law materialized, marched towards the table, picked up the pot and—before a word of protest could be spoken—had thrown the whole lot down the drain.

Saturn was a planet to be wary of. On Saturday, the day of *Shani*, Muni knew that she must not oil her hair. Nor wash her hair on a Thursday; the health of brothers was at risk. She must constantly ensure that the broom was not left standing head up, or slippers left facing downward. Sometimes it was difficult to keep track of all these different things on various days, but her mother-in-law Dhanwanti never forgot. Unwilling to keep pace with the changing times, her rule of law swung from one solipsistic sensation to another. It was a fetish of commandments.

Dhanwanti, Dhano for short, had been born on 9 January 1911 to Chachi Bhagwanti, Bebe Gurdei's best friend, in the still new town of Nairobi. The bazaar had just been burnt to the ground. Many infants and children had died of the plague, but Dhano had been among the lucky ones.

At their wedding ceremony, when the Brahmin priest had asked Hiralal: what would you like to call your bride? He had replied, Pushpadevi. Extraordinary powers were attributed to names and the act of name-giving. Hiralal thought that with the new name, she would bloom forth as a lotus. Over the years, Dhanwanti's passion for religion flourished. She prayed with fervour and knew all the mantras. She visited temples and walked long distances to meet with the various priests, both Punjabi and non-Punjabi. She explored preternatural effects in her world. 'Propitiate the evil influence of Mangal on a Tuesday, the devil Shukar on Fridays,' a tantric priest told her.

Grains and stones of all sorts were found hidden here and there; occasionally mantras were found written on crushed pieces of paper. Sometimes, seeds were discovered under Muni's bed, and one of the children told, 'Throw them where four roads meet.' Muni was perhaps the perennial intruder, a suspect who might win away the affections of the son. The grains became talismanic objects carrying the power to determine life or death, the secret stories behind them revealed to no one. The night when Muni had a bad dream and cried out in her sleep, Krishanlal made a decision. 'We must leave,' he said. The relationship with his mother had to change. He knew that his father would not be happy, but would eventually understand.

They left for the coastal town of Mombasa, to what they hoped would be a better life. To release them from the continuing adolescence that life under the parental roof imposed upon them,

My parents Krishanlal and Krishna soon after their marriage

even though the joint family was still very much the norm. They were a little afraid of the scandal and alarm it might cause. In the end, it was but short-lived, a three-month escape.

'Krishna is not keeping too well. The stomach is heavy, she feels constipated, bloated all the time. Perhaps the hot and humid climate does not suit her,' Krishanlal wrote to his father from Mombasa. Hiralal insisted that they return. They did not question his authority; fortunately, his bidding was fair. Pale and fragile, Krishnanlal's young wife returned to Nairobi in a sorry state. When the women of the household saw her, they knew immediately what was wrong. 'There is no need to take her to the doctor,' yelled an excited Gurdei. 'You better go to the *halwai* instead and get some *mithai*. *Motichoor laddus* will do just fine. Why do you stare at me, young man, don't you know that Muni is with child?' Krishnanlal had not known; neither had Muni. How was she to know that throwing up every morning could be related to being pregnant or the ceasing of her monthly periods was a sign of conception?

Why, even her menarche had come as a dreadful surprise. She could still remember the day. 'One day sitting on a chair, I felt all wet underneath. I was afraid and ran to the toilet. I saw blood and was mortified. I did not understand how I could have hurt myself down there.' Behind closed doors, Amma had handed her an old but clean piece of cotton cloth—perhaps the remains of what was once an old *salwar*. Without daring to look her still-petrified daughter in the face, or giving her any sort of an explanation, she had said, 'You will have to expect this every month now.' It was said in a hurried and matter-of-fact manner. Before the young girl could digest the sentence, let alone have time to ask any questions, Yashoda had left the room, banging shut the door behind her. Left alone with the cold and unemotional voice still ringing in her ears, Muni had stared at the white cloth dangling in her hands for a long while before giving way to tears. Instantly, she had felt unclean all over. She looked down at her body as if anew.

The onset of her periods was a subject of deep shame. They did not discuss it, and Muni had not dared talk about it openly with any of her friends at school—with the result that she grew up in complete ignorance of her own body. Now that their Muni was expecting, Yashoda and Gurdei looked after her for a few days before sending her back to the in-laws. They showered her with love because they knew that her vibrations, her good feelings, would affect the child in her womb. Muni craved the sour and the pungent: *achars* were made. They roasted cumin seeds and added ginger to her food, 'an effective antidote against morning sickness,' said Bebe Gurdei. 'Sure to be a girl . . . her hips are broadening', Bebe Gurdei's friends looked closely at Muni, predicting the gender of the baby in a matter-of-fact way.

* * *

Emergency was declared on 20 October 1952: it would be known as Kenyatta Day after independence. Times were hard for everybody during this period. While the colonialists were adamant about keeping the land and its resources, the Mau Mau movement, dominated by peasants still practising their traditional beliefs, continued the fight in every possible way—with the aim of reclaiming their land at any cost. To bond people together in this time of crisis, members had to undergo the *muuma*, the commitment oath encompassing rituals developed from traditional Kikuyu practices. Traitors to the *muuma* oath were tortured; the Mau Mau did not spare its own people, especially if they were informers. To the colonials, the whole thing sounded barbaric, sub-human and savage.

The ordinary *mwananchi* was caught in the middle. In the event, the colonial government used severe methods to trace insurgents. African newspapers and political parties were banned. Mass arrests took place. It became an offence to be in the company of a Mau Mau fighter or to be a supporter. Hanging of such persons became commonplace. Thousands were sent to the gallows, many more to detention camps without trial. Property of convicts was confiscated. All of this was done under the name of a superior power. It was a dirty war.

Bribery and corruption became commonplace. British officials, Asian businessmen and African home guard loyalists to the colonial power—many were guilty of the act. Loyalists and home guards were well rewarded with all kinds of favours by the colonial power for 'screening' and harassing suspects. British officials accepted bribes from businessmen to obtain contracts.

Accused of managing the Mau Mau, declared illegal under colonial rule, Jomo Kenyatta was arrested and taken to Kapenguria for trial. His trademark leather jacket still on, Kenyatta arrived in the remote little northern town 48 km north of Kitale near the Uganda border, to which access was restricted, giving the government full control of the hearings and reporting of the trial. Achroo Ram Kapila, Fitz de Souza and Jaswant Singh, brilliant young lawyers of Kenya, were to play an important role in his defence. The team included D.N. Pritt, Britain's able and notorious lawyer, known for his communist sympathies. Jawaharlal Nehru sent Chaman Lall, a prominent Indian lawyer and MP. The political trial started on 3 December 1952.

In this climate of a police state, Muni's pains continued to be acute, even though the month of December 1952 brought with it warm, long and lazy afternoons, with occasional showers and breezes during early morning and late evening. The Kapur family had gathered together for their usual Sunday lunch of *paronthas* stuffed with potatoes, cauliflower and radish dipped in bowls of yoghurt or swallowed with milky cardamom tea. But Muni was in no condition to enjoy either the extended family meal or the agreeable weather. She lay restless in bed. Her labour pains were becoming unbearable. She shifted constantly, sometimes she screamed with pain. 'My son, your wife's time has come,' Taiji told Krishanlal, 'better call the *dai*.' By the time Sarla, the midwife, arrived, Muni had calmed somewhat; she slept. 'You may as well share some lunch with us,' suggested Hiralal to the midwife, indicating a seat at the table.

Sarla had swallowed only a few mouthfuls when the screams started again, this time with agony. Without saying a word, as if it was a routine affair—and it probably was for her—Sarla left her half-eaten meal on the table, and rushed to the room behind. 'Push, push,' she urged Muni, but the poor young woman, eyes shut tight, hands desperately clutching the bedsheet, did not understand what to do. It took a long time, a very long time. Muni was afraid and very tired. 'I am going to die,' she thought. She tried to pray, but no words came. The only sensation she felt was pain. 'Perhaps I have become pain,' she thought. 'Is it this hard to give birth? Did my mother have to suffer so much for me?' She was drenched in sweat by now. The touch of the *dai*, normally known to give faith and courage, trembled with some anxiety. She was uneasy and debated with herself about calling a doctor to perform a caesarian.

All was calm outside; there was still a curfew on. Another shriek, Muni screamed in more pain. There was a momentary silence. It was over. The umbilical cord was cut. In the height of the Mau Mau terror, a child was born. 'What is it? What is it?' were the shouts from the living room. 'Lakshmi has come to our house!' shouted Hiralal. I came into this world on 7 December, as the trial of Kenyatta at Kapenguria entered its fourth day.

The image of goddess Lakshmi was celebrated. A matrix of organic life, she was seen as a reflection of the universe, sublimely oblivious to the viewer, defying spatial boundaries. Smooth as sap-filled plant stems, her limbs twisted in serpentine undulation. Unashamedly sensuous, she existed in the timelessness of being, at peace with its own fullness. A perfectly oval face, her eyebrows described the curve of a bow, thighs the banana stalk, the walk that of an elephant—Lakshmi looked right through her worshippers and encouraged a quiet receptivity.

Hiralal's sister Savitri was all excitement. A box of sweets was opened and shared. But sweets were not distributed outside the immediate family—not until three years later when Muni gave birth to a son. For the moment, a messenger was dispatched to tell the entire family.

Lajpat Rai and Yashoda arrived in no time. They did not come empty-handed—especially not on this occasion. On their way, they had picked up customary gifts: a gold necklace for their daughter and gold bracelets for each of my tiny wrists. Other guests arrived soon after. Calling on the family in a ceremonial fashion, some wished the new father better luck next time. Krishanlal did not even hear these apologists. He only saw Lakshmi. He was exuberant, totally in awe of the creation. Whenever someone asked, 'Who has the child taken after?' his only reply was, 'Why, my beautiful Kina, of course!' He cried with happiness; tears coursed down his face. He hugged Kina's head repeatedly. It was a delicious feeling.

Muni lay exhausted and alone, isolated from everyone except the *dai*. Even Taiji, Hiralal's brother's wife, had held her hand for a few brief moments to give her some courage, before joining the celebrating party. It was not until *dai* Sarla had washed the baby, sponged the mother and cleaned the room with antiseptic that Krishanlal and other family members had been allowed into the room to see the child. That day, and for seven days after, Krishanlal's mother had neither lit the sacred lamp, nor had prayers been said; the house had become impure. 'In my time, people were not even allowed to see the child during this period of impurity,' Amma had shared with her daughter.

Morning and evening, the two *dais* came in turns—Sarla and twin sister Sita. They gave the child a bath, washed nappies and massaged the baby and mother. They disinfected the room with *ajwain*. Carraway seeds were also burnt over the charcoal *jiko*. For the first three days, Muni was sponged. On the fourth day she had a luxurious bath with *ajwain* and tea leaves. 'You girls are lucky to have someone look after you,' Gurdei nudged Muni on one of her visits. 'I had to do it all by myself. To enable me to finish the housework, I would not hesitate to give *post* (a mild intoxicant) to put my infant to sleep.' 'Hai Ram,' exclaimed some of Muni's sisters-in-law. Their eyes were wide open in shock. They stuffed their *dupattas* in their mouths, trying to suppress laughter. 'But look at my infant now, he hasn't done too badly, has he?' chuckled Bebe as she pointed out her son Lajpat Rai. 'The *"post"* put him into such a deep state of sleep, that many a time I even had to pinch him to wake him up.' The *dupattas* fell from their mouths as the girls burst out in open laughter. 'I let him cry for some time before feeding. It exercises the lungs and gives the child a real feel of hunger.'

Gurdei was obviously enjoying the attention of the young people, and wanted to reveal all. 'And when he had an upset stomach, I chewed grains of aniseed and spit them into the child's mouth. If he had rashes, I smeared his bottom with coal ash.'

Forty days had passed. The little girl was now ready to be received in front of the small family shrine where Krishanlal lit the *diya* each morning. I was now ritually inducted into the family. Later, they took me to the Sanatan Dharam temple. Orange marigolds were put round my neck, and the attending priest put the sacred red mark between my brows. Preparations for the *naamkaran samskar* (the naming ceremony) were finally done. The priest lit the sacred fire. Krishanlal held the infant in his lap and whispered the name he had chosen for her in her ear. 'Neera' he said—not once, but three times. There had never been a doubt in his mind that his first child would be a girl. All through her pregnancy, he had held his Kina's hand, singing the two names that were going round and round in his head—both feminine. And indeed, their second child, born a year later, was also a girl!

In this matter, Krishanlal defied tradition. He had not waited for the priest to assign the first letter of the name after astrological calculations based on the child's time of birth. Nor did he want a typically Punjabi name—Veerawali or Sukhwanti. No Lajo or Chandrani. He did not even care to choose a name from any of the mythologies, as was very common. 'Don't you realize,' he had laughed, 'the names have been revealed to me?' The romantic Krishanlal! The dreamer, the idealist, the writer, the poet. 'Our children will be our dreams fulfilled,' he had shared with his beloved Kina. 'Two Sanskrit names, Neera for the deep waters, Renu for the earth—that will be our little universe.' They were to have four more children over the years—all boys.

* * *

He had never been an oath-taking revolutionary. Rather, he was a missionary-educated moderate, but in this time of crisis, Kenyatta became a unifying symbol for the people. The Mau Mau rebellion continued with greater intensity; the settlers' hysteria did not let up. The trial of Jomo Kenyatta lasted over four months; it ended on 8 April 1953. The proficient team of multi-racial lawyers defended the accused in an exceptionally skilful manner. They exposed the corrupt nature of the British colonial government for having 'bought' witnesses. Moreover, the political trial only highlighted the injustices of colonialism in Kenya—nationally as well as internationally. However, the course of the trial had already been set from the beginning—Kenyatta had to go. He was imprisoned for seven years with hard labour.

Day and night, police patrols moved about the streets. Roads were blocked; residents of the city, especially Africans, were regularly harassed. The level of crime increased, from petty robbery to serious armed burglary and murder. Few Asians had arms, but most Europeans kept guns in their homes and on their person. The colonial government was forced to recognize that changes had taken place among its subject peoples.

The British government in London condemned Jawaharlal Nehru of India who continued to pledge his support for the Mau Mau fighters. Apa Pant, the Indian high commissioner, also continued to actively support the movement morally and materially with money, arms and aid. Pio Gama Pinto, a young agitator in Kenya, worked closely with some Asian and African associates to fight for freedom. He helped to supply arms and money to the Mau Mau fighters in the forests of Nyandarua. With other veterans like Haroon Ahmed, D.K. Sharda and Ambu Patel, they published anti-colonial literature. All this further fuelled the settlers' allegations that Asians in Kenya were working on behalf of the Mau Mau. They led a vituperative campaign against Asians in 1953. Spiteful remarks were made; harsh words were used. 'Subversive elements', they said. 'They are communists', 'Catalytic forces behind the Mau Mau', 'Vultures over Africa', 'the brains behind African nationalism'. 'Where do your loyalties lie?' they questioned. Still split apart by communal and religious affinities, they did not come out in full force. However, the Asians continued to play a significant anti-colonial role. This served as a brake against settler demands for complete transfer of power from London to Nairobi.

Everyone was caught off-guard in April 1954. There was police everywhere, especially in the *landhis*. They even came to River Road, to Grogan Road and to Parklands. The city of Nairobi was under siege——Operation Anvil, they called it. Every house was checked for Africans, their movement was closely monitored. Their papers, especially the *kipande*—detested symbol of British colonial power—were thoroughly checked. Woe to those who did not happen to have their work and pass papers to the city, worse still if they happened to be of the Kikuyu tribe. Many were sent to concentration camps. Pio Gama Pinto was also detained.

26

Moving On

Rann gai siappe dukho rowe apo apne . . .
(When women go for mourning, each weeps for her own troubles)
—Punjabi wisdom

When his first grandson was born to Krishanlal and Muni, Hiralal was happy beyond words. The boy had been born at his maternal grandparents' house in Pangani. Hiralal insisted that Muni return home even though the forty-day period of ritual impurity had not been completed. As soon as Krishanlal brought Muni and the infant home, Hiralal bade them wait at the door. The *puja thali* with coconut, *diya* and flowers was waved around the head of mother and child, a *tikka* was applied on their foreheads, and also on all those present. Oil was poured at the door before they entered, sweets were offered. This time Hiralal insisted that their priest Laxminarayan Shastri come to consecrate the birth and select the first letter for the name after astrological calculations. The letter 'V' was appropriate and so the boy was called Vimal. But Hiralal was not to have the good fortune to share the growing up years of his grandson. He was to die less than two months later.

It was in the coastal town of Mombasa in 1954. He was struck by a car and closed his eyes in the world, perhaps to be reborn in the endless cycle of karma.

The suddenness of Hiralal's passing was stunning. It came without warning or lingering illness. The whole household plunged into sorrow. As soon as his body was brought to Nairobi, they rubbed it with curd. It was washed, dressed in new clothes, placed on a narrow plank, and hoisted up on the shoulders of the men of the family. Old and young, men and women—their heads covered—wept and beat their breasts. 'Hai, hai, our beloved Bauji has left us.' The lamentation would last for thirteen days.

At the crematorium, his body was placed in a rectangular pit for the sacrificial fire, and more wood piled over it. Mourners went around it paying their last respects. As the eldest son, Krishanlal lit up his father's body. The flames rose higher, recitation of the Vedic mantras continued. He could not utter a word; his face drenched with tears, he bid adieu to his father. Ghee mixed with camphor, saffron, and other aromatics were cast into the fire. The body was completely consumed. On the fourth day, his bones picked out of the ashes were submerged in the Indian Ocean.

As in birth so in death. The family was considered impure for twelve days. On the thirteenth day, they donned fresh clothes. In an attempt to establish a communion with the dead, Brahmin priests were invited on the fortieth day to conduct the necessary prayers and to partake of lunch. 'O ancestor, Pitri-deva. Please proceed to vaikunth (heaven) now. Take leave of your family and go. Your family bids you peace.'

They invoked ancestors long gone. Brahmins were gifted beds, money and clothes; these were supposed to reach the departed soul. As for Dhanwanti, since her husband was no more, her obligations as a householder ceased. During the entire shraddh ceremony, performed to ensure his soul a peaceful transition into the other world, she was virtually excluded from the various stages of the ceremony. She took the segregation religious rites hard. She felt isolated, deprived of the solemnity of the occasion.

Her younger son was appointed to carry on these duties. He would wash and dry the feet of the Brahmins, while Muni had to do all the cooking unaided; she even had to serve them. The menu included seven varieties of vegetables—bereft of garlic or onions— besides rice, puri and kheer. When the Brahmins had had their fill, they touched Muni's covered head and blessed her. 'Beti (daughter), you have fed us with a lot of love and care, may the gods bless you.' By now, she was completely exhausted, and smiled rather weakly. Hands joined together in front of her chest, she paid obeisance without saying a word. She herself had not yet eaten. Moreover, she had not even had time to feed her children. She went into the privacy of her room and burst into tears.

After Hiralal's death, the family had to vacate the official public works department house. They were given six months notice. Hiralal's death had fetched them a certain sum of money from the driver of the car which had accidentally run him over. With some financial help from their *mamas*, their mother's brothers, the family managed to buy a piece of land in the Parklands area. Krishanlal spent all his off-duty hours supervising the building up a spacious family house in the short span of time. The *mamas* and their families also moved in; it was a chaotic 30-odd member jamboree. It didn't last long. Misunderstandings and fights galore became the norm— soon rather than later.

The thin transparent membrane enveloping her lungs and lining the walls of the thoracic cavity became inflamed. She was constantly coughing and had difficulty breathing. When Hardei died of pleurisy on 5 September 1955—eleven years after her husband—it would not be a moment of mourning, for her life's mission had been fulfilled. She had lived long enough to earn the title of *padnani*: the gods had blessed her with a long enough life to enable her to see her great-grandchildren. The occasion merited thanksgiving. Dry fruit and gifts were distributed. Each great-grandchild got ten shillings, grandchildren got much more, while her wealth and treasures were distributed amongst her children. By the time Hardei died, Kirparam had already become part of a forgotton past; a blurred memory. Their separate journeys to Nairobi at the turn of the century were part of family lore.

Krishanlal and Muni shifted house once again, this time for good. Living amidst a very large and extended family was taking its toll on both, but especially on Muni, as her mother-in-law would not hear of separation from her brothers. Moreover, their own little family was increasing. Muni had given birth to another son.

Hiralal was not here to witness the birth, nor would he have the pride or the pleasure of cuddling another grandson. However, Gurdei was to lavish her 'shila' with all kinds of tokens of her love.

Their move would not mean that Krishanlal would shirk his responsibility towards his siblings; on the contrary. As the eldest son, he saw it as his duty to ensure that his younger brothers and sisters continued with their education—especially now that Bauji was no more. More importantly, marriage of the remaining five unmarried sisters was a heavy responsibility. It entailed looking for appropriate grooms and accruing sufficient dowries. Together with his younger brother, he would carry out the family dharma.

Once again, they would try their luck in Mombasa, they decided. Krishanlal opened a grocery store by the beach. It was hard work with long hours, and didn't do too well. He returned to clerical work, once again for a firm selling spare parts for motor cars. This time, it would be for a bigger firm set up by Allen and Cooper—who had initially sold Landrovers from a wooden hut; by 1956 it had become a large enterprise. Very soon their workshops spread their tentacles in many parts of the country. Volkswagons, Suzukis, Mazdas and heavy commercial vehicles: Krishanlal slowly got to understand them, and his hard work paid off.

Surrounded by coconut palms and huge tamarinds, the small rented house at Nyali Beach on the north coast became their little paradise—with friendly African and Arab neighbours. For the first time since their married life, Muni felt free; she could breathe easy. She still had to work hard as they never had very much money, especially now with four young children to look after, but at least there was no nagging. To add to their income, she started tailoring garments for sale. Soon, word spread and *waswahili* neighbours came for clothes for their children. Neighbouring kiosk owners displayed them in their small dukas. Muni was truly happy.

They had three coconut palms in their little *shamba*. It was heavenly to have the juice of freshly picked coconuts as often as possible—whenever the owner sent someone up the trees. The coconut palm was the life blood of Swahili society. At the birth of child, the afterbirth and cord were buried with the child's shaved hair. A coconut sampling was planted at the site and the tree would normally become the possession of the child. In Kiswahili, there are special terms for every part of the coconut tree and for each stage in the development of the nut. Food, firewood, shelter, timber for doorways, oil for cooking and lighting, coir, roofing, utensils— no wonder the tree was almost revered! With relatively little maintenance, it continued to bear the nut for 50–100 years.

Two years later Krishanlal was transferred from Mombasa to company headquarters in Nairobi; before they shifted back, he decided to take Muni and the two young boys to India for a holiday; my sister and I were left with our grandparents Lajpat and Yashoda, and Gurdei, of course. Muni's first visit to India was a complete culture shock. Although she could speak the language, although she wore the sari, although they were used to the food, yet nothing was the same. The heat, the humidity, the crowds, the lack of toilet facilities—all that, and more! Her precious nylon saris, Kenyan tea, packets of biscuits, chocolates, facial creams . . . all her 'foreign' goods—friends and contacts in Bombay grabbed them without her permission. Even though she learnt to adjust to Indian ways, it continued to be 'them' and 'us'!

By the late 1950s, decolonization became accepted as a necessary step. Britain started readying to leave Kenya, though the settlers were furious. The latter became more and more alarmed as *uhuru* reverberated everywhere. Deprived of a collective voice even now, at this crucial juncture, feelings of insecurity heightened amongst the Asians. There were frequent attacks, especially against the dukawallahs. Tensions mounted, soon to become deep-rooted. *Uhuru* drew nearer. Finally the day arrived.

The queen's husband was the guest of honour at the ceremony. At first, the new flag refused to open . . . Kenyatta grinned and the night breeze whipped it open for the first time over the territory. At midnight of 11 December, Kenya's new flag, with a Maasai shield and spears in the middle, displayed its bright red, green, black and white colours. The police band played the new national anthem. Gone forever was 'God save the queen . . .'

Many radical changes had taken place since Kirparam had stepped into the territory in 1898. The union jack, which had flown for sixty-eight years over the then 'British territory in Eastern Africa', was finally hauled down by the Duke of Edinburgh on 12 December 1963. Kenya became a fully independent nation. At Uhuru Park, Prince Philip and Governor McDonald handed over the instruments of independence to Jomo Kenyatta; he would lead the country as its first President.

'This is the greatest day in Kenya's history and the happiest day of my life', said a beaming seventy-year old Jomo Kenyatta, his trademark flywhisk swishing in the air, to a crowd of over 40,000. The crowd cheered, so did we all; I too was there with Renu, Vimal, little Sunil and our father Krishanlal. (Mum stayed home to look after our youngest brother Ashu, who had been born at the beginning of the year). A church leader prayed; other religious leaders looked on. A firebrand in his youth, a passionate politician, Kenyatta's charismatic and eloquent speech had us all spellbound. He was articulate, persuasive and inspiring.

'Harambee!' shouted Kenyatta, the gathering shouted their approval. 'Haraaaaaambeeee . . .!' he roared again. The word probably was of Indian origin. Railway workers in the late 1800s chanted 'Hari Amba! Hari Amba!' as they 'pulled together' on the lines. 'I bow to you O goddess Amba, you who ends all miseries . . . glory to you O divine mother, relieve your devotees of hardships . . . O mother, consort of Shankar, bestow upon us prosperity and happiness . . .'

'Harambee' would gain an immense centrality in the political scene, especially of the 1960s and the 1970s, and a permanent place in the Kiswahili language. Many Harambee schools were to be set up. A main street would be called Harambee Avenue; important government buildings, including the office of the President, Parliament buildings and other key government ministries would be called Harambee House.

But the old man was to embrace his enemies. Kenyatta would 'request' the British troops to remain in Kenya. A defence agreement between Kenya and Great Britain would keep the British army in their current headquarters at Nanyuki. Bruce MacKenzie, a non-African, would be appointed minister of agriculture. MacKenzie was a British spy.

Those settlers who chose to leave sold 'their' land at profitable rates to the new government. Land and properties from Europeans was to be redistributed to dispossessed peasants: however, much of it would be sold to large-scale African private investors. A new African elite would be born. Slums soon sprouted in the urban areas. Donating to a Harambee cause would gain the new elite status . . . and they would donate generously. This new tribe would be called the *wabenzi* as their Mercedes Benz cars bestowed further status on them. (Today they should perhaps be called '*wapajero*' or '*wa4-4*'!)

On the eve of independence, 1,80,000 Asians, most of whom lived in urban centres, calculated their gains and losses. Decisions had to be made fast. Considerably apprehensive about our future and those of our children, we Kenyan Asians asked ourselves some important questions. Will we be regarded as foreigners in this land that gave us birth, a land that was adopted by our grandparents? Should we continue to stay on, as they had done? Or should we choose the British passport? Until the eve of independence, Kenya, India or even Britain were possible 'homes'. The newly independent government gave the Asians two years to decide whether or not they wanted to become citizens. The majority regarded themselves as permanent residents of the country where they lived, saved, invested and eventually retired. Only about 3,500 Asians left immediately—as compared to over 11,000 Europeans out of 53,000. However, processing of applications was slow, perhaps deliberately; many Asians would thus miss the two-year deadline and find themselves on the fence.

They had come a long way in adjusting, readjusting. Once more they were to adjust themselves. To adapt, to react—rather than act—that would be the key. Most Asians tending to remain would become

more and more apolitical on the national front. And those who
had played active roles were ignored and unsung. Except for Joseph
Zuzarte Murumbi, whose father was Goan and mother a Maasai,
not a single Kenyan of Asian origin would be elected to the new
cabinet, even though several of them—Makhan Singh, Pranlal Seth,
Pio Gama Pinto, J.M. Nazareth, Haroon Ahmed, Fitz de Souza,
among others—had played key roles, many at personal risk, for
independence. Makhan Singh would be sidelined completely, too
radical for the new regime.

Soon after independence, persons of non-African origin would
have slim chances, if any, for positions in the Public Service
Commission. A policy of Africanization versus Kenyanization would
be born even though the newly composed Kenyan Constitution
would prohibit discrimination on racial grounds. President Jomo
Kenyatta would refer to us as 'guests', as had Pandit Jawaharlal
Nehru some years previously!

Despite such remarks made by political leaders, Krishanlal and
Muni saw themselves as Kenyan. They decided to stay and adapt
to their new situation—as their ancestors had done. Not only
because their family was growing, as one more son had been born
at the beginning of the year, but they sincerely believed that they
belonged here. They had no other home. They were born here, as
were their parents. The question of another 'home' did not even
arise; their going to Britain was never discussed. Neither Krishanlal
nor Muni had even visited the country. They did not see any reason
to leave. Kenya was their home, as even India could not be. The
gradual decline of strong links with India that had begun in
Yashoda's generation, to continue speedily after the second world
war, was now in overdrive.

Cultures and lifestyles too had changed. Going were the days
of poets of the calibre of Tausif Hassan or Pandit Laxminarayan.
The days of *hakims* and *vaids* were also numbered. The dukawallah
of the old days was fast disappearing from the scene, but his image
would linger for some time to come. Vanishing very fast also were
the different characteristics that made a Lahoria, a Bharochi, a

Chakwalan, or a Mianiite . . . who knew the ways of their ancestors any more? Or even where Punjab lay on the map? Muni worried because her grandchildren could not speak their mother tongue. She spoke to them in Punjabi, but they replied in English, as if it were a shame to speak the language. With her own last-born, she too had to make a conscious effort.

Even before the independence of India and the birth of a new Pakistan, the new generation of Indians in Kenya had slowly started losing contact and familiarity with their parents' places of origin. Children born during and after this period were on the road to a slow but sure deculturalization. Marked changes in food habits, mode of dress and language were evident. Specific mother tongues had been banned in government schools soon after the second war.

It had been a period of total imposition of English mannerisms and language: they were made to pay a symbolic ten cent fine for having spoken in 'vernacular' at school. The younger generation was quickly being alienated from Punjabi, Hindi and Urdu. They would know neither one nor the other language well enough to appreciate the nuances of the poetry of the likes of Pandit Laxminarayan Shastri. The sophistication of the *shairi* of Tausif Hassan would become almost baffling. What could once strike instant rapport was now to fall on deaf ears. It had been a most intriguing form of expression, given an appreciation of the aesthetic and a certain philosophy of life. Nothing could substitute this education, or the stability it brought within.

New, independent Kenya would for a long while continue to adhere to the path laid down by its masters. In government schools, each morning, one and all had to attend an assembly where a short Christian prayer was said. Courses of study would be literary, Cambridge-style. Neither exposed to the best of the other cultures, nor to the best of our own, we were not introduced to the best of world literature nor exposed to classic Asian, African or European cultures.

At least the desegregation of schools had begun. I was eleven years old at the time of independence and until then, and even a little while thereafter, we continued to study the history of William the Conqueror and English nursery rhymes. The image of Kefa, a very tall Luo boy, at least twenty-five years old, made to sing 'London is burning, London is burning, look yonder, look yonder, Fire, fire, and we have no water!' was so flabbergasting that it is still pinned to my memory. It was meaningless for us then, as it must have been for Kefa. Did we know why London was burning?

We had *uhuru,* but it also gave rise to an ideological rift. Pio Gama Pinto, of the progressive faction in Kenyatta's political party, the KANU, asked for recognition of the Mau Mau freedom fighters and for equitable distribution of land and wealth. In a bid to show 'no confidence' in the new government, barely four months old, Pinto master-minded a coup. So Pinto had to go. In 1965, he was assassinated. It was a great blow. Pio had not only fought hard the colonial power and neo-colonialism, but he had also tried to build strong ties between the Asians and Africans. Joseph Zuzarte Murumbi, who had replaced Oginga Odinga as vice-president would resign soon after. It is said that the death of Pinto had hit him hard.

For the moment, African attitudes towards Asians were strained, they believed them to be 'the problem' because of their economic advancement . . . 'One day his duka will be mine!' they said. The average Asian looked upon the African as his cultural inferior. Through the major period of colonial rule, segregated in every way—in schools, residential areas, hotels etc.—the African and the Asian had been socially distanced. The famous 'divide and rule' policy that kept them apart meant that neither had a cultural appreciation of the other. The relationship was generally restricted to master-servant, worker-employee, or to trade.

The Africans were dependent on the dukawallahs for sale of their farm produce. They saw the *muhindi* handle 'big' money, flaunt cars, parade gold jewellery . . . the common African did not often see the *mzungu* handle bank accounts and cheques—places where 'big' money really lay, but which the common *mwananchi* (citizen) did not yet have access to. Increasingly, the African felt that the

Asian (rather than the European) was responsible for his suffering and deprivation. They did not know that at least two-thirds of the corporate as well as most of the large-scale agricultural estates were in European hands.

A trade licensing Bill would be introduced in 1967 to further restrict Asians from doing business in downtown areas. The little vegetable and fruit shops of Mayarams and Sitarams would have to go . . . Fearing discrimination, uncertain of their future in Kenya, more Asians would decide to leave.

Christmas Eve, 1966, was the night Krishanlal received a long distance telephone call at the small guesthouse in Malindi where our family of seven was spending its annual vacation. 'It is nothing, just work and the office; we must leave first thing in the morning', Krishanlal replied when Muni asked. Muni had noticed that he was avoiding her eyes. Her hands trembled; she sensed that all was not well, but her husband bade her go to sleep. As for himself, he lay on his back, not daring to move.

The pain in Krishanlal's breast was acute. Lajpat Rai had always treated him with the same affection that he had for his daughter; he had consulted them on matters of importance. Krishanlal's eyes continued to remain wide open. He turned to look at his wife. 'How will I share this with her?' he thought. 'It will bring her so much suffering'. By the time they reached Voi, Krishanlal could not contain his sorrow any more. Muni was heartbroken. 'Maa,' she called out from the car as soon as they arrived in Nairobi. Mother and daughter clung to each other before the tears and the words flowed. 'It is too late,' Muni said between sobs, 'I should never have gone.'

Lajpat Rai, son of Devidayal and Gurdei, died of cirrhosis of the liver. His body—including the bed that he was sleeping on—took on the yellow hues of jaundice. Perhaps it was hereditary. Others said it was superfluous heat: too much ginger, too much garlic, and he had of late taken to drinking brandy neat every night. According to Ayurveda, all these lead to an excessive production of heat in the body and ultimately destroy the liver. Why or how

Lajpat Rai—who had for so long been health-conscious, ever since he had acquired the Ayurvedic health store—started letting himself go, no one could say. 'Bring me some oranges and coconuts,' Lajpat had told Muni, encouraging his daughter to proceed to the coast for their vacations. Muni's mind had been far from their long-awaited holiday. Thoughts of Bauji had been constantly with her. Now Bauji was no more.

The family started disintegrating when Lajpat Rai passed away; the atmosphere at home became bitter. Gurdei only learnt about the death of her son when they were taking him for the last rites. With her arm around the shoulder of their faithful servant Moilo, she shuffled weakly down the path towards where the body of her son lay covered in a white sheet. Slowly, the women helped her descend the two steps. She would not believe it for a long while, 'You are lying,' she kept on insisting. When she finally broke down, a big part of herself died with her son.

Bed-ridden now with a broken leg that would not heal, in her usual stubborn attitude to things new, Bebe Gurdei flatly refused to be admitted to hospital. The leg got worse, until finally it became utterly useless. Her eyes had clouded; she could not see very well, but her hearing was still good. 'He looked after me. He came to talk to me. How could he, my son go before me, while I am still in life', a feeble voice broke the hushed silence. It was the silent suffering of a mother. She had invested her entire being in bringing up her son, been mother and father to him. She had learnt to be separate, but she could not survive this second cut in the umbilical cord. Faithful Moilo was assigned to look after Bebe's few needs. Surrounded by her grandchildren and great-grandchildren, Bebe Gurdei died a very lonely woman a year after her son.

The shock of three successive deaths in the family so depressed Yashoda that she started spending more and more time in solitude. Soon after the death of her husband, her sons saw it fit to have her passport changed: she would retain her rights to the United Kingdom. It was a decision in which she had no choice, but one that would decide her fate in the remaining years of her life. She could not continue to stay in Nairobi as long as she wanted. Why must she come here as a visitor, she asked herself time and again, why must it be so? It was here in Nairobi that she had grown up under the loving care and protection of her father.

In one of her diaries, she wrote: 'Each one of my sons says the house is his. They fight for it even while I am still alive. Yet, it was my husband and I who had it built. We put in extra rooms for the children. The extensions landed us in bad debts. In the anxiety of the debts, my husband has passed away, and now it is I who has to bear the burden. Maybe I too will die with the same worries. I always told him not to borrow money, but who listens to me? The burden has fallen on my head. It was written thus in my kismet.'

The house in Pangani was put up for sale. Now, more than ever, she belonged nowhere. In a small corner of her heart, she wished she had had the courage of her mother. To defy tradition and live alone, as Hardei had done after Kirparam's death. So that she wouldn't have to answer to anyone. So that she could come and go as she pleased. Or eat what she desired. Her life now seemed a long agony of repression. Had she learnt to display her emotions more openly, she would have suffered less, perhaps. There was always this reserve in her—a privacy wherein she allowed no one. No, not even Lajpat had had access to that space.

Most of her grandchildren—and she had many by now—were less keen to hear stories from Hindu mythology—or any other mythology, for that matter. However, reading for the one or two who took some interest gave her some satisfaction. In the morning after a bath when the mind and body had been purified, her white hair lay undone upon her shoulders. Every now and then, she pushed up the thick glasses hanging loosely upon her frail nose.

Then slowly and softly, she began, 'The Ramayana begins with an extraordinary episode. Valmiki the hunter became a poet as a result of this episode. One day on his usual hunting expedition, he saw a pair of birds.'

'Which birds, Amma?' I remember asking her.

'I don't know. Anyway, the male and female birds were together (she didn't say making love). Valmiki shot an arrow at the male bird. Immediately, he expressed a painful sound. This *soka*, or pain, came out as a melodic sound and it became a *sloka* (verse). Thereafter, Valmiki meditated. And the hunter turned writer. He composed the Ramayana, which is essentially a book of responsibilities and duties.'

I suppose I must not have given Amma much indication of having understood, but somewhere the incident stuck and many years later, long after Amma had passed away, the stories revived; they were relived with much emotion.

Somewhere, the fine line between illusion and reality started getting blurred. She felt increasingly secure in her terrible insecurity. Amma became more and more restless with age. The change in her life led her nowhere. Downcast, hopeless and easily disheartened, convinced that the world had done her wrong. Her psyche started being dominated by the lost paradise of her childhood. She found some solace in memories of her beloved father. As if in a dream in which she is always a child, a fairytale that reality cannot make prosaic. The images grew until they took on colours. She filled herself with them more and more, but she couldn't live therein. Yashoda died on 5 August 1976 in London. She had just crossed her seventieth birthday.

27

Uneasy balance

Maang ke laye chand lamhe zindgani
Baade naseem ki pur lutf shokhian
Shame khizan key shaitani fitney
Phir doondhay laakhon tinkey anmit vishwas key
Aur goondh key in sub ko mehnat key behisaab pasiney mein
Banaya mahobat ka ik pyar saa aashiana . . .
Janatey hain aashianey hain barq key jhooley
Vishwas dekhiye, hum phir jhoolein . . .

(Our few requested moments of life were granted
Filled with pleasures of delicate early morning breezes,
While the naughty play of autumnal evenings found small straws of
undying faith
Mixed in the sweat of hard work and dedication . . .
Here we made our little nest of love.
Knowing fully well that the nests were prey to the sways of lightening,
Yet look at our faith . . . we carried on rocking)

—'Aashiana', Allaudin Qureshi.

B y now my father was quite happily resigned to his destiny of
selling spare parts for cars as a means of livelihood. In fact,
Krishanlal's passion for cars drove him to change the family car
every six months when he could. He looked after them as if they
were newborn babies, cleaning, caressing and constantly checking
on them. At the office, he knew by heart every spare part of the
cars they sold—name, number and place of storage. During the
rally, when spares were urgently needed by competing cars, the crew

would come for Krishanlal even at midnight. In fact, this was the most hectic period of the year, the four days of Easter. We had become used to the fact that papa would be in and out of the house at odd hours tending to the safari *shauris*.

We would all go to the city hall to check the fate and results of the cars participating in the rally—or even better, wait for the cars to return. With a picnic basket, as the wait could last many hours before the first cars started zooming by. The welcome committee could stretch 30–40 km to cheer in finishing competitors—young, old, Asian, African, or European. Many would be stretching forward to applaud or wave them in. The interval between one car and the next could be long, but nobody seemed to mind. It was a way to relax, to be out in the open, usually on Mombasa Road.

'Will it be a wet safari or dry this year?' The fickle weather was an important issue at this time of the year—for those concerned with the rally in any case. Like the British, whom Krishanlal would lampoon for always discussing the weather, during Easter even papa was concerned about it. Most times, it rained. There could be entirely wet rallies, as happened the year of freedom: 1963. Out of the eighty-four entrants, only seven reached the finishing line. The tracks had turned to rivers, roads ceased to exist. Life-threatening torrents descended that April; a soggy morass of black cotton soil made driving difficult.

The rally through 6,000 km of East African territory was never easy by any standards. The sheer expanse of the savannah or the beauty of the pink flamingoes by Lake Bogoria took it through the most awe-inspiring terrain, as also the roughest. It meant passing through dense jungles or bumping over gravel roads. At other places, the choking, penetrating dust crept through the cars for kilometres. Heat in the south could be merciless, while misleading road signs or none at all could be a challenge for the navigator. Herds of elephants or a couple of lions—not forgetting rhinos and cattle— could block the roads. In waterlogged and sodden earth, tyres had to be girded with heavy chains to keep the glued mud at bay. No wonder, the safari (from the Arab-Persian word 'safar' for journey) through such a diverse land with different temperature zones, gloried in the reputation of being the toughest in the world.

At its inception in 1953, the all-white committee chose to call it the Coronation Safari—to coincide with the crowning of Queen Elizabeth II. In February 1952, Princess Elizabeth spent a night at the 'Treetops' in the Aberdares Forest (one of the places where the Mau Mau fighters were in hiding at the time). She woke up as queen the next morning, following the death of her father King George VI.

In tribute to her, and also to raise the profile of the British empire, the motor car rally in Kenya was set to coincide with the new queen's coronation in England. Over the years, the event became more commercial—with a direct bearing on vehicle sales. Entrants began arriving from Europe, consequently it gained international importance. But even then there was hesitation about changing its name—some felt it would be sacrilege. It was seven years before it was finally called The East African Safari Rally.

The route was made longer and tougher—through Embu/Meru, Thomsons' falls, the white highlands, across the equator, towards the twisty mountain regions of western Uganda, Lake Victoria region, through lush, green and dense forests of the Aberdare mountains. It then crossed over to Tanganyika, past the majestic Kilimanjaro, returned to Kenya via the coastal regions of Mombasa, passing through a game-infested route, and back to the finish in Nairobi. Ford, Saab, Rover, the French R4L, VW Beetle, Toyota, Mercedes, Datsun, Peugeot—they all took part.

Krishanlal's modest role also increased. He was more often out of the house than in. He also had to cater to the chase cars loaded with spare parts and mechanics, serving as mobile garages. However, there was always the extra forgotten spare part. With the arrival of international stars like Erik Carrlson and Pat Moss, the rumpus was complete. We barely saw papa over the week. The celebrities never won against the unassuming local drivers with their small machines and shoe-string budgets—not for a long time anyway.

His British bosses called him 'Chris', pretending that 'Krishanlal' was a mouthful. They respected him, trusted his integrity and honesty, yet were not ready to increase his salary. Muni would often urge him on, but each time he asked politely, they would hand him a bottle of whiskey or take him out for a meal, and the matter would end, papa quite pleased by the small token. One day he got all worked up; he promised my mother that he would do it. At first the talk with the bosses at headquarters proceeded in the usual polite manner, but as Krishanlal's excitement mounted, he banged the official rubber stamp repeatedly on a piece of paper. The chief looked at him in amazement; Krishanlal smiled, lifted the rubber stamp and before anyone anticipated his next move, had banged the stamp onto the chief's forehead! He was in the throes of a small epileptic attack. They rushed to get him a glass of water. The drama over, they had laughed over it, and Krishanlal got his increment after all.

At the time of independence, multi-partyism was a written part of the Constitution. By 1969, Kenya had emerged as a *de facto* one-party state. Under Kenyatta's rule, Kikuyu hegemony prevailed; the control was evident. Kikuyu presence in the army was increased. In protest, other ethnic tribes took to the streets. However, opposition to the government could not be voiced openly. Certain words could not be used, the word 'president' for example. There can be only one President in the country, he said. As such, no-one else could be 'president' of any association, be it a sports organization, a religious or a social body or a business partnership. Other words also could not be spoken out loud—Mau Mau, for instance. Kenyatta wrote of the Mau Mau as 'a disease which has been eradicated and must never be remembered . . .'

'Kenya is becoming a country with ten millionaires and ten million beggars', so said J.M. Kariuki, a minister in Kenyatta's government. Himself a Kikuyu and a former Mau Mau detainee, he escalated the political temperature, especially by voicing his concern for the *wananchi*. He was found dead a few weeks later, brutally murdered in the Ngong forest. Tom Mboya, the minister

Author with a Samburu family

for economic planning, had also been shot dead in broad daylight in the centre of town. University of Nairobi students took to the streets to voice their anger and ask for justice. *Chai*—corruption—quickly gained Kenya the reputation of a corrupt nation in the international media. *'Nchi ya kitu kidogo'*, 'land of a few something' seemed to become a new slogan.

We, Kenyans of Asian origin were continually called 'paper citizens', we were not 'real' Kenyans, they said. Our nationality was suspect; our citizenship attacked. My brother Vimal, with three straight 'A's for his advanced level exams, was refused admission to the department of medicine in the University of Nairobi. Thankfully, he got a scholarship to the University of Edinburgh later. At the age of nineteen, I obtained a 'green card' without much ado to study in Canada. A very unhappy year later—a year wasted, or so I thought then—I returned without any regret, never to go back to a land where I did not belong emotionally or culturally.

I had no degrees, nor did I have much work experience, but I could speak Hindustani, English and Kiswahili. Air-India offered me a position at the airport. Within five years I would rise to the position of assistant airport manager and when the position above me fell vacant, I naturally expected to be promoted. However, the job would go to my junior, an African. Moreover, I was a woman. The 'Africanization policy' as laid down by the government had been clearly defined. I resigned from my post and from the organization.

I lost a job, but gained an art—for a lifetime. On the eve of my departure for higher education to Canada, a friend had taken me out for dinner at the Hilton Hotel. As entertainment they had invited a young Kenyan Indian girl to dance. She performed a peacock dance. For the very first time in my life I witnessed any form of Indian classical dance. It was love at first sight! I can still recall the dancer's bright blue-green tight-fitting costume. Huge peacock feathers rose from behind her back. As she held the ends between each hand and mimed the walk and soft delicate leaps of the peacock trying to attract the peahen, I was transported to a dimension I did not know existed. That night in the privacy of the room I shared with my sister, dancers leapt up and down from everywhere; I dreamt again and again of the beauty of the movement, of the use of a body in this way. I did not know it then, but in retrospect, I can see it as the moment in which the door to a spirituality of sorts was opened.

Something inexplicable kept on haunting me. I was not at peace. I was not even excited about the journey I was about to undertake. I had begged my father to send me to Canada to study chemistry. Now that it was here, the enthusiasm seemed to wane even before the term had had begun! I think in the subconscious of my mind, all throughout my short stay in the dark, wintry laboratories of Canada, that peacock dance continued to mesmerize me. Somehow, I felt that I did not belong anywhere but in the world of Indian dance (and in Kenya at that time). I returned, and started learning from the few teachers teaching Indian dance in Kenya. It was during this time that I was employed by Air-India and an opportunity to learn dance at the feet of gurus opened up. Some years, as often as every three months, I was sent for training at the Air India College in Bombay. I started with Kathak.

In the meantime, Air-India brought in a well-known Odissi dancer to perform in Nairobi. I was put in-charge of looking after her. I saw Odissi dance for the first time ... and another awesome feeling went through my being. Protima Bedi and I became friends. She decided to prolong her stay in Nairobi. I gave her my bed. I took extended, unpaid leave. We returned to India together and she invited me to stay with her. I continued with Kathak classes, but got more and more influenced as I watched Protima practice. My practical self said, leave it for the next life, the three-dimensional, triple-bend position is too divergent from the straight lines of Kathak ... but in the confines of my room, I would imitate Protima's positions. I left Kathak and took up Odissi. Physically, spiritually, mentally, modern and deeply ancient at the same time, it seems to fit my personality; I have never looked back!

It was through dance that a love for my roots and my Indianness and Indian culture developed, reinforced by successive dance gurus and teachers—from Pushpa Vara, Roshan Kumari, Madhurita Sarang, Debi Basu, Guru Kelucharan Mohapatra, Surendranath Jena to Pratibha Jena. I bought books like *Teach Yourself Hindi*. My mother's help here was invaluable. My father's radio and theatre influence rubbed off on me. His way of reciting Urdu *shairi* opened further avenues in my newly born artistic sensibility. I would sit on the floor in a white khadi sari and read Gandhi or Rabindranath Tagore's *Geetanjali*. Books on philosophy, oral tradition, literature were devoured.

My parents never forced anything upon us, but their own practice of the Hindu tradition and way of life definitely built up my emotional awareness. In every generation there is an artist in the family. My grandfather acted in Shakespearean and other plays. My father had to work as a 'distributor of automobile spare parts' to survive financially, but continued to write poetry and act in plays. Perhaps, I am that artist in this generation, even if the word 'artist' is still not looked upon as glorious or honourable in most Punjabi homes, as it was to some extent in mine! One of my brothers once told me, 'Oh, so you are just going to dance your life away?' I take it as a compliment and salute it as a continuation of the dreams of my grandfather and of my father.

In 1978, Kenyatta died—the 'promised land' still far from reach of the ordinary *mwananchi*—whose *uhuru* had not yet arrived. Vice-President Daniel Arap Moi became the new head of state. A *rungu* (knobbed stick) in hand, *Rais* Moi shouted 'Nyayo!' The crowd hailed him, hoping for a brighter future. It was now the turn of the Kalenjin tribe to reap the fruits. And things began to change for the worse. There was mass deception. Many Kenyans lost faith in governmence, but nobody could openly criticize the government or the head of state without reprisal.

A group of radicals studied Marxist ideology secretly to usher in a more egalitarian society. However, those publishing 'seditious' literature were tortured and imprisoned. Freedom of press was at an all-time low. Academics were oppressed and detained. As in Kenyatta's time, the memory of freedom fighters and war heroes was not evoked. We lived in a period of historical amnesia. For over forty years of independent rule, stories about the Mau Mau would be erased from memory. Other heroes were also wiped out from history. There would be no protest marches or outcry in the papers. For nearly twenty-five years, Moi's rule would be marked by virtual autocracy. Yet, each Sunday, the news at 9 p.m. opened with the President at mass and prayer ceremonies in different churches; he was a devout Christian. Towards the later part of his rule, international donors, who in the past had turned a blind eye, would begin to call for multi-partyism if economic aid were to continue.

Class and ethnicity meshed together to deepen social and cultural divisions, holding the country back. Every *mwananchi* was at some stage a victim of *chai, kitu kidogo,* crime or murder. Disparities between the 'haves' and the 'have-nots' led to disproportionate class structures; they were all guilty of it, black, brown and white—and all were quickly losing their strong cultural values and work ethic.

During his election campaign of 1979, the MP for Parklands, Krishan Gautama said, 'There are no Asians in Kenya. There are only Kenyans and non-Kenyans . . .' However, three years later, on 1 August 1982, Kenya's mainly trader Asian community bore the brunt of looting, violence and rape that followed a coup d'etat by the air force. The coup was not successful, but the attack on the Asian community was aggressive.

There was a blackout over much of the city that Sunday night. A contingent of ground troops seized strategic institutions like the Voice of Kenya radio station and Jomo Kenyatta international airport. Bullets could be heard. With the killing and looting that transpired, within no time the city degenerated into chaos. Rumours quickly spread. Somebody rang up my mother and told her there was a coup in town. Not knowing what the word meant, she went calmly to the neighbours to pass on the information. Immediately, our Muslim neighbour burst into a flood of tears. 'Do you know what that means . . . it means that we are all in trouble, that our children who are to arrive sometime today from Mombasa may never make it . . . it means that all hell is let loose . . . oh my children . . .' she sobbed ceaselessly. But, the government of Moi would react fast to crush the insurgents with its loyal members in the army and GSU.

News had not yet reached the town of Mombasa. My brother Ashu and our neighbour's daughter only learnt about the ruckus when their coast bus arrived at Athi River. Here, they had to pass much of the night in deep anxiety, not so much for themselves but the apprehension that they knew their respective families would be feeling. There was no way of communicating with them, although they were very close to Nairobi. At about 7 the next morning, passengers were told to alight and show their identification papers. Those not carrying them could be in trouble. Fortunately, both had theirs. With ID cards in their mouths, hands held straight up in the air, they 'walked' a short distance on their knees.

It was like a ransacked ghost town. From the railway roundabout upto to Kirinyaga Road, no cars, buses or taxis, not another soul apart from them was visible. As they walked down the hill near the Globe cinema roundabout, dead bodies were scattered here and there. Looted stuff from broken shops lay littered everywhere . . . food, gold, jewellery, furniture . . . that part of the city lay in total chaos. Fear for their safety, which had been absent initially, now surfaced. Luckily, not much later, a Sikh gentleman speeding by in his car spotted them. 'What are you doing here?' he asked. And even before they could reply, he had quickly opened the door and dragged them inside. They arrived safely at home, but the girl's mother could not stop crying. All this while, she hugged and scolded her daughter for having gone to Mombasa! Surprisingly, both Muni and Krishanlal had taken the episode in their stride.

'*Muhindi enda* . . . go away' they chanted. Fallacies and misconceptions between brown and black *wananchi* sprang up ad nauseum. Some would call the era 'the ugly 80s' when seeds of all sorts of propaganda were planted to create hate relations. Stereotyping and fingerpointing bred general mistrust. A deep fear was further instilled in their hearts. Some Asians left during this time. Now they would look not just at Britain as a possible home, but also Canada and Australia.

Many evenings, playwright Allaudin Qureshi and I discussed the plight of Kenyan Asians. My involvement with theatre started in 1975 when his group Natak, looking for a dancer, roped me in. My Hindustani was basic, but I learnt to speak it more or less correctly. Natak's plays, including originals written by Qureshi, were generally in Hindustani. *Parchhayian* (shadows) or *Anarkali*—I was mesmerized; the stage gripped me as nothing else had done before. My love for theatre became paramount, a *junoon* (obsession) of sorts, perhaps passed on to me initially by my grandfather Hiralal but more importantly by my father Krishanlal. In March 1983, less than a year after the fatal coup, *Aashiana* (nest) was scripted— as a plea of the mostly lower middle working class Asians, living in the *veda*-houses of Eastleigh—a riposte to racial pressures and prejudices.

With neighbours and friends leaving the country, including many in the character Javan's family, he cries out:

No, this cannot be! I will remain here. This is my nest; my place is here. It was here that my father, my grandparents shared their happiest moments, it was here that they exhaled their last breaths . . . I was born here . . . do you expect me to leave the land that gave me birth . . . O natives of this land, look at me, I am one of you. Don't think of me as a guest . . . come towards me, let us build a great nation together . . . I am weakened by all that has come to pass . . . please give me strength so that together we can destroy this fear . . . take me as one of you . . . let us make our nest prosperous . . . a home built on confidence and mutual respect . . . but, people are leaving . . . how will our nest be built?

The audience was limited to those who could understand Hindustani. For four nights, we played to a packed hall with a capacity of over 400 seats at the Kenya national theatre. We put in our all, our enthusiasm, emotion and time—voluntarily. Krishanlal and Muni never complained about the late nights. Whenever they asked me where I was going, my usual reply was 'Matha tekne . . . to prostrate at the temple . . .' My temple was the theatre. By this time, plays by Africans were regulars at this theatre; some were of a revolutionary nature. Politically controversial writers of the time like Ngugi wa Thiongo frequented it. Word went around that it was not 'safe' to be seen here so often. Theatre was progressively perceived as a place where radicals, dissidents, and other trouble-makers tried to stir up emotions. Plainclothes officers hung around the place. They strolled in front of the main gate or 'dropped into' the bar upstairs where everyone met after an exhausting rehearsal.

The site for the theatre had been well chosen; it lay bang opposite the Norfolk hotel in the appropriate English tradition—people went to the theatre after drinks or a sumptuous meal, or had supper after theatre. In its constitution, theatre did not have a racial bar. Even in the colonial days, Asians could, and did, perform.

Unemployment continued to reach acute levels; there was much social unrest, poverty and crime. This was when Sanjiv, the baby of the family, returned from Australia after learning computer engineering Wherever he went, they wanted to make him work longer hours for less pay. Many other Kenyans became equally vulnerable as more and more companies managed to recruit persons who fitted the bill. Amongst those recruited were recent arrivals from India or Pakistan.

At first they were invited by the government to fill positions in specific areas, like the banking industry and teaching. Special permits were allocated to them. In search of better economic opportunities, others started coming on their own. Some were professionals, computer-savvy and of managerial grade; however, many were unskilled or semi-skilled workers, including cooks, tailors, clerks, teachers, salesmen—employed in supermarkets, retail outlets and hotels, in manufacturing industries and construction firms. The new arrivals were racially profiled as connected with illegal activities such as smuggling of goods and prostitution. Young girls were seen dancing to Bollywood music on rooftop restaurants, in bars and nightclubs, some became call-girls.

They come; they make money, they leave no sooner they have made enough—to other destinations, mostly the west. They 'take off', so they became known as 'rockets' to the dwindling communities of third and fourth generation Kenyan Asians. Others said they are rockets because they are ready to seduce women. 'They are different . . . they have an attitude problem . . . they are not like us . . . here for quick money . . . they take away jobs from us . . . they work illegally, without work permits or fake ones . . . these 'rockets' are foreigners to Kenya . . . many are unable to speak proper English or Kiswahili . . . it is distasteful to have them around . . .' were some of the mostly negative perceptions. Real or imaginary, they seemed to pose a threat.

Over the tumultmous 1980s, Krishanlal's health started deteriorating. Finally on 27 February 1988, at the age of 59, he passed away. Seeing him lying there on the floor in his final shroud—grey and frail—feebly, she held on to him. She felt the ground open under her feet. She cried her heart out. Krishanlal's recurring illness finally took its toll. He lay lifeless. With piteous sobs, Muni clung to him. She kissed the blue lips of her Krishan for the last time before they took him away from her forever.

A white sheet covered his body up to the chin. His complexion had turned blue, like that of Lord Krishna. The peace which had eluded his body since many years was at last his as he lay there serene in death. A lifetime had passed—one that had encompassed great highs and abysmal lows.

Nourished by the stability of family life and strengthened by creativity, his identity had grown; Krishanlal would continue to paint, write and participate in plays till late in life. Despite frail health, he sacrificed much for his family, immediate and extended. The joy was always his as he raised children and siblings at the same time, observing their successes with pride, taking their failures in stride. Enriched by religious beliefs right from early childhood, his search for the truth would never fade. He had sought it in the god as Krishna, in Jesus Christ, and even in the self. A devotee once asked the nineteenth century saint Paramhams Ramakrishna: 'Where can I find God?' He had replied, 'Look between two thoughts'. Perhaps Krishanlal's incessant introspection had led him there.

At last Muni took hold of herself and folded her hands together in front of her chest in a last namaskar to the man she had spent thirty-six years with. My sister and I were near collapse, but we put an iron control over our feelings to embrace and hold our mother. We were trembling all over as we struggled with our emotions.

A wife and six children, yet during his last moments he was all alone. Krishanlal passed away in 1988 in a cold hospital bed. The direct cause of his death was not epilepsy or the operation conducted upon his femur two weeks before. On the death certificate, the doctor had written: cardio-respiratory arrest, severe malaria.

Krishanlal had received blood transfusion at the hospital two weeks before. All of us were so numbed by the suddenness of it that a query with the hospital was never made at the time.

Muni had seen him the night before; she thought that he looked fine. He was supposed to come home the next day. At the same time he kept saying, 'Look, there comes a golden chair for me, can you see it?' Muni couldn't; she laughed. 'But I can see it clearly', Krishanlal insisted. 'This tells me I am going to get fine. Look! Medicines for epilepsy that I have been taking since the last forty years were not given to me today by the nurses, yet I feel fine . . .' Somewhere in his subconscious he must have known that the end was not far. 'Please call my children. Neera, tell her to come back; she will know what to do . . .' his last words to his wife before she left him for the night.

Krishanlal died at midnight, but the hospital did not call my mother until 8 the following morning. 'There, that must be papa calling,' Muni told her youngest son Sanjiv. 'Let's hurry up and bring him home . . .' she had barely finished her sentence when the cold voice of the nurse on the other end of the line announced the dreadful news. The telephone receiver fell from Muni's hand, she thought she had heard wrong. She was in a state of shock. Sanjiv, who had been driving mum to the hospital every day, who had been there for his parents in these difficult times, was all of a sudden too stunned to react immediately. Renu arrived within a matter of minutes . . . but it was too, too late. I was in Bombay taking lessons in dance; Sunil in Bangalore, doing a masters course in Christian theology. Ashu lived in Canada, Vimal in Australia. With the exception of Ashu, who had to complete another uninterrupted year before being allowed rights to live in Canada, we all took the first flight back.

Neither Krishanlal nor Muni had denied any of their children the freedom to choose their lifestyles. In the event, while growing up, we were surrounded by mainly American Christian missionaries in our area; they enticed us with free lessons in cookery. We learnt to bake chocolate cakes and brownies; we made marshmallows;

we went camping to Kijabe for a few nights. We did not hesitate to participate as the break from a large family living in a cramped one-bedroom house was welcome. During such sessions, we were asked to kneel down and accept Jesus Christ as our saviour. I remember having done that, and for a few years announced myself as 'born again'. Sunil took it seriously and continued to profess the faith. The missionaries came home; they visited papa at the hospital in his time of need. They held his hands and prayed for a healing touch. But papa did not recover, and now that he was no more, Sunil asked for his body to be taken to the Baptist church for blessing before finally being cremated according to Hindu rites at the crematorium at Kariakor.

Between the logs, they could see the form of the man who had given them life. As he took the torch in his hand, the elder son could feel its glowing heat, but he stood motionless, bewildered. After a forty-eight hour journey from the other end of the world, had he come this far to extinguish a body that had given him life? Vimal could not bring himself to set the body of his father aflame. He was still trembling from the flight. He had not bathed, eaten, or recovered from the journey from Australia. He was still numb from the shock of the news he had received over the telephone from Nairobi. A body now lay before him, he could see it but he would not believe it. Blurred images kept recurring before him.

The torch released a flood of memories and his hands started shaking. The images of a loving father and a caring man stood as clear before him as if he were still present. A young handsome man obsessed about cars and theatre, poetry recitals and *bhajans* . . . of visits to the radio station each Sunday morning. Here papa was encouraging them to participate in a children's programme called '*Bhaiya Moorti*'. Those on-the-air story-telling and singing sessions would be etched in their memories for a lifetime to come. Now he was gone.

Vimal regretted that he had not even had the time to get to know his father as he became a man; he had left for Edinburgh to build a career for himself. But how could his father go when he

was not too far from his promise? 'Why is life so unfair?' he cried.
For once, just this last time, he wanted to tell his father how much
he had meant to him . . . The torch continued to burn, he felt the
heat, but he was beyond caring. Vimal stood transfixed, as if rooted
to the spot.

Krishanlal's first epileptic attack had been incited when as a
young boy of not yet ten he had witnessed this ceremony for the
first time. It had been at the *antyeshti samskar* of his grandfather
Chunilal. When Hiralal had put a torch to the seemingly asleep
Chunilal, and the body had in no time erupted into flames,
Krishanlal had been struck dumb to the point of paralysis. How
could they do this to his grandfather whom he so loved, he had
cried within his soul! The dramatic ceremony so affected the
sensitive boy, that he would never be the same again. Krishanlal
had had a fit then; he had fallen on the floor unconscious. It would
mark him for the rest of his life. Many other attacks would follow.
And leave a deep impact in the subconscious of the growing
adolescent. The trauma never left Krishanlal.

And now Vimal's limbs seemed paralysed, refusing to cooperate.
The fire of the torch grew fiercely. Krishanlal's younger brother led
the young man forward, urging him on, 'My son, this is something
that only you must do.' Instinctively folding their hands, Vimal
and younger brothers Sunil and Sanjiv bowed their heads. Voices
saturated with emotion, their sounds quivered as they murmured
the prayer. '*Om bhur bhuvah swaha* . . . create an image of the sun
in your heart, let the sun's rays dispel fear and weakness from the
heart . . .' Reciting the Gayatri mantra, the Sanskrit prayer that
they had learnt from their father, they lit the pyre. The fire spread
quickly, and flames leaped on high.

Fire, the brilliance of intelligence, ardour of strength, glow
of health . . . energy of passion, of anger and of lust . . . the very
universe resulting from the spark of the divine desire. The One
wishing to be many; personified as the god Agni—to this very god
they cast offerings of ghee, grains and herbs. Creating, sustaining,

and witnessing rituals and sacraments, be it a marriage ceremony or honouring the ancestors—the same fire would now consume Krishanlal's body with the final rite of cremation.

The three brothers looked on, their faces wet with tears; they knew that their brother Ashu, who could not make it for the ceremony from Canada, would be crying alone. Vimal saved one flower from the pyre to send to Ashu, as he was finally ready to let go of his father's earthly remains. '*Om agneya swaha, Om somaye swaha, Om lokaye swaha, Om anumateya swaha, Om swargaye swaha* . . .' the mourners folded their hands.

The elders of the community got together to install the heir. A white turban was tied on the head of the eldest son. Muni got up silently, went into the bathroom and bathed. She emerged in a white sari, without any make-up or jewellery. The usual red dot on her forehead that she had taken to since the day she got married was gone forever; she would apply it no more. Her hair remained unadorned. A sense of calm and poise was at last evoked. The moving dignity of the moment reduced the onlookers to tears.

The old charm and vivacity has not deserted her, nor has the warmth of her affection diffused. She may have a receding hairline and put on several kilos. Her walk has definitely slowed down, her knees have given way, but she has lost neither her welcoming spirit nor an abundance of joy. She still has a soft and gentle approach to people, not to mention humorous. Muni, alias Krishna, is ageing gracefully.

The railway that was once Kriparam's lifeline and later that of the land, has all but lost its lustre. Even its identity—the famous Uganda Railway was renamed Kenya-Uganda Railway, then East African Railways and Harbours; today it is known as Kenya Railways. People don't flock to the now modest railway station to say their goodbyes in large numbers. The momentum of the rail that quickly superseded the fear it first wrought has all but faded away. Perhaps, an air of romance still hovers around it, and the nostalgia can make the trip an unforgettable experience, especially if one can afford to travel other than third class. You will still be travelling along the same narrow track for a night journey that extends to fourteen hours and has been reduced to thrice weekly.

Nairobi, which was born at the time of Kirparam Ramchand's arrival, has also travelled its own journey and traced its proper course during this span of over one hundred years. By the end of the 1980s, Nairobi had become a typical urbanized third world city. The re-introduction of multi-partyism in Kenyan politics gave it a new lease of life. *'Matatus'* '30-cent communal buses' painted in vibrant colours and dynamic themes, driven at break-neck speed, with loud music blaring from within, lost their colour and some of their madness with the present government, as also their blaring horns and reggae music. Fast food joints and little kiosks have sprung up like mushrooms next to highrise buildings. The television set has become more and more common, the use of mobile phones has exploded; however, many a common *mwananchi* continues to walk around with a small transistor covered in a plastic bag, next to his ear, while little street children, many of them orphans, sniff glue elsewhere.

In the Parklands area, a little corner of India has sprung up. Known as the Diamond Plaza, here one can buy anything—from the latest Bollywood videos and audio cassettes to utensils, saris, readymade or tailored *salwar kameez* and fashion jewellery. Tiny restaurants serve snacks and restaurant meals, even cybercafés and international phone bureaus which charge more for local calls have sprung up. Westlands, once a no-go zone, has also become a very middle-class Asian residential area, while the economically weaker Asians remain in Ngara and River Road.

Forest land has been systematically destroyed. Shortage of land for cultivating *shambas*, unemployment, and the lights and sounds of urban Nairobi have attracted more and more peasants from the rural areas. Bars, restaurants, hotels, hairdressing salons, butcheries and groceries—sprawling slums which have sprung up in pockets all over the city—they have them all. The slum of Kibera, a refuge for Sudanese soldiers of the Kings' African Rifles (KAR) of the early 1900s, is today one of the densest in the world; it has grown exponentially. It is estimated that sixty per cent of the 3.5 million people of Nairobi today are slum-dwellers, living in insecure and unhygienic conditions—while African and Asian elite are increasingly moving to once forbidden white-owned residential areas, Muthaiga being one of the more expensive class havens. Others, including many of Nairobi's expatriates, have moved out to the suburbs of Gigiri, where the present UN Habitat headquarters are located. Or, to Karen (named after Karen Blixen of *Out of Africa* fame) in the Ngong hills—complete with a racecourse nearby and horse shows every other Sunday. This was where the white settlers had set up their farms in the 'happy valley' days of the early twentieth century.

Nairobi has also gained the reputation of 'a pot-holed city of Nairobbery'. Crime, security and corruption continue to remain dominant issues, with a cost of living that keeps escalating. But blessed with a very hospitable climate and its haven of game reserves, the 'city in the sun' is a tourist attraction. As a base for multinational companies and many NGOs, the Nairobi of today is one of the more expensive cities in the world to live in.

With forty-three years behind us, and only three heads of state since, we may have gained independence from colonial rule, but other than that—economically, socially, politically and even culturally—we still have a long journey ahead of us. The 'dawn of a new era', and the 'second liberation' slogans we had greeted the new government of President Kibaki with, when he came to power in 2002, have faded fast. Poor economic growth and uneven distribution of wealth still loom large. Promises to reduce corruption and poverty have been disappointing. Ten percent of the population controls half of the country's wealth.

Notwithstanding, there is greater freedom of expression today. People can voice an opinion without fear of being put behind bars, politicians can be criticized, as also the head of state—and his entourage. The media is in a better position to air its views; caricatures are drawn, jokes are written. People are growing, stirring, awakening in an embryonic but vibrant society. With real expansion of FM radio, and debates through the media, the public continues to demonstrate greater awareness. Increasingly aware of their rights, Kenyans are definitely heading towards a slow but sure maturity for a national consciousness—even if political parties continue to play tribal politics.

However, unless one happens to have an established business, the path ahead is slow and tortuous. For many, religion has taken on tremendous importance. Mosques and Hindu temples have been built, but churches predominate. Muslims make up about thirty per cent of the population; the majority are Christian. Intense missionary activity which began with the first missionaries who penetrated into the 'dark' continent 200-odd years ago has given birth to hundreds of Christian sects. Baptists and Protestants, Seventh Day Adventists, Anglicans, The Lost Tribe of Israel, the House of Yahweh and many more today throng big and small independent churches at every corner and every street of every area each Sunday in a promise to save souls—not necessarily uplifting them from poverty or improving their socio-economic status.

It is not rare to see evangelists arrive in huge stadiums filled with hundreds of worshippers to make the blind see, the deaf hear, the lame walk or the faint-hearted have hope. Or even to have a 'revelation and salvation of the nation'. All it needs is donation. Thousands of the hopeless continue to attend such miraculous meetings. The church is getting more and more politicized, with preachers guiding their flock to a certain 'party alignment'. More Kenyan Asians today embrace Christianity, and meet for fellowship with African brethren. In my family, two of my brothers chose to convert and marry according to Christian beliefs. I had no problem about that, but some Christians had a problem with me.

I was once filmed dancing and interviewed by a local TV station. In the end however, the board decided that my dance was too pagan to go on air! On another occasion, I conducted a month long workshop for a group of African dancers (all Christian believers). We decided to use a theme common to Indian and African tribal traditions. A huge pot symbolizing fertility, the mother earth, the womb, was built and dancers were to emerge from it. Some of the dancers were terribly perturbed; their respective churches saw it as idol-worship and as pagan; they created a dramatic uproar. I had to have several discussions to try to convince them that it was not necessary for them to deny their ancestral traditions in order to be good Christians. However, a couple of them left the workshop.

Zest for life and humour have not diminished, despite all odds. Uchumis and Nakumatts supermarkets may have bombarded the city, but we still love to bargain in the hustle and bustle of markets, whether buying vegetables from mama mboga, women vendors going door to door, or in small retail shops. We still venture towards the majestic Rift valley to instill in us a spiritual experience as also a day out towards the Ngong hills, or at the foot of Mt Kenya. Yes, *Ngai* surely lives there!

Kenyan by birth, Kenyan-Asian by culture, French influence through marriage ... all in all, I consider myself lucky to have had such diversity in my life. My sister Renu married a Sikh, my brother Sunil's wife's grandmother was a KiMeru. We are called Kenyan-Asian, South Asian Kenyans, Kenyan-Indians or Kenyans of Asian origins ... but perhaps just the term Kenyans should be sufficient.

Epilogue: My journey to the ancestral land

I have not slept many nights in the excitement of this trip. Finally, it seems that we will make it. I have been dreaming about it for the last two years, ever since we arrived in India. The year before, when in Paris, I had not dared to dream. India was awesome enough, but Pakistan? Not once did I even tell myself that I would go there. It had seemed another planet, not just a 'forbidden land'.

My husband's posting to various countries brought me in contact with cultures other than the ones I had been exposed to, used to. For a long while, they did not overly excite me. Perhaps, I was ethnocentric, and withdrew into my 'Kenyan-Indian' cocoon—whatever that meant. The depth and satisfaction I was seeking did not come. I realized that I knew neither the Kenyan nor the Indian cultures, nor did I know their histories well—leave alone anything on the Kenyan-Indian! There was a gap somewhere. I had to open up. I had to let myself be exposed to others, to learn from them, to appreciate them. It took many years of love, of pain, of growth and the nurture of marriage—to finally come to terms with myself, to accept myself as a simple human being interacting with other human beings. It was the beginning of a spiritual journey.

Once the cocoon had burst I felt freer, almost as if I had got rid of excess baggage. I felt ready to continue my journey—back in time. Of course, we were Kenyans, and of course we had Indian roots, somehow, but how? My mother mentioned Bhera-Miani. Someone else said Lahore. I couldn't even trace Bhera and Miani on the map. It all seemed very vague—they must have been tiny villages of no importance, lost in obscurity. I didn't pay much attention. I looked at some old family photographs that seemed interesting and put them in an album.

Years went by. In between, my dance performances became rare. My health had suffered. I started thinking about my 'roots' again. We were in Paris then. I flew down to Nairobi to talk to the family. This was my first serious attempt to listen to family stories. The probing has not been easy. Those who 'knew' are no more. Some thought that it was a waste of their time—they were not willing to share. Who was I to demand that private lives be exposed? Secrets are best buried with times gone by. Others were vague, their answers differed every time to the same question; or I got no answers at all. Many times I felt that I was hitting a dead end; I seemed to get nowhere. Rarely, except with my mother, did I get straight answers. More and more often, I came to the conclusion that perhaps I too was wasting my time. My husband Alain nudged me on. He thought it was important enough to persist.

Christmas last year, Alain and I go to Nairobi to be with the family for a few days. Alain leaves before the New Year. I am left with my mother. I listen to her talk about her life. It's beautiful. Another kind of a bond develops between us. We are no more just mother and daughter, but very close friends as well. I meet a friend in Kenya who has been to Miani: she talks about it. The town suddenly seems to take on a reality. I realize that neither Bhera nor Miani are in the India of today; they are now a part of Pakistan. She gives me an address in Lahore for me to get further information. Some hope at last! For the first time I become serious about wanting to visit the land of my ancestors. The land that was India before they left for Kenya over a hundred years ago, but would be known as Pakistan fifty years before I made the journey back.

Returning to India in the beginning of February, I find that India has tested an atomic bomb. Pakistan retaliates, and relations between the two sour. My dreams of visiting Pakistan get a little frayed. I still insist that I want to go. The first Delhi-Lahore bus starts, with Atal Behari Vajpayee, the prime minister of India, as its first passenger. Easter holidays are not far. Alain and I are booked to go to Kathmandu. Alain has been nominated to take charge of a centre there. Each day I talk to Alain. He is still apprehensive. Connections between the two countries are still not normalized. One reads about all kinds of problems on the other side of the border. I persist, I plead. Alain gives in, reluctantly. I start making the bookings. My search for a guide book on Pakistan in Delhi bookstores is entirely futile. 'Not permitted, customs officials would impound them on arrival', I am told! A friend lends me a very old and not very informative book. However, my own version of the picture starts to form. The dream takes on a reality.

On 31 March, Alain and I board the PIA flight PK271 for Lahore. I am terribly excited. The airhostess reads a prayer from the Koran. We are quickly served food. No sooner have we finished eating, than we land. It was only forty-five minutes away, but the borders have been closed for over fifty years. We deplane and I touch the soil to my forehead, in salutation to my ancestors. I think of them. Perhaps somewhere they are watching, maybe they are urging me on. I laugh and cry at the same time. I almost cannot believe it.

Sunfort Hotel Gulberg, Liberty Market. We check in. Women in bright *salwar-kameezes* embroidered all over in gold, and decked up in gold jewellery. My excitement has not worn off a bit. I admire them and tell them so. They stare at me so hard, as if I am completely mad. Perhaps I am so. Nothing seems to dampen my spirits for the moment. We order drinks—no alcohol is allowed. Only foreigners working here have access to a limited quota, for which a permit is issued. Exotic fruit cocktails; I choose peach. A sip, and my hair stands up. I try another. This time my eyes pop out. So much sugar, almost unbelievable! I should have known. All Punjabis love sugar. My father put sugar in everything, sugar and milk with lots of thick milk cream. He would have been so happy to be here with me.

At 9 next morning, the taxi comes for us. We have not yet finished our breakfast. The buffet service has been temporarily suspended due to the Id holidays. Qazafi, a young man from Baluchistan, fluent in French, offers to guide us in town. For a fee, of course.

Lahore Fort. Badshahi Mosque. Very young girls all dressed up in their best. Lots of make-up—lipstick, eye shadow, kohl—they resemble little dolls. Id festivities continue throughout the town. Men play cricket in the lawns of the Fort. The old town is clearly visible from the ramparts. Alain spots a *hijra*—a transvestite—gaudily made up, in a rickshaw on the street leading to Hira Mandi. By now the heat is quite oppressive. I cover my head with my *dupatta*, thankful that I brought only *salwar-kameezes* to wear here. It seems to be the dress of one and all—men and women, boys and girls. 'Zia-ul-Huq, a previous head of state, encouraged the vogue—even in offices, but the present younger generation find it is too comfortable for serious and disciplined work!' Qazafi explains.

The beginning of Hira Mandi, the famed red light district of Lahore. I had heard about it as a young woman—innumerable stories about beautiful, talented and cultured courtesans of the diamond market. We begin with lunch at Coco's Café, a surrealist restaurant, full of portraits of women—in an Islamic state. I am quite taken aback. The owner, the son of a prostitute, is also a professor of fine arts at the university. The restaurant is otherwise empty. 'Respectable Lahori society does not frequent the restaurant,' we are told. 'Only foreigners do!' A menu is passed around. No vegetables. I eat rice and chapatis. There is plenty of meat. Alain has been craving for a steak for many days. In India, beef is not served. On this side of the border, it is the norm. One eats a lot of meat here. Not one, but two or three different kinds of red meat served at the same time, such as mince and biryani. There is chicken cooked in various ways, especially in thick gravy. Vegetables are rarely served. For a vegetarian, it is lentils.

Our walk in Hira Mandi is quiet. A few people—only men—are visible. I am the lone woman walking those streets. When I do look up, I see a face—perhaps a faint glimpse of the famed beauties peering through the curtains at these strangers. What would it be like to be a part of the crowd here on a normal day? Of course, I would not come here alone. A woman in Pakistan is rarely unaccompanied on the streets—another woman, a man, even a child will do. Would I, who could easily pass off as a Pakistani woman, incite an emotion—walking with a 'white' man?

Most of the shops are closed. Id festivities are clearly in evidence everywhere—a week, maybe longer—an opportunity to reunite, to catch up on the last threads. We carry on down Gumti Bazaar and the jewellers' street. Hiralal Kapur, my paternal grandfather came from Africa to this part of town on his bi-annual visits to the family in Lahore. The lanes narrow. Electric wires hang dangerously, a bit too low. Some jewellery shops are open. The designs are very familiar. It could have been a shop on the streets of India. The jeweller invites us in to have a look at more designs. His Punjabi reminds me of home—a Punjabi that I am distinctly familiar with, a Punjabi that I know so well, a Punjabi that is different from that spoken on the other side of the border. We walk on towards the rope-making streets. Ropes used in all kinds of ways, to make stools, and beds. We watch an old man at work. With very deft fingers, he weaves the rope bed, the charpoy, *vaan da manja*, the rope-bed that my great-grandmothers used to sleep on.

Wazire Khan mosque, a real wonder in coloured ceramics of the time of Shah Jehan. The Lodhi tombs in Delhi's beautiful and harmonious Lodhi gardens must have been similar, when the ceramic was still intact. I cover my head—women do so when visiting the mosque (not necessary for men). A pond in the courtyard for ablutions, a few tourists, floral designs and paintings adorn the walls. Fully carpeted and very fresh, the interior of the mosque invites us for a much-needed rest. No priest comes to disturb our peace, asking for money. No alms, no beggars—speaking of which, I notice how rare it is to see a beggar here. Each of us is absorbed in our own thoughts, drinking in the beauty of the place. One notices on the streets a lot of very fair-complexioned young men and girls with green or blue eyes, perhaps from up north, perhaps Afghans. Some in tribal clothes, others in *salwars*; none in chadors—except for two women with the Afghan-type burqa, covered from head to toe, with a lattice-like opening for vision. We drive back past the river Ravi.

The next day we drive up on the Mall, a vast road of colonial times. I can clearly visualize Hindu and British shopowners of the past on both sides of the Mall. We pass by Faletti Hotel, the hotel that seems to have become a historical monument. It was from here that the British engineer Radcliff had slaughtered the subcontinent into two. Lahore, beloved of the Punjabis—Hindus and Muslims—went to Pakistan.

Lahore Museum: Alain is extremely excited. All sorts of statues from the Gandhara civilization—many exceptionally Greek in influence—standing Buddhas with moustaches and togas, we realize that Greek civilization was very strong here at the time of Alexander, and for a long time after. Alexander met Porus in Haranpur on the river Jhelum, the town where Hardei, my great-grandmother was born, so it is said. It is my turn to get excited. The area near Peshawar, Swat, Taxila, Mardan, right up to Afghanistan was strongly influenced by the two great civilizations, Greek and Buddhist. A few stupas still exist in these well-watered valleys, clear cut hills and a pleasant climate.

During the fifth and sixth century BC, the region formed part of the Achaemenian empire of Persia. In the fourth century BC, it was occupied for a brief period by the Greek legions of Alexander. After the short spell of Greek rule, and on the departure of the Macedonian king, a powerful dynasty established its rule—the Mauryan empire. Ashoka was responsible for the spread of Buddhism in the subcontinent. During this period, a group of monks arrived in Gandhara, and Buddhism found roots here. Kirparam's ancestors belonged here; someday Alain and I should surely like to go up north, to the land of the Hunza and the Kalash. Blonde and blue-eyed kafirs; 'Kalash' because the women are always in black. They are thought to be descendants of the Greeks . . . who knows?

Finally on Friday, we take the Lahore-Islamabad highway for Bhera. The highway is very impressive. We can actually do 120 km per hour. At this rate, within two hours we are in Bhera. Eltesham Piracha is at the station to meets us. We leave our taxi and cross over on the other side from where he drives us to his house. At first impression, it is like a hot dusty village. Soon after we have passed numerous gates and entrances to the town, we come upon lush green fields. We drive towards the Jhelum river. Potters are at work, soil from the river being turned into pots. The language of the old man is so familiar—just the way grandfather Lajpat Rai, also of this region, used to speak. It feels good. An old Hindu temple lies close by. It is bereft of the usual temple sculptures. Later I learn that it was a temple built by a Hindu family, the Mehras who lived there at the time of my great-grandparents—here, I get myself photographed standing in the place of the goddess.

We meet Piracha's mother, a very strong woman; the Pirachas are one of the oldest families of these parts, I learn. Alain is reminded of an old family of Italian or Sicilian origin. We are served all kinds of drinks—sodas, teas, *halwa* . . . We walk the streets and see some old havelis, many of which lie empty, closed, abandoned; they must have been beautiful at one time. The doors are intricately carved. We walk in the Khoja Mohallah, before driving down to Miani, half an hour away by car.

Beautifully carved wooden doors to *havelis*, many two to three storey high, but in a dilapidated condition. Partition years, change of owners, urbanization—it's painful to see such neglect. And yet they retain their majesty, they still have many stories to tell. I think of Kirparam's mother. When she had learnt of the death of her elder son, she had fallen with shock from the third-storey balcony of one such *haveli* of Miani. There is one *haveli* that is particularly intricately worked upon. The owner, a professor—post-partition—retains the original name of the *haveli*—Krishna Niwas (abode or residence of Krishna). A Hindu name, a name of the god Krishna, in an Islamic state . . . we appreciate this with much surprise. The haveli has one hundred rooms, very surrealistic, most of these are locked up. The present family occupies only part of the second floor. They are nice enough to open the ground floor room for us. Here, we marvel at the ceiling, painted in very vivid colours: the story of Vishnu lying on the cobra, with Brahma issuing forth from him. Another beautiful painting of Vishnu resting before re-creation of the world. Vishnu has certainly helped preserve this painting, for the condition is very good. We take some pictures, but dare not stay too long, for we do not want to disturb them.

Before leaving the town of Miani, which is much smaller than Bhera, and seems poorer too, I want to buy some pots, as a souvenir of the soil of our ancestors. The owner, a young man, refuses to accept money from us, but our guide, who is from Miani, insists on paying him and at the same time will not accept money from me. We see some temples on the main street, doors locked. Apparently, the shops in front are in dispute, so the whole area has been shut down. We walk over to another *haveli*, the Chaddha *haveli*. What was once a residence of the Hindu family has now been converted to a school. People living on the ground floor, classes above, while the rest has collapsed, or been broken down . . . who knows?

We hear children screaming '*Afreeka ke log* . . . people from Africa . . .' How do they know, we wonder? Women peep at us through curtains. Not a single woman is visible on the streets. The same gentleman who paid for my pots insists on buying us a drink before we leave. I leave very reluctantly, but I know that it has been a long wait for our host. We had never met him before, yet the hospitality extended by him and his family has been incredible. He has been with us since 11.30 a.m. Now it is nearing 6 p.m. Eltesham Piracha tells us that some government official had once come and stayed with them for a week, researching Bhera and its history. The outcome was supposed to have been a book; Eltesham has yet to hear from him.

I am in a daze. It was all too short and too sudden. I was not even prepared. I had been so unsure about whether we would get here . . . but we did! I don't know if I have learnt anything from this trip that is going to be useful to me. I certainly did not find a lead into my family roots, nor saw their *havelis*, nor identified their *mohallah*. In fact, I didn't really expect to be able to reach Bhera. The fact that I did was perhaps in itself an achievement. Whoever I had talked to in preparation for our voyage had put me off by saying that it would be too risky to go into the interior, especially with Alain. Moreover, I had not been able to trace any literature about Bhera, not even about Pakistan. How wrong they all were! Not only did we make it, but we were treated with such affection and respect that it was hard to part. So near, yet so far, incredible. Now, I have been to the region. I have stood on the soils of Bhera, Miani and Lahore—the earth that my great-grandparents walked upon over a hundred years ago. In a way I have paid my tribute to them.

We arrive at the taxi. The driver is most upset, and shows it clearly. We insist on taking him to the restaurant for a meal. The others are shocked. 'But he is only a driver . . . let him be . . .' We head further north to have a quick look at the Salt range. Massive red mounds of hills, powerful and majestic they stand. The highway cuts through. They have enough salt to last another 300 years or so. In the fading evening light they are even more impressive. Grey, at times mauve, then orange, and finally an earthy brown, they change colour with the light. With nature as such, it is difficult not to believe in God. We turn back from Kallar Kahar, heading back towards Lahore. I had wanted to photograph the Jhelum, but the light has suddenly gone.

There is a full moon. I feel blessed. Alain and I look at each other. He holds my hand and whispers, 'We did it.' It is a magic moment, especially to know that I am not alone in this pilgrimage. The quest has not been in vain. The journey has served a purpose. I feel elated. How I long to call my mother. I know that some day soon, I would like to return with my mother—for a longer period— *Inshallah!*

We take a walk in the Shalimar gardens on Saturday. It is only 10 a.m., but there are already quite a few people enjoying the beauty of these Mughal gardens designed by Jehangir over 300 years ago. The sun comes in quite strong, but is not yet oppressive. Some young students from Peshawar want to be photographed with Alain. He is exotic for them, I suppose. Alain returns to the Museum, while I walk the streets of Anarkali. It is like a souk of Fez or of Marrakech. Here, I buy a pair of *khussa jutties*. I remember my great-grandmother Bebe Gurdei, who wore these for special occasions.

We stop at the famous Parsee Hotel, the Avari. They have a strawberry festival on and Alain is keen to try their strawberry fruit cocktail. While waiting, our eyes fall on the yellow tablemats; they depict the story of Lahore. Lahore, *loh-avar* from the Sanskrit *awar* for fort, and *loh* for Lav, the son of Sita and Rama, who founded the city.

Bina and Syed are a lovely couple. They pick us up from the hotel, and we drive towards their house in Model Town, a quarter designed by the Hindus in the 1920s. After partition, prosperous Pakistanis were given access to it. They have a beautiful house, spacious, very tastefully furnished. We have never known these people before, and yet the way they welcome us in their house, with such warmth and generosity, I don't know if I could reciprocate. It must be a *rishta*—a relationship of sorts—left over from the last life. A sumptuous meal awaits us. Near midnight, Manju and her husband, who are also visiting from Delhi, arrive. I am very happy to meet them, for their ancestors too are from Bhera. Manju's father-in-law was born in Bhera. She promises that he will call me as soon as possible, because Bhera is very dear to him. He was twenty at the time of partition when he had to leave Bhera. 'We have many houses in Lahore where we can stay, but this time we decided to stay here with Bina and Syed. It had to be because we had to meet you,' Manju tells me.

Back in Lahore and a meeting with a master of *Khayal*—a style of music. The son comes to pick us up at the hotel. The maestro is a very dramatic-looking personality. Not very aged in years, but looks a character straight out of a Shakespearean or Dickens classic. Except under the eyes, his skin has lost colour all over the face. He has a shock of white hair, frail body, no teeth . . . and yet he can sing—sing with gusto, in fact. The voice erupts with force that seems to emerge suddenly and mysteriously. The proud son shows us extracts on the video from some of their performances.

We learn soon, however, why the son had been insisting we meet his father. 'You have come to your *peke* (father's place). We have to make sure you are looked after.' I am not used to this kind of conversation, not even in India. However, my previous theatre experience comes in handy. I can play the game, but a little uncomfortably. The evening soon takes on an emotional turn with the old man giving us bits of his life in India, now on the other side of the border: Birth in Amritsar; musical training at the Gwalior *gharana* (school); singing *shabads* and *kirtans* from the sacred Sikh *Gurbani*. Pieces of his life he no more dare declare, let alone sing. His plea, his last ambition before dying, is to sing in Delhi.

We feel his pain. At the same time, one can sense that he is not as weak as he looks. Incessantly, the photographer clicks us with him, and very quietly, he gives directions when and how to picture us together—in conversation, sitting, standing. He thinks we are in a position to help, alas! I hope we can do something for them.

Monday, 5 April, is our last morning there. After breakfast, I decide to rush to Liberty Market to buy a few souvenirs. Alain is not very fond of shopping and does not join me. I have not been able to pick up anything in the last few days because Id holidays meant a long break; most of the shops were shut during this period. The flight is at 3 p.m. We have to leave for the airport at 1.30. Shops do not open before 11, at the earliest. This means I can only do a really limited souvenir. I discover lovely *khussa juttis* and *bareeze*—special material for *salwar kameez*, so-called because it has small holes for ventilation in summer—very similar to the *chikan*-work embroidery of Lucknow. I end up buying shoes for the entire family. I need much more time to reflect before buying, so the rest hopefully next time. My crossing the street alone invites a few stares. I quickly cover my head with my *dupatta*, and feel a bit more confident.

It is quite interesting that when we had arrived at Lahore airport, we had not been subjected to any kind of checking or security measures. Customs officials had not asked us what we had brought; our bags had not been opened. Everybody seemed to pass through. It had all been very swift. Departure was a different matter. Our passports were checked to see that we had not overstayed, our bags were checked, thoroughly. Each of us was asked if we were carrying any gold and how much foreign money we had on us.

A not-so-sympathetic looking official pointed towards Alain with his head and asked me in Urdu what he was to me—although he could very well read that on our passports.

'My husband,' I replied.

'Have you any children?' he asked.

'No,' I said.

'Why not?' he asked, almost in an accusing manner.

I nearly lost my cool, but did not want to create a scene. Controlling myself, I said, 'Allah ki dein hai . . . That is a gift of God'.

He did not sound convinced, but this time he kept quiet. His eyes, however, followed me until I had finally turned the corner to take the stairs for the departure lounge. Thankfully, Alain had not understood a word!

I had a few Pakistani rupees left—not enough, though, to buy the book on Pakistan, which I had been looking for all over in the Lahore bookstores, but had not found. Mall Road, the main street of Lahore, has three or four bookstores, but compared to Delhi, or any other big cosmopolitan city in the world, a very poor collection of books. A little paperback on Pakistan, with a brief history, and a tour guide written by Isobel Shaw was better than anything that we had seen. The shopkeeper was quite happy to accept Indian rupees. The reverse is not the case on the other side of the border.

The five days have flown. It has been a very rich emotional experience. Many more questions, so much more to learn, to share . . . Inshallah, I will be back!

My ancestors came from Jhelum to Tana. It took years to understand that I had to make the trip from Tana to Jhelum—a trip in the memory of four generations and three countries. The cycle is now complete. I offer it to the younger generation so that it may realize that a tree whose roots have not dug deep can easily be blown off by the wind—nor will it blossom.

Epitaph

From the unreal, lead me to the real
From darkness, lead me to light
From death, lead me to immortality.
      —Brihadaranyaka Upanishad

Time stood still. They were important not only for their presence and what they stood for, but equally significant was their absence and what they left us with. My ancestors became alive for me long after their death. They now live within my soul as if I had always known them: the previous generation. Memories from a recent past. A dying culture. Old photographs, pieces of conversation. Impulses of yore that continue to have an existence in the marrow . . . this fog of nostalgia envelops me, like a vision from an about-to-be-forgotten past. I feel as if I am back among the spirits of my great-grandparents, of my grandparents' generation—many of whom had lived through the two world wars. Some showed an extraordinary determination to take destiny in their own hands.

If I hadn't heard these stories from my grandparents and parents, from friends and colleagues, I may not have shared all this with you. The mysterious world, whose history is rooted in far-off places. A journey in time and space, receding into the subconscious, and re-emerging only after the journey has come full circle. But since I am beginning to understand my history, I have begun to have strength in my present and hopefully be able to handle my future.

In the midst of chaos, a ceaseless striving for order remains. An eternal search for what is constant, coherent and true—amid change that is perpetual as the river's flow. I know that much of the tradition has dissolved into time, I still consider myself lucky to be part of an era that was, but is now being lost very fast. An epitaph is at this moment being written. Part of a past, perhaps favoured by Lakshmi, that many attained affluence in the land that they shared—bound by fate, identities and loyalties. Surely, these migrant peoples, of whom I consider myself a descendant, did not just remain visitors for ever. In the end, their new lands owned them as much as their old lands once did. They may have had loyalties to time-honoured traditions, but they also borrowed from their new worlds, and were perhaps swamped by neither. In future, where you live will become a matter of choice, traditions will not prevent you from integrating.

Gigantic oceans and rivers will bring with the flow an ultimate reality for each one of us. Becoming the Ganga of other worlds. The Ganga of the mind. Destroying the worlds of illusion. Emptying itself into eternity. Developing into a profound humanity. Or so I hope. The Tana will continue to flow, as will the Ganga. And the Jhelum. The itinerary from Shiva's matted locks to the snow-covered peaks of the Himalayas and to the foothills of Kerenyaga has been a long one. It took three generations and over a hundred years. Perhaps only now our roots are being implanted firmly and we are able to interlace with others.

Glossary

Swahili words

Amanyahanga	:	(Maasai) people of clothes
askari	:	soldier/security guard
bilori	:	glass/tumbler
boma	:	administrative centre
bui-bui	:	woman's covering cloak, full length veil (very often in black)
bwana	:	master, gentleman
chotara	:	half-breed
chungwa	:	see *mchungwa*
debe	:	four-gallon tin (from the Indian word *dubba*)
dik-dik	:	dwarf antelope found on the dry savannah of Africa
dissidabba	:	three-tiered tiffin box
duka	:	shop
dukawallah	:	shopkeeper
fitina	:	discord/feuds
fundi	:	craftsman
gharries	:	cars
gunia	:	sack
Hakuna kitu	:	Have nothing
hamali	:	a porter, carts pulled by men
jahazi	:	ship
jembe	:	hoe
jiko	:	cooking fire (usually using coal or wood)

jikoni	:	kitchen
kanga	:	woman's garment
kaburu (carts)	:	two-wheeled ox-carts
kahawa	:	coffee
kaniki	:	dark cotton material
kanzu	:	men's garment (long robe)
khat	:	see *miraa*
kiboko	:	whip
kikapu	:	plaited basket
kipande	:	piece (identity card, as used here)
kitenge	:	woman's garment, also called *kanga*
kofia	:	hat/cap
kudu	:	a striped African antelope, the male of which has long spiral horns.
kraal	:	settlement
landhis	:	barrack-like accommodation made of brick with corrugated iron roof for the railway maintenance staff
mabati	:	metal sheeting
malli	:	wealth
Mama mungu	:	woman of god
makuti	:	coconut leaves for thatching
matata	:	trouble/quarrels
Mbuyuni	:	Baobab tree
mchungwa	:	orange
miraa/khat/ Catha edulis	:	Cathionine is the major psychoactive component of the plant *Catha edulis*, also known as *khat* or *miraa*. The leaves are chewed for a stimulant effect. An evergreen shrub native to East Africa
Moran	:	young Maasai warrior
moshi	:	smoke
Muhindi	:	Indian
mwananchi	:	citizen (singular)
mzungu	:	white man, European

Ngai	:	God (among the Gikuyu and Maasai tribes)
nyayo	:	follow the footsteps
panga	:	a large bush-knife
posho	:	rations/maize flour/French beans
sawasawa	:	okay
shamba	:	cultivated field/plantation
shauris	:	advice/affairs
shifta	:	bandit in Amharic (Northern Kenyan, Southern Ethiopia)
shuka	:	a piece of cloth
simba	:	lion
sokoni	:	marketplace
sufuria	:	saucepan
wageni	:	guests
Wahindi	:	Indians
wananchi	:	citizens (plural form of *mwananchi*)
wazungu	:	Europeans, white men (plural form of *mzungu*). A Swahili handbook of 1909 defines the word *mzungu* as a strange or startling thing
uhuru	:	freedom

Indian words

aaliyan	:	mourning songs
achar	:	pickle
ajwain	:	caraway seeds
akhara	:	wrestling arena
alif	:	the first alphabet in Urdu, equivalent to 'A'
amar rahe	:	long live
anna	:	grain
anna and *paise*	:	units of the rupee (Indian currency)
angeethi	:	small burner using charcoal or wood
Angrez	:	English people
angutha-tek	:	one who gives a thumb-print instead of a signature

antyeshti samskar	:	death rites
atta	:	wheat flour
attar	:	perfume
Ayurveda	:	knowledge about healthcare from the Vedas (Hindu scriptures of knowledge)
azadi	:	freedom
Bhabhi	:	sister-in-law (brother's wife)
bacchi	:	girl child
badam	:	almonds
bahi	:	register
balti	:	bucket
baithak	:	sitting room
balushaiyan	:	confectionery made of flour and syrup
bania	:	grocer/merchant
barfi	:	confectionery made of milk and sugar
baya	:	an offering, an oblation
Bebe	:	term of respect for an older woman (in Punjabi culture)
beta	:	son
bhagat	:	devotee
bhajans	:	religious songs
bindi	:	round mark applied in the middle of the forehead by Hindus
biradari	:	extended family
bitia	:	term of affection for a young girl
Bohra	:	the word means trader. As a proper name, a Bohra is member of the Dawoodi Tayyibi Ismaili Shia community
boondi	:	gram flour balls coated in syrup
brahmachari	:	celibate student
buaji	:	father's sister
burqa	:	veil
chai	:	tea
Chacha and Chachi	:	father's younger brother and his wife
chakki	:	grindstone
chamar	:	cobbler

chandan tikka	:	sandalwood mark on the forehead
chapati	:	thin, unleavened Indian bread
charan amrit	:	foot nectar (usually of gods/goddesses)
charpoy	:	string bed, cot
choli	:	woman's short blouse
chowk	:	crossroad
chhote	:	small, young, little
chulha	:	kitchen stove
chunni	:	scarf
chura	:	low-born, outcaste
chust	:	narrow
coolie	:	labourer/porter
cowrie	:	sea shell
dai	:	midwife
dakshina	:	charity, a donation
dal	:	lentils
dandasa	:	bark of neem tree, used as toothbrush
darshan	:	sight, the act of seeing, both in the normal sense and also inner vision
darwaza	:	door
darzi	:	tailor
dawa-daru	:	medicine-liquor, often used colloquially together
dayan	:	witch
dharma	:	moral duty
dharamsala	:	lodging/house for pilgrims
dhoban	:	washerwoman
dhobi	:	washerman
dhol	:	drum
dholki	:	small drum
dhoti	:	piece of cloth 5-6 yards long tied from waist, generally worn by Hindu men
dhow	:	lateen-rigged ship with one or two masts, used chiefly in the Arabian region
dhurrie	:	carpet

diya	:	earthen lamp
diya bati	:	the light of an earthen lamp
doodhwalla	:	milkman
dulha, dulhan	:	bridegroom, bride
dupatta	:	a wrap, scarf
dvija	:	twice-born
dvipa	:	two
firangi	:	white person
gaon	:	village
genhu	:	wheat
Ghadr	:	Revolutionary movement to overthrow the British
ghagara	:	long pleated skirt
ghat	:	river bank
ghee	:	clarified butter
gopi	:	milkmaid
gotra	:	literally, Sanskrit for cow pen, meaning larger clan
gram devatas	:	village deities
gudda	:	male doll
guddi	:	female doll
gulab jamun	:	confectionery made of milk and soaked in syrup
gulkand	:	thick rose syrup
gulal	:	red powder used during Holi festival
gulli danda	:	name of a game
gurgabian	:	high-heeled shoes/sandals
gurhuti	:	first food given to a newborn
Habashi	:	Abyssinian (Ethiopian)
Hai rabba	:	O God!
haiza	:	plague
hakim	:	physician
halwa	:	sweet dish made of carrots or semolina
halwai	:	confectioner
haramzada	:	illegitimate, a term of abuse

havan	:	an offering, oblation to fire
havan kund	:	fire altar
hookah	:	oriental tobacco pipe with a long flexible tube which draws the smoke through water in a bowl
izzat	:	respect
jaloos	:	procession
jalsa	:	festival
jadu tona	:	the art of magic
jahaz	:	ship
jaimala	:	garland
jalebi	:	a kind of spiral confectionary made of gram flour and cooked in syrup
jamedars	:	headmen
jamun	:	rose apple fruit
Jat	:	farmer-soldier caste of mostly Rajput Hindu ancestry. It was Jat Sikhs who came to Kenya with the police and army at the beginning of the colonial era
jau di roti	:	barley bread
jhumka	:	bell-shaped pendant of women's earrings
Johri gali	:	jewellers' lane
jua	:	gamble
jutti	:	lady's shoe
kacchi lassi	:	buttermilk
kameez	:	long loose shirt
kanjariyan	:	prostitutes
kanyadaan	:	giving away the bride (performed by the father)
karhai	:	pan
karam kar	:	do good works
karela	:	bitter gourd
kathakar	:	storyteller
kesar	:	saffron
khalassi	:	sailor, seaman
khandani	:	ancestral, of the family

khasmakhaneya	:	husband-eater
kheer	:	rice pudding
khichri	:	dish of rice and lentils cooked together
kirtan	:	songs in praise of God
kissa	:	a story
kucci	:	primary
kuccha	:	unripe, raw, non-cemented in the case of houses, roads
kula	:	family line, lineage
khara	:	saltish, not very potent
kurta-pajama	:	loose long shirt and pants
kushti	:	wrestling
laddu	:	confectionery made of gram flour and sugar
Lalaji	:	honorific generally reserved for a Punjabi merchant
lateen	:	triangular sail at an angle of 45 degrees to the mast
log	:	people
lungi	:	a piece of cloth wrapped round the waist
luqat	:	a kind of fruit
maas-sharab	:	meat-alcohol
madrassa	:	a school for Koranic studies
Mangal	:	name of the planet Mars; a masculine, dry, fiery planet connected with energy, confidence and ego. Also, Tuesday, well-being, mantra, chant/spell
masnavi	:	a long romantic narrative poem with rhyming couplets
mathian	:	deep fried crisp but thick salty biscuits
mauli	:	sacred red thread tied round the wrist during religious ceremonies
maya	:	illusion, the belief that the universe is only what we perceive with our sense organs
mendiyan	:	braided hair on head
mendiyan kanak	:	braided hair on head like braided wheat
meru danda	:	name of a children's game

mishar	:	water carriers
mishri	:	sugar candy
mistri	:	craftsman
mochi	:	cobbler
mohallah	:	neighbourhood
muftikhor	:	person always looking for freebies
mugdar	:	dumb-bells
muhurat	:	auspicious opening, beginning
Muklava	:	newly married woman's first return to parental home
mundan samskar	:	head-shaving ceremony
mungre	:	seed-pod of radish
munshi	:	clerk, learned man
murabba	:	fruit preserves
murki(an)	:	long looped earring(s)
murabbae	:	preserves
murti puja	:	idol worship
musafirkhana	:	resting place for pilgrims
mushaira	:	poetry recital session
mushtandeyo	:	hooligans
naamkaran	:	naming ceremony
nabz	:	pulse
nadi	:	vein
nakhoda	:	captain of the dhow
nakhra	:	fuss
nai	:	barber
nastik	:	atheist
naukar	:	servant
Navaratri	:	nine nights (Hindu festival)
nichi jat	:	lower caste
paan-supari	:	betel-leaf and nut
pahare	:	mathematical tables
phaini	:	very fine wheat noodles cooked in milk
pandit/pundit	:	learned, skillful person
pakoras	:	vegetables deep-fried in a paste of chick-pea flour

paltan	:	platoon/gang of persons
pansari	:	grocer/pharmacist
papadums	:	crackers, usually made of lentils
parnani	:	maternal great-grandmother
paisa	:	money
palan-poshan	:	upbringing
paranda	:	long black strands of thread with colourful tassels, used to lengthen and decorate plaits
paraya-dhan	:	wealth of another
parnana	:	maternal great-grandfather
parontha	:	fried bread
patija	:	nephew
peepul	:	fig tree
penji	:	elder sister
petha	:	melon
phaini	:	very fine wheat noodles cooked in milk
pidi	:	low stool
pir	:	saintly, holy man
potli	:	small bundle
praji	:	respected term for a man (usually older man), elder brother
prasad	:	sanctified food
priti-bhojan	:	food served at the temple
prerna	:	inspiration
pugree	:	turban
puja	:	worship
punya	:	virtue, virtuous deed
puri	:	deep fried small unleavened bread
Purvasamskaras	:	a purification rite of another age/time to sublimate inferior impulses and emotions
qaida	:	a school/study/text book
quam	:	community
rakhi	:	thread tied around the wrist during a festive occasion (Hindu)
Rama	:	god-like hero of the Ramayana (Hindu epic)

Ramlila	:	dramatized performance of the Ramayana
saab log	:	sahibs
sada dena	:	give, extend an invitation
samskar	:	rite
salwar-kameez	:	very loose pants and long loose shirt
sanyas	:	renounce worldly life
sarai	:	rest house
saroor	:	metal bar
Satsang	:	religious gathering
sattvic	:	pure
sehra	:	prothalamion, poem sung at a wedding, or a bridegroom's veil, usually made of flowers
sevian	:	deep fried salty noodles of chick-pea paste
shabad	:	religious verses (especially those from the Sikh *gurbani)*
shagun	:	auspicious gift
shairi	:	Urdu poetry
shakkarparey	:	confectionery made of wheat flour and syrup
shani	:	the planet Saturn associated with darkness
sharab	:	alcohol
Shastra(s)	:	scriptures
shavasana	:	corpse-like yogic pose
sherbet	:	syrupy drink
shervani	:	long coat worn by men
Shukar	:	The planet Venus associated with gentleness and femininity, or day, Friday,
shunya	:	void/empty/zero/vacuum
sirmunniye	:	one who has cropped hair
sithanis	:	songs full of humour and satire
sloka	:	Sanskrit verse
surma	:	antimony, a powdered collyrium (usu. to beautify the eyes)
Tayaji and Taiji	:	father's elder brother and his wife
tambaku	:	tobacco
tantric	:	a class of mystical doctrines (Hindu/ Buddhist)

tappa	:	a kind of verse for song
teeka	:	an injection
thali	:	steel or brass plate
thanda	:	cold
thurra	:	seating platform
tiffin	:	(Anglo-Indian) light meal, esp. lunch
tika	:	mark (usually Hindu) painted on the forehead, an ornament for the head
tikkiyan	:	waved/coiled parts of hair
tilak	:	mark made on forehead (Hindu), coronation
tonga	:	a horse-drawn (or bullock) cart
topee	:	hat/cap
tulsi	:	holy basil
vaid	:	doctor of Indian medicines
vaikunth	:	heaven
veda	:	compound
Vedas	:	sacred Hindu texts
vehmi	:	superstitious
vrat	:	religious fast
wadaiyan	:	congratulations
wade	:	elder, big
Vilayat	:	England
Vivah	:	wedding
yajman	:	one who performs a yajna (a religious ceremony) or offers gifts to brahmins
yoni	:	vagina
zila	:	district

Other

Freemason	:	member of an international order established for mutual help and fellowship, which holds elaborate secret ceremonies.
sola topee	:	sun hat made from the pith of a swamp plant of the pea family